Pathways to
in Health Care

Pathways to Careers in Health Care

Christopher T. King
Philip Young P. Hong
Editors

2019

W.E. Upjohn Institute for Employment Research
Kalamazoo, Michigan

Library of Congress Cataloging-in-Publication Data

Names: King, Christopher T., editor | Hong, Philip Young P., 1972- editor.
| W.E. Upjohn Institute for Employment Research, issuing body.
Title: Pathways to careers in health care / Christopher T. King, Philip Young P. Hong,
editors.
Description: Kalamazoo, Michigan : W.E. Upjohn Institute for Employment Research,
2019. | Includes bibliographical references and index. | Summary: "The authors in
this book present findings, lessons, and recommendations that emanated from HPOG
research and evaluations for consideration by policymakers, program operators, and
other researchers"— Provided by publisher.
Identifiers: LCCN 2019040213 (print) | LCCN 2019040214 (ebook) |
ISBN 9780880996662 (paperback) | ISBN 9780880996679 (ebook)
Subjects: MESH: Health Workforce—economics | Health Occupations—education |
Government Programs—economics | Program Evaluation | Socioeconomic Factors |
United States
Classification: LCC RA440.9 (print) | LCC RA440.9 (ebook) | NLM W 76 AA1 |
DDC 362.1023—dc23
LC record available at https://lccn.loc.gov/2019040213
LC ebook record available at https://lccn.loc.gov/2019040214

The facts presented in this study and the observations and viewpoints expressed are
the sole responsibility of the authors. They do not necessarily represent positions of
the W.E. Upjohn Institute for Employment Research.

Cover design by Carol A.S. Derks.
Index prepared by Diane Worden.
Printed in the United States of America.
Printed on recycled paper.

Contents

Foreword

The Health Profession Opportunity Grants (HPOG) program is an important federal effort to improve labor market opportunities for disadvantaged populations and help meet employer demand for skilled labor. It was established by Congress almost 10 years ago to address two important problems: a shortfall in the number of qualified health care workers to meet growing demand, and the increasing need for postsecondary education to secure a job with a living wage for families.

When the Patient Protection and Affordable Care Act, which contained the authority for the HPOG program, was passed by Congress and signed into law by President Barack Obama in March 2010, unemployment was high (the Bureau of Labor Statistics [2010a] reported that the seasonally adjusted unemployment rate for the civilian labor force was 9.9 percent, just slightly below the peak rate of 10 percent that had been recorded just six months earlier). The recession was declared officially over just prior to the ACA's passage, in July 2009, but the recovery lagged, and it took six years for the unemployment rate to return to the 5 percent territory it had occupied before the Great Recession.

When HPOG was implemented, the health care and social assistance sector was projected to gain 5.6 million jobs over the next 10 years—more than any other occupation group (Bureau of Labor Statistics 2010b). Health care jobs are expected to continue growing—14 percent between 2018 and 2028, faster than the average for all occupations—and add about 1.9 million new jobs (again, more jobs than any other occupational group) (Bureau of Labor Statistics 2018). This projected growth is mainly due to an aging population. The timing of HPOG coincides with baby boomers aging and leaving the workforce, which affects both the labor supply and health care demand. The first of the baby boomers turned 65 in 2011. According to the Pew Research Center, from then until 2030 approximately 10,000 baby boomers will reach 65 every day (Passel and Cohn 2008). By 2030, when all baby boomers will have turned 65, fully 18 percent of the nation's population will be at least that age, compared with around 12 percent when HPOG began.

These data underscore the need for programs like HPOG. The grant program is playing an important role in preparing low-income individuals for labor market opportunities and increasing the ranks of qualified workers to meet demand. As the following chapters describe, in HPOG's first round, 32 grants were awarded to government agencies, community-based organizations, postsecondary educational institutions, and tribal-affiliated organizations in 23 states. And over the course of its first five-year grant period, the program served almost 40,000 individuals.

In addition, HPOG is playing a critical role in building evidence about how to meet the needs these data highlight.

At the time of implementation, evidence about the career pathways approach required in the law was thin but promising. The HPOG research and evaluation portfolio—described in this volume—is an important contributor to the evidence base.

As a demonstration program, HPOG's authorizing legislation required that a federal evaluation be undertaken. Of the $85 million appropriated annually for the program, the Administration for Children and Families (ACF) set aside a significant proportion—$10 million per year—for evaluation activities in order to build evidence. ACF developed a thoughtful and comprehensive research and evaluation portfolio that includes eight projects aimed at answering questions about implementation, systems change, outcomes, and impacts. The research and evaluation strategy was also designed to support the collection of program administrative data and to build local program partners' capacity to use data and evidence.

The HPOG University Partnership Research Grants are an important component of the strategy. Five University Partnership Research Grants were awarded to support university-led studies developed in partnership with HPOG programs.

The chapters that follow focus on HPOG university partnership research and two of the projects in the portfolio: the National Implementation Study and the HPOG Tribal Evaluation. They provide an overview of findings and lessons and demonstrate the richness of the insights the researchers drew from partnerships with program operators, including those in American Indian/ Alaska Native communities.

The findings from the National HPOG Impact Evaluation—36-month impacts and 72-month impacts—will be released in 2019 and 2021, respectively. Those findings will provide answers to a number of questions about program effectiveness. But in the meantime, the pages that follow offer important lessons about program implementation and outcomes and about building partnerships between the research and practice communities. These partnerships pave the way to ensuring that the lessons in this book and those that come later are useful, usable, and ultimately used to improve these programs and—more generally—to benefit the education, training, and employment fields.

On January 14, 2019, President Donald Trump signed the Foundations for Evidence-Based Policymaking Act of 2018 into law. The legislation represents a bipartisan recognition of the importance of data and evidence in helping to design and improve policies and programs. The HPOG research and evaluation agenda and the projects and partnerships described in this volume are excellent examples of how to achieve those goals.

— Molly Irwin, Pew Charitable Trusts

References

Bureau of Labor Statistics. 2010a. Databases, Tables & Calculators by Subject. Washington, DC: Bureau of Labor Statistics. https://data.bls.gov/timeseries/LNS14000000 (last modified September 13, 2019).

———. 2010b. Occupational Outlook Handbook. Washington, DC: Bureau of Labor Statistics. www.bls.gov/ooh (last modified September 4, 2019).

———. 2018. Occupational Outlook Handbook: Healthcare Occupations. Washington, DC: Bureau of Labor Statistics. www.bls.gov/ooh (last modified September 4, 2019).

Passel, Jeffrey S., and D'Vera Cohn. 2008. "U.S. Population Projections: 2005–2050." Washington, DC: Pew Research Center.

Acknowledgments

The authors would like to express our appreciation to both Molly Irwin, now at the Pew Charitable Trusts, and Hilary Bruck for their leadership of the Health Profession Opportunity Grants University Partnership Research Grants program, which supported the underlying research for the volume, if not its writing. We would also like to thank all of the contributors to this book who have made important contributions in the Office of Planning, Research and Evaluation's multipronged evaluation of the Health Profession Opportunity Grants Program.

And last, but certainly not least, we want to acknowledge the support of our families during the writing of this book. They also serve who stand and wait—even while making faces.

1
Introduction

An Overview of the Health Profession
Opportunity Grants Program

Christopher T. King
University of Texas at Austin

Philip Young P. Hong
Loyola University Chicago

The Patient Protection and Affordable Care Act passed by Congress and signed into law by President Barack Obama in 2010 effected major changes in the financing and delivery of health care in the United States. It also authorized creation of the Health Profession Opportunity Grants program (HPOG), a demonstration effort within the U.S. Department of Health and Human Services to provide opportunities for education and training that lead to jobs and career advancement in health care for recipients of Temporary Assistance for Needy Families (TANF) and other low-income individuals and to respond to the increasing demand for health care professionals. As a demonstration program, HPOG also featured a mandated federal evaluation to assess its success and a corresponding research program—the HPOG University Partnership Research Grants (HPOG UP), a collaborative effort between the program operators and academic researchers from different disciplines—to observe various aspects of its operations.

HPOG unites two important innovations in workforce development programming for serving low-income populations in recent decades, career pathways and sector strategies, by actively fostering the use of the former in the context of one major sector—health care. Health care is one of the only sectors that continued to exhibit growth year after year in periods of general economic expansion as well as decline. Health care employment even continued to expand in most states and communities across the United States through the Great Recession in 2008–2009. In addition to offering insights into these strategies and their evolution, the authors in this book present the findings, lessons, and recommendations that emanated from HPOG research and evaluations for consideration by policymakers, program operators, and other researchers.

SECTOR AND CAREER PATHWAY STRATEGIES: THE LARGER FRAME OF REFERENCE

As Christopher King and Heath Prince explain in Chapter 2, career pathways and sector-based strategies have come of age in the past few years. Sector strategies grew slowly from "one-off" efforts intended to rationalize and improve workforce development programmatic relationships with employers and postsecondary institutions in the 1980s and 1990s, often instituted separately, to become more widespread practices throughout much of the workforce system by the 2010s, even before the evidence base was there to fully support their claims to effectiveness. Now these strategies are firmly ensconced in U.S. workforce development policy.

Per Conway et al. (2007), sector-based workforce strategies target specific industries or clusters of occupations, intervene through credible organizations, support workers competing for quality job opportunities, address employer needs and industry competitiveness, and create lasting change in labor market systems helping both workers and employers. They aim to improve the economic situation of workers through increased employment, wages, benefits, and earnings over time, while also seeking to improve employers' access to workers with the necessary skills, to increase business productivity, and to boost regional competitiveness. Sector strategies act as *integrators* of wider regional economic and workforce development activities. They were pioneered starting in the 1980s by the Bay State Skills Corporation (now the Commonwealth Corporation) in Massachusetts and 1990s by the Wisconsin Regional Training Partnership and Project QUEST in San Antonio, and they expanded in the 1990s and 2000s with considerable support from foundations (such as the Annie E. Casey Foundation and the Charles Stewart Mott Foundation), as well as state and federal governmental partners.

Sector strategies represented a decided departure from more traditional approaches to job development within the workforce field. Too often, local workforce programs focused almost exclusively on the supply side of the market, offering job search assistance, job skills training, and other services, and then preparing job seekers to secure jobs with employers that their staff had cultivated at some point near the end of their program participation. This came to be seen as overly focused on the job seeker and too limited in terms of real employer engagement. Job development and placement efforts tended to be scattershot, untargeted, and disconnected from employers' real skill needs in the workplace.

By contrast, sector-based workforce strategies began from workplace skills that employers within growth sectors of the labor market need—sectors that were often targeted by these strategies included advanced manufacturing, information technology, hospitality, and logistics and transportation, as well as health care, although health care has almost always been on these lists at the state and local levels.

As sector strategies spread over time, they evolved to incorporate what are now referred to as *career pathway strategies*, which are of two main types.[1] The first type, wholly situated within postsecondary institutions, is organized around an articulated set of courses that lets individuals learn skills and earn postsecondary credentials for specific occupations, such as nursing and allied health careers. These pathways identify key entry and exit points that allow individuals to reach a certain point in their pathways; leave for a period of work in the labor market, if necessary; and subsequently return to pursue further training, with earned credits that "stack" toward completion of a particular diploma or degree (e.g., an associate's degree in nursing). The second type is more employer based, identifying occupations that appear to have the career pathways already built in and focusing more on preparing individuals for them based on completion of courses leading to industry-recognized certificates. Today's career pathway and sectoral strategies, while distinct, are integrated approaches to workforce development in a growing number of communities.

It may be useful to articulate more clearly how these policies are expected to operate and, importantly, what outcomes they aim to produce in labor markets for job seekers. Figure 1.1—taken from David Fein's (2012) insightful working paper on career pathways as a frame-

Figure 1.1 Theory of Change for Career Pathways

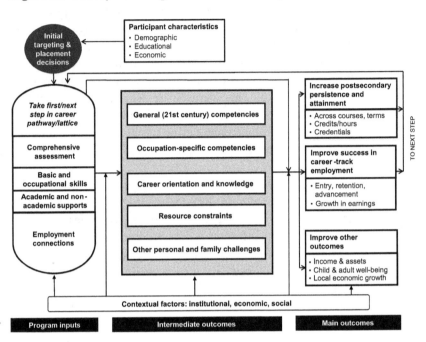

SOURCE: Fein (2012).

work—attempts to capture these in relatively simplified form. Given the emphasis sector strategies place on the employer role, it is important to note that these strategies are also intended to produce positive outcomes for employers, such as reduced employee turnover, increased productivity, and profitability.

Sector and career pathway strategies have now been largely codified in U.S. workforce policy as part of the Workforce Innovation and Opportunity Act (WIOA) of 2014, but, as King and Prince indicate in their chapter, based in part on recent research and local case studies they conducted for the Annie E. Casey Foundation, challenges remain in implementing, sustaining, and scaling. Among these are scarcity of resources, limitations of program requirements and funding silos, competing state and local priorities, varying emphases of community and technical colleges, relevance to employer needs, poor participant supports, and various implementation barriers. The contributors to this volume address many of these challenges in the context of the health care sector.

King and Prince conclude with observations and recommendations for policymakers, followed by a brief update on the emerging evidence on the effectiveness of these strategies, which is generally strong across industry sectors—including health care—in terms of impacts on program persistence and completion and labor market outcomes of interest.

HPOG, HPOG UP, AND OPRE'S RESEARCH AGENDA

In Chapter 3, Hilary Bruck, Amelia Popham, and Kim Stupica-Dobbs provide a detailed description of the HPOG program, focusing particularly on its first round of grants (referred to here as HPOG 1.0) and its origins and goals, as well as the associated HPOG UP research and evaluation programs. They also situate the program in the larger context of the Office of Planning, Research, and Evaluation's (OPRE) extensive research agenda, which is guided by five principles: rigor, relevance, transparency, independence, and ethics.

HPOG 1.0 programs are explicitly based on a health care career pathways framework in postsecondary education, which posits that instruction should be organized as a series of manageable and well-articulated steps, accompanied by strong supports and connections to employment. HPOG builds on OPRE's nine-site Pathways for Advancing Careers and Education initiative that was introduced by the Administration for Children and Families several years earlier in 2007. That project is the subject of a separate, rigorous longitudinal evaluation.

The HPOG 1.0 research and evaluation portfolio contains eight projects, each driven by its own research questions. This volume features chapters addressing two of these projects, notably the HPOG National Implementation Evaluation (NIE) and Tribal HPOG Evaluations and the HPOG UP Grants.

Bruck and her coauthors conclude with a discussion of program and research plans for the future and offer a series of reflections and lessons learned.

FINDINGS FROM HPOG'S NATIONAL
IMPLEMENTATION AND TRIBAL EVALUATIONS

Although we do not have HPOG program impact results yet, we can learn from two major process and outcome evaluations of the program. In Chapter 4, Alan Werner, Pamela Loprest, and Robin Koralek provide an overview and findings from HPOG's NIE for OPRE. The NIE focused on the 27 nontribal HPOG 1.0 grantees that received five-year grants in 2010. The evaluation was organized around three major research questions: 1) How were the programs implemented? 2) What changes in service delivery systems were associated with their implementation? 3) What outcomes occurred for individual participants?

The NIE addressed these research questions in three related studies, respectively: the Descriptive Implementation Study, the Systems Study, and the Outcome Study. Werner and his coauthors summarize the findings of the Descriptive Implementation and Outcome Studies. Among other things, they find the following about HPOG 1.0:

- Programs served more than 36,000 individuals—mainly unmarried minority women with children—engaging mostly in health care occupational training. Approximately 30 percent of participants were in school and 41 percent were working when they enrolled in the program.

- By 36 months after enrollment, most (78 percent) participants who began training had completed at least one health care course of training, spending an average of 3.5 months in training.

- At 15 months after enrollment, most (73 percent) participants were employed, more than half of them in health care jobs. As with other sector-based programs, those employed worked full-time on average; those employed in health care earned higher hourly wages and enjoyed better employment benefits than those working in other sectors.

- Participant employment and earnings increased through 12 quarters after exit, with steeper increases in earlier quarters. Completers and noncompleters experienced these increases, but employment and earnings were notably higher for completers.

While these are solid results—in line with findings from other sector and career pathway evaluations—they are *outcomes*, not net *impacts*. For the full story on HPOG's impacts, we have to wait for the interim three-year and longer-term six-year impact estimates that are slated to become available in 2019 and 2021, respectively.

In Chapter 5, Michael Meit et al. address the second of the HPOG evaluations, the HPOG Tribal Evaluation, addressing the American Indian/Alaska Native (AI/AN) communities. They focus on the five Tribal HPOG 1.0 grants awarded to tribal organizations and tribal colleges:

1) Blackfeet Community College in Browning, Montana

2) Cankdeska Cikana Community College in Fort Totten, North Dakota

3) College of Menominee Nation in Green Bay, Wisconsin

4) Cook Inlet Tribal Council in Anchorage, Alaska

5) Turtle Mountain Community College in Belcourt, North Dakota

The evaluation examines the structures, processes, and outcomes based on three key research questions, respectively: 1) What frameworks and relationships did the Tribal HPOG grantees create to implement training and service delivery? 2) How were training and support services delivered? 3) What outcomes did participants achieve, and was health care workforce capacity enhanced in tribal communities?

Their analysis of the HPOG Performance Reporting System data and qualitative interview data for the five tribal grantees finds the following:

- Structures were put in place to strike a good balance between managing the academic programs and support services to meet the needs of AI/AN students and to produce program success.

- Processes were enacted to streamline recruitment through informal word of mouth, screening for eligibility and academic readiness, and ongoing student engagement from orientation throughout participation in Tribal HPOG to allow smooth implementation.

- Outcomes for the tribal programs included enrollment of a total of 2,270 students—mainly unmarried AI/AN women with chil-

dren—mostly in training for the occupational category of nursing assistant, aide, orderly, and attendant, followed by licensed
practical and vocational nurses. Approximately 20 percent of
participants were employed in a non-health-care field and 15
percent in the health care field at the time of enrollment in the
program.

- By 36 months after enrollment, nearly half (48 percent) of the
students who began training had completed at least one health
care course of training, and fewer than one-fifth (18 percent)
exited without completing the training.

- At five years after enrollment, most (65.3 percent) students
completed one or more health care training programs. Among
students who completed and exited the program, most (69 percent) were employed at the time of exit. Among those who found
employment at exit, most (85 percent) were employed in health
care. Of those who were working in the health care field at the
time of enrollment, 39 percent experienced a wage increase during program participation.

Meit et al. conclude by reporting qualitative data for various stakeholders—students, staff, and employers—on their general satisfaction
with the Tribal HPOG program. Many students appreciated the Tribal
HPOG program for its financial and culturally competent support services that made it possible for them to persist through to the finish line.
There was a marked improvement in soft skills among the students.
Staff were impressed with the impact not just on students but also on
their kids and other older family members. Lastly, employers found it
helpful to hire Tribal HPOG students who know and respect the history
of AI/AN people. This benefits employers as providers connect with AI/
AN patients and communities at large.

ENGAGING EMPLOYERS IN HEALTH CARE CAREER
PATHWAY PROGRAMS

One of the longer-running themes in workforce development policies and programs is the need to engage employers more fully and in

meaningful ways. This issue has been addressed in myriad ways over the years with varying degrees of success through such diverse efforts as mandating that employers play a major/majority role in program governance, offering substantial subsidies for employers providing on-the-job training, and more recently requiring governors to implement sectoral strategies statewide in their WIOA programming. In Chapter 6, Janet Boguslaw, Jessica Santos, and Trinidad Tellez examine ways New Hampshire health care employers and other key stakeholders might improve the training, hiring, retention, and advancement opportunities of racial, ethnic, and linguistic minorities entering or seeking to advance in health professions through the New Hampshire Health Profession Opportunity Project (HPOP). This is an important subtopic of the employer engagement issue.

HPOP trained 1,051 low-income individuals to pursue health care occupations, of whom 80 percent completed training in health care and 74 percent attained employment, with 88 percent of those employed finding positions in health care. One of HPOP's key foci was on workforce diversity; the program successfully engaged 28 percent of students from racial, ethnic, and language minority populations. This was in response to the increasing diversity of the New Hampshire workforce, even as minorities face institutionally based challenges in hiring, retention, or advancement in careers despite their own efforts and motivation.

By conducting in-depth qualitative interviews, literature reviews, local data analysis, and the engagement of employers and other stakeholders, this study focuses on the following research questions related to racial, ethnic, and linguistic minorities in New Hampshire: 1) How can state health care employers create a more diverse workforce and foster greater recruitment, retention, and advancement? 2) How can the workforce development field better prepare and support both workers and employers in the health care sector to improve minority hiring, retention, and advancement along career pathways in the state? 3) What opportunity structures or bridges need to be developed or leveraged to build and sustain a more diverse and upwardly mobile minority health care workforce in New Hampshire?

Based on in-depth interviews with a wide range of New Hampshire health care employers—hospitals, long-term care facilities, home health care agencies, community health centers, mental health centers, and dental services across HPOP's four geographic areas—and with industry association leaders, job developers, incumbent health care workers, and community leaders, as well as with incumbent health care employees across a range of positions, the authors find that health care workers of color face a range of institutional, relational, and organizational barriers to career advancement:

- Discrimination against diverse populations in health care is embedded in institutional structures and deep-rooted in the absence of formal organizational commitment to and understanding of the value of workforce diversity across professional positions and variations in leadership. This creates unequal opportunity for racial, ethnic, and linguistic minorities.

- Informal labor networks function to restrict access to new opportunities for entry and advancement for health care professionals of color, limiting inclusion and equity. This subtler form of network-based structural exclusion is perpetuated by informal internal labor markets within firms.

- Employers at the level of director or unit manager are skeptical about the need to hire for a diverse workforce with the greater benefit of improving community wealth, patient outcomes, or business performance. They tend to understand and make decisions that impact diversity in the context of their perceived bottom line.

Boguslaw and her coauthors suggest that these structural issues together contribute to a new way of thinking about policies and practices that improve the entry, retention, and advancement of diverse populations in health care positions. Employer engagement is critical to developing career pathways that advance health professionals of color, and that workforce development programs will move forward with greater success when tied to the related agendas of improving health care performance and reducing area health disparities. They suggest a framework for culturally effective health care organizations by investing in seven core elements: 1) leadership, 2) policies and procedures, 3) data collection and analysis, 4) community engagement, 5) language and communication access, 6) staff cultural competence, and 7) workforce diversity and inclusion. They maintain that this combined approach will generate improved quality of care, safety, and patient satisfaction; reduced health disparities; and increased revenue.

Another set of issues garnering greater attention in workforce and education programming in recent years as career pathways strategies have matured involves the provision of appropriate supports to participating students to assist them in successfully navigating the less than hospitable landscape of these publicly funded programs from enrollment and participation through to completion (certification and degree attainment) and labor market success. Several groups of HPOG UP researchers and their program partners addressed quite different aspects of the supports issue.

CULTURAL COMPETENCY IN RURAL, TRIBAL HEALTH CARE CAREER PROGRAMS

Cultural competency is an issue seldom addressed explicitly in workforce and education programs in the United States, nor is it typically articulated in the context of requisite program supports. Yet, in more rural and tribal areas of the country, cultural competency among providers and provider institutions is likely to play a larger role in students having successful program experiences and outcomes.

Loretta Heuer of North Dakota State University led a team that included President Cynthia Lindquist of Cankdeska Cikana Community College, Marilyn Klug of the University of North Dakota, and Mary Leff of North Dakota State University, in partnership with Cankdeska Cikana Community College's HPOG program, Next Steps. The project goals were to engage in service research projects to develop practices for supporting the recruitment and retention of American Indian people into professional nursing programs in North Dakota, and to explore ways to encourage interest in health careers among American Indian youth.

This research team presents in Chapter 7 six interdisciplinary projects, as well as numerous nursing recruitment/retention projects led by the North Dakota team. For each of the projects the research team tracked key outcome measures and reported their progress based on set goals. In general, the desired outcomes were achieved at the project level. Key accomplishments included the following:

- To encourage American Indian students' interest in health careers, a series of educational opportunities were initiated and evaluated. Pre- and posttests, course evaluations, and focus groups were used to assess the culturally competent curriculum content and student engagement. Findings demonstrated an overall student satisfaction and appreciation for the opportunity to be introduced to the health care industry through HPOG.

- More than 500 students completed the Youth Education & Employment Survey, with a response rate of 64 percent. The data provided a comprehensive look at American Indian students as a whole in terms of their aspirations and perceived self-sufficiency in relation to future career goals. Many students indicated motivation to study and work in the health care field.

- Four annual conferences were put together for state nursing educators and employers to create a forum for generating ideas and strategies for improving the recruitment, retention, and employment of American Indian students in the nursing profession.

- Multiple video projects highlighted the lived experiences of participating student nurses and mentors to identify promising practices used by Next Steps to support student success. Excerpts were used to develop video materials for recruitment and retention of American Indians in Nursing.

- An oral history project, *Voices of American Indians in Nursing*, was also completed, with 14 nurses representing multiple generations and career choices in a documentary, *Essence of Healing: Journey of American Indian Nurses*.

Heuer and her coauthors provide a general reflection of what is important in working on projects with the tribal nations. They recommend academic researchers have cultural competency in connecting with the tribal communities—basic knowledge and respect for the differing worldviews, values, and beliefs. They also mention some key cultural foundations to understand: American Indian traditional values focus on the group by taking care of people, focusing on the present, and respecting elders' knowledge and wisdom.

ROLE OF SOCIAL SUPPORTS IN A HEALTH
INFORMATION CAREER PATHWAY PROGRAM

Over time, workforce and education programs have come to rec-ognize the importance of social supports for effective program partici-pation, completion, and, ultimately, successful outcomes. They have devoted an increasing amount of attention to the design and provision of social supports in addition to the content of their program offerings.[2] These supports take varying forms, including the provision of child care and transportation assistance, academic and career coaching or navi-gation, financial counseling and assistance, peer supports and network development as part of social capital.[3] When the Affordable Care Act authorized the HPOG program in 2010, it explicitly stated that "instruc-tion should be organized as a series of manageable and well-articulated steps, *accompanied by strong supports and connections to employ-ment*" (emphasis added).

The authors of Chapter 8, Cheryl Hyde and Karin Eyrich-Garg, engaged with the Health Information Professions (HIP) program as their training program partner in their HPOG UP research. HIP was coordinated and primarily staffed by the Center for Social Policy and Community Development at Temple University, with additional pro-gram partners including District 1199C, the Philadelphia Workforce Investment Board, the Department of Public Welfare, Philadelphia Workforce Development, and area health care/medical industries. HIP operated as a five-tier training program in various aspects of health information management. Using a participant-centered approach, HIP offered employment training, as well as career coaching, child care and transportation assistance, interviewing techniques, and guidance with job placement and internship.

Hyde and Eyrich-Garg examine the social supports of low-income HIP program participants—their social support networks and primary group memberships—in order to understand their impact. Specifically, they explore the extent of participants' social support and whether their participation in the training program bolstered this assistance. Their research focused solely on Tier 1 participants, those enrolling in the lowest tier, Medical Office and Accounts/Electronic Health Records training. The primary Tier 1 target population was TANF recipients, though the program expanded its pool to include individuals at or below 250 percent of the federal poverty line.

Based on a combination of in-depth interviews with participants (N = 141) at four points in time—program intake, program exit, six months postexit, and one year postexit—as well as eight program alumni focus groups (N = 72), and extended interviews with HIP program staff, the researchers found that the primary group memberships—the most popular of which was religious in nature—were largely homogeneous in terms of race, gender and education. Their social support networks were small and expanded only a little throughout the program. Participants relied heavily on friends for social assistance but most did not include training staff in their six-month post-exit networks. They also found little evidence that the participants created bridging or linking social capital, although they did belong to more professional/business associations and Internet groups, mainly medical coding and health professions.

Hyde and Eyrich-Garg suggest that programs need to understand that networking is not just a key strategy in finding employment but also a skill that needs to be learned and honed for subsequent advancement. Rather than just encouraging participants to network, program staff need to develop networks and then assist participants in accessing them. In addition to developing participants' human capital, training programs also need to facilitate their social capital development, specifically the kind that links network-poor individuals with opportunity pathways.

A FAMILY-CENTRIC APPROACH TO HEALTH CARE CAREER PATHWAYS

Sector and career pathway strategies tend to be more focused on and driven by the needs of employers in their particular sectors and stress the demand side of the labor market more than traditional workforce development programs have done over time. Where they engage with providers and specific target populations, they generally are concerned with addressing the education and training needs of individual participants so that they can obtain the necessary skills, degrees, and/or certifications required to secure positions in these sectors and progressively advance in them.

Chapter 9 by Teresa Eckrich Sommer, Patricia Lindsay Chase-Lansdale, Terri Sabol, and Christopher King describes Career*Advance*®, a career pathway program in Tulsa's health care sector that is unique in targeting the parents of children participating in Head Start, Early Head Start, and Oklahoma early education programs and serving them with a structured array of evidence-based services, which are intentionally coordinated for parents and children. It remains the only sector-based career pathway program under study that offers human capital services to children and parents simultaneously.

The Community Action Project of Tulsa County (CAP Tulsa) began enrolling parents in Career*Advance*® in 2009 and soon expanded its scale and scope in 2010, when it received the first of two HPOG grants. Program services include quality early childhood education, sector-based career training, stackable credentials, coaching and peer supports, and incentives and other financial supports (e.g., transportation assistance, child care vouchers). It is a much more intensive, family-centered approach to services organized around an early childhood education platform, in this case one of the best in the nation, as rigorous longitudinal evaluations have clearly shown.

Initial quasi-experimental evaluation findings for Career*Advance*® from the research partnership with CAP Tulsa under the HPOG UP program (as well as additional support from the W.K. Kellogg Foundation and the Foundation for Child Development) include the following results:

- Sixty-two percent of enrollees achieved at least one health care certification in one year versus just 3 percent of matched comparison group members, a rate well above that for all community college students nationally after six years.

- Though enrollees did not increase their overall employment rate versus comparison group members, at 52 percent, they enjoyed a 23-point gain in health care employment.

- They did not experience increased earnings after a year but also did not report higher levels of material hardship, possibly because the program's financial supports more than offset their lost income during participation.

- Parents in the program also reported higher levels of commitment to work, greater self-efficacy, and higher levels of optimism compared to their comparison group peers, without any significant increase in perceived stress, psychological or other, after one year.

- Participants' children increased their attendance by three points over the year and reduced their rates of chronic absence, results that may foreshadow future impacts for these children.

The research team's implementation research, featuring site visits, participant interviews, and participant and staff focus groups, yielded several themes. Operationalizing a two-generation mission within a sector-based program faces many challenges, among them basic skills and English-language levels for parents. In addition, parents require intensive support services, including coaching, peer supports, financial supports, coordinated parent/child schedules and others, although from the research, it is not possible to determine the effect of any single component on their success. Deeper relationships with employers via workforce intermediaries (e.g., Tulsa WorkAdvance) can help match the needs of employers and adults needing employment in a given sector in part through better sequencing of school and work activities. In addition, programs like Career*Advance*® necessarily rely on sustained mutually beneficial partnerships that need considerable care and feeding over time to become and remain effective. The future direction of the program after HPOG 2.0 support ends in 2020 is yet to be determined, but current research shows that a two-generation approach within a health care sector-based career pathway program is feasible.

PSYCHOLOGICAL SUPPORTS AS HUMAN CAPITAL INVESTMENTS IN HEALTH CARE CAREER PATHWAYS

As discussed, workforce and education supports can take many different forms. Child care and transportation assistance may be among the most common, with coaching, career navigation, and social capital recently receiving increasing attention. Another form that has not been accorded much recognition, and certainly has not been funded to any significant degree, is psychological supports.

Philip Hong, Timothy O'Brien, Terri Pigott, Jang Ho Park, Brian Holland, and Rana Hong examine the role of human capital investments in the form of psychological supports in health care career pathways programs offered at two prominent area health care centers. The Southland Health Care Forum in Chicago Heights offered medical assistant, certified medical assistant, and licensed practical nurse track training coupled with robust psychological supports provided by program staff, including the program manager, program specialists and coordinators, instructors, and job developers. Gateway Technical College in Kenosha, Wisconsin, also built strong psychological supports into the intensive coaching model provided by HPOG program specialists to strengthen participation in and success with a wide range of health care career opportunities, including community pharmacy technician, dental assistant, health information technology, health unit coordinator, medical assistant, medical billing clerk, medical transcription, nursing, nursing assistant, physical therapist assistant, radiography, and surgical technology.

In Chapter 10, evidence of psychological self-sufficiency (PSS) is presented by demonstrating positive change over time as an empowerment process of switching from barriers to hope. This PSS process contributes to the economic self-sufficiency (ESS) outcome. Its HPOG UP research partner, Loyola University of Chicago Center for Research on Self-Sufficiency, evaluated empowerment-based workforce development processes during participation in training and education—the extent to which PSS affects ESS—as they relate to employment placement and retention outcomes for HPOG students.

HPOG participants filled out Loyola's surveys at the start, middle, and end of the program/employment, as well as at six-month follow-up. Survey instruments included questions on basic demographics, employment-related intrapersonal and noncognitive skills, employment hope, and perceived barriers to employment. Rigorous statistical analyses were conducted to develop the PSS measure, consolidating discrete variables into testable domains by validating both the employment hope and perceived employment barrier scales. Further, the research team explored the performance of one of the derived domains—employment hope—as an intermediate variable to examine the process-to-outcome relationship.

A total of 834 (92 percent) participating HPOG students at the partner sites were surveyed. Seventy-three percent filled out the second survey, and 70 percent the third survey. Twenty-six percent filled out the fourth survey. Based on analyses of the survey and qualitative focus group data, Hong et al. found the following:

- About 70 percent reported having increased their employment hope, while 57 percent reported having decreased their perceived employment barriers.

- PSS increases between Time 1 and 2 and stays the same at Time 3, and then drops at Time 4. ESS generally increases over time, paralleling the PSS growth pattern and dipping along with PSS at Time 4.

- PSS scores increased at a higher rate during Times 1–3 for those participants who received career counseling and job search services compared to those who did not. The drop in PSS score was statistically significant for those who did not receive this service.

- PSS scores were higher at Time 3 for those who were employed at exit compared to those who were not. PSS scores remained much higher at Time 4 for those who were employed at exit. And PSS scores for those who were working at Time 4 were much higher at Time 1 and 4 compared to those who were not working at Time 4.

- Participants who maintained higher PSS levels also were more likely to complete the HPOG program; the group that completed the HPOG program had a much higher PSS score at Time 4 compared to those who did not complete the program.

- Structural equation modeling analysis of the PSS theoretical model indicated that PSS significantly contributes to ESS and that increases in PSS lead to growth in ESS outcomes.

- Qualitative findings suggest the importance of the relational aspect of HPOG program delivery that helps bring together the disconnected system, resources, direction, and motivation. Psychological supports by HPOG staff helped remove participants' fear and anxiety about continuing in the program. These relationships provide the comfort, confidence, and conviction necessary to increase and sustain PSS during program participation.

Hong et al. suggest that workforce development practitioners apply the PSS theory and focus on clients' growth and maintenance of PSS when working closely with participants toward achieving their ESS outcomes. Investing in psychological capital in the form of PSS as a human capital development strategy could be translated into providing self-sponsored retention support during job readiness training before participants enter the labor market. Further, Transforming Impossible into Possible (TIP®), an innovative evidence-based intervention developed during the project, can help invigorate the internal strengths necessary to keep moving participants toward their ESS goals.

BOOK ORGANIZATION AND THEMES

Following this introductory chapter, the first major section of the book, Chapters 2–5, delves into broader issues and national-level findings regarding HPOG 1.0, while the second section, Chapters 6–10, offers insights from the five HPOG UP researcher/program collaborations that are more topical and area specific. Chapter 11, the final chapter, offers concluding observations and policy recommendations.

Broad themes about HPOG 1.0 explored here, all of which are addressed more fully in the topical and concluding chapters, include:

- **Who is being served?** HPOG 1.0 programs, as intended, have served large shares of TANF and other low-income populations, most of whom are women of color, many of them parents. Participants have not always been the hardest of the hard to serve, but most have had education and other barriers to participation.

- **How are they being served?** Also, as intended, the programs have offered participants a wide range of social and psychological supports, while connecting them to an array of education and training services and employers for at least their initial job in health care. Supports provided have included tuition assistance, child care, case management, peer supports, and help with strengthening psychological capital for job readiness, employment, retention, and advancement—that is, self-esteem, self-efficacy, and psychological self-sufficiency.

- **What have been the near-term outcomes of the programs?** Participants have generally succeeded in securing credentials and obtaining jobs in health care at high rates in the near term after completing programs. Unfortunately, fewer participants—about one-fifth in programs nationally and one-tenth from tribal programs—have gone on to reach the next step on their career pathway by obtaining a second credential.

Notes

1. Jenkins (2006) published a clear exposition of career pathways in the context of the knowledge sector.
2. Among other efforts worth noting along these lines are the Institute for Women's Poverty Research's *Student Parent Success Initiative* (https://iwpr.org/issue/special-websites/student-parent-success-initiative/); Sarah Goldrick-Rabb's work on postsecondary education at Temple University and earlier as founder of the Wisconsin HOPE Lab (http://saragoldrickrab.com/research/); and Mario Luis Small's work at Harvard on the role of social capital in varying contexts (https://scholar.harvard.edu/mariosmall).
3. Career navigators found their way into mainstream program contexts like workforce and postsecondary education based on their success serving disabled populations as part of national efforts such as the Disability Program Navigator Initiative of the U.S. Department of Labor from 2003 to 2010. See the online disability employment resource site for America's Job Centers at www.disability.workforce gps.org.

References

Conway, Maureen, Amy Blair, Stephen L. Dawson, and Linda Dworak-Munoz. 2007. *Sectoral Strategies for Low Income Workers: Lessons from the Field.* Washington, DC: Aspen Institute, Workforce Strategies Initiative.

Fein, David J. 2012. *Career Pathways as a Framework for Program Design and Evaluation: A Working Paper from the Pathways for Advancing Careers and Education (PACE) Project.* OPRE Report No. 2012-30. Washington, DC: Office of Planning, Research, and Evaluation, Administration for Children and Families, U.S. Department of Health and Human Services.

Jenkins, Davis. 2006. *Career Pathways: Aligning Public Resources to Support Individual and Regional Economic Advancement in the Knowledge Economy.* Barrington, RI: Workforce Strategy Center.

2

Career Pathway and
Sector-Based Strategies

A Broader Look

Christopher T. King
Heath J. Prince
University of Texas at Austin

OVERVIEW

Career pathway and sector-based strategies have come of age in the past few years. As discussed in previous literature (e.g., Glover and King 2010; King 2014; King and Prince 2015; Prince, King, and Oldmixon 2017), they evolved from "one-off" efforts intended to rationalize and improve workforce development programmatic relationships with employers and postsecondary institutions in the 1980s and 1990s, often instituted separately, to become more widespread practices throughout much of the workforce system by the 2010s, even before the evidence base was there to fully support their claims to effectiveness. Now, these strategies are firmly ensconced in U.S. workforce development policy and practice. New rigorous evaluation studies are published every year, further documenting their impacts on employment, earnings, and other outcomes of interest.

Several national foundations (such as Annie E. Casey, Ford, Hitachi, JPMorgan Chase); the National Fund for Workforce Solutions; National Governors Association (NGA); and, more recently, the U.S. Department of Labor have fostered the spread of these strategies on a wider basis across many industry sectors and regions and for varying groups of job seekers. And, as the chapters in this volume clearly demonstrate, the U.S. Department of Health and Human Services, through its support for both the Health Profession Opportunity Grants

(HPOG) program and its rigorous research agenda—including HPOG University Partnerships fostering collaborations between local programs and academic researchers, the national and tribal evaluations, and its ongoing Pathways for Advancing Careers and Education evaluation (e.g., Martinson and Gardiner 2014)—has contributed to both our understanding of and the expansion of these strategies, especially in the health care sector, with an intense focus on welfare and other low-income populations.

In this chapter, we clarify what career pathway and sectoral strategies generally entail and offer a brief history of their evolution. We then explain how these strategies have been codified in U.S. workforce policy and provide some examples of how they are being implemented in practice in selected sites around the country. We examine some of the challenges and opportunities that arise in successfully implementing, sustaining, and scaling these strategies, and then conclude with an update on emerging evidence and offer some final observations and recommendations.

STRATEGIES DEFINED

For decades, workforce strategies tended to be focused almost exclusively on the supply side of the labor market. Local programs traditionally outreached and enrolled job seekers ranging from new labor force entrants with few if any skills to workers who were displaced or dislocated from a particular industry by the effects of trade or technological change. These programs devised a set of activities and services to address the needs of these job seekers—often including job readiness and job search and skills training via community and technical colleges—and then sought to place them with employers. Missing from this traditional approach were, at the very least, two major pieces:

1) Substantial engagement with employers in key industries and sectors around their common skill needs and efforts to understand the nature of career progression within them—in other words, serious attention to the demand side of the labor market

2) Working with key education and training providers, especially community and technical colleges, to get them to structure

their offerings in ways that fostered the provision of credentials meaningful to employers, and sequenced and scheduled so that job seekers/students could more readily navigate them

In a larger sense, the strategies to address these missing pieces can be seen as attempts to rationalize, to more coherently structure opportunities both in the workplace and in our mainline education and training institutions to lead to better outcomes for job seekers and employers. Sector-based strategies arrived on the scene well before career pathway strategies appeared, so we will start by examining them.

According to Conway et al. (2007), whose Economic Opportunities Program team at the Aspen Institute has been a major force in fostering knowledge about such strategies and their diffusion for over a decade, sector-based workforce strategies

- target specific industries and/or clusters of occupations;
- intervene through credible organizations (often workforce intermediaries);
- support workers competing for quality job opportunities as measured by wages, benefits, and advancement opportunities;
- address employer needs and industry competitiveness; and
- create lasting change in labor market systems helping workers and employers.

In sum, sectoral strategies aim to improve the economic situation of workers through increased employment, wages, benefits, and earnings over time while they also seek to improve employers' access to workers with the necessary skills, increase business productivity, and boost regional competitiveness. Further, sectoral strategies act as *integrators* of wider regional economic and workforce development activities (Glover and King 2010).

A key element in the evolution of the definition of sector strategies, however, has been a greater emphasis on designing sector strategies in such a way that they are clearly employer led and demand driven. As the strategy has moved into the next phase of its development, the role of employers has become more clearly articulated, which has, in many cases, also meant that a clearer division of labor among employers, the public workforce development system, and the postsecondary education system is becoming established.

Career pathway strategies generally are of two main types (King and Prince 2015). The first, which is wholly situated within postsecondary institutions, is organized around an articulated set of courses that lets individuals learn skills and earn postsecondary credentials for specific occupations, such as nursing and allied health careers. These pathways identify key entry and exit points that allow individuals to reach a certain point in their pathway, leave for a period of work in the labor market, and subsequently return to pursue further training, with earned credits that "stack" toward completion of a particular diploma or degree (such as an associate's degree in nursing). Success in this type of pathway—one that most HPOG projects follow—is generally gauged by progress or advancement through the specified course work, credentials earned, job placement and retention, and earnings progression.[1]

The second type of career pathway is more employer based and tends to identify occupations that appear to have the career pathways already built in and focuses more on preparing individuals for them based on completion of courses leading to industry-recognized certificates. Success for this pathway is measured by placement and retention in the occupation and earnings gains.

More often than not, today's career pathway and sectoral strategies, while distinct, are integrated approaches to workforce development in a growing number of communities. As we have previously written,

> While many career pathways programs claim to be sector-based, this is rarely the case, and for good reason. Sector-based strategies emerged independently and prior to career pathways as a framework for organizing investment in skills training. Over a relatively short period of time, however, what began as an effort to define advancement paths for workers participating in sector programs became a distinct career pathways approach to training as the workforce development field began digesting the expanding literature on the relationship between income and postsecondary credentials. This shift in emphasis from aggregating employer demand for skills within a sector to one focused on postsecondary credentials marked the beginning of what are known now as career pathway models. (King and Prince 2015, p. 197)

CAREER PATHWAY AND SECTORAL STRATEGIES EVOLUTION IN BRIEF

The early antecedents of sectoral strategies can be found in efforts by the Commonwealth Corporation (formerly called the Bay State Skills Corporation) in the early 1980s, and the Wisconsin Regional Training Partnership and San Antonio's Project QUEST in the early 1990s (for more detail, see King and Prince [2015]). Each sought to engage employers in a much more systematic manner than traditional workforce programs across a varying mix of industries reflecting the local labor markets and serving differing target populations, not to mention different sources of funding and organizational bases. The Annie E. Casey Foundation's innovative JOBS Initiative, an eight-year, sector-based effort, followed in the mid-1990s in six diverse communities: Denver, Milwaukee, New Orleans, Philadelphia, St. Louis, and Seattle (Hebert and Waldron 2007). A number of these and the organizations that ran them, such as the Seattle JOBS Initiative, continue to serve job seekers and employers today.

As more states, localities, foundations, and nonprofit organizations continued to innovate and experiment with these strategies, and as researchers conducted more studies on their implementation and results, they began to coalesce into a complementary set of practices. Washington State adopted a statewide approach in which it supported "skills panels" in every workforce area of the state. Pennsylvania devoted its own state tax revenues and leveraged additional federal and state funds to support the creation and operations of workforce intermediary organizations in communities across the state. The Southwest Industrial Areas Foundation secured foundation and public resources to spread variations of the QUEST model in many other communities, including Austin, El Paso, and the Lower Rio Grande Valley (Texas); Monroe (Louisiana); Oklahoma City (Oklahoma); Tucson (Arizona); and others. And, leading foundations (Annie E. Casey, Ford, Rockefeller, and Hitachi) teamed up with public partners (at one point including the U.S. Department of Labor) to launch the National Fund for Workforce Solutions that was administered for several years by Jobs for the Future in Boston (see Giloth 2004 and Conway and Giloth 2014).

The HPOG program, which is directed and overseen by the Department of Health and Human Services/Administration for Children and Families and incorporates an intentional career pathway approach into the health care sector, is clearly a direct lineal descendant of, and draws much from, these earlier programs.

CODIFICATION INTO U.S. WORKFORCE DEVELOPMENT POLICY

The Workforce Investment Act of 1998 sought to explicitly shift U.S. workforce programs from having an almost exclusive focus on job seekers, skills training, and the supply side of the labor market under its predecessor, the Job Training Partnership Act (JTPA) of 1982, stressing that it had a "dual-customer" focus, serving employers and job seekers equally (see Barnow and King 2005). Yet, the reality in many if not most local areas was that programs continued to stress job seeker services and related outcomes. In fact, under the Workforce Investment Act, there were no performance standards for employers, only participants. As the preceding section notes, some states, local boards, and nonprofits began to design and implement versions of sector-based strategies, later adding career pathway approaches to them. Moreover, states—including Washington State and Pennsylvania—took strong positions in support of such strategies, even creating their own funds to support their creation, operation, and expansion over time (see the discussion below).

Largely influenced by the perceived success of sector and career pathway strategies over the past two decades and growing evidence from rigorous evaluations making the case for them (e.g., King 2014; Smith et al. 2012; Maguire et al. 2010; Martinson and Gardiner 2014; Roder and Elliott 2011, 2014; Smith, King, and Schroeder 2012), the Workforce Innovation and Opportunities Act (WIOA) passed both houses of Congress with surprising bipartisan support and near unanimity and was signed into law by President Obama in July 2014. WIOA further bolstered the status of sectoral and career pathway strategies. The U.S. Department of Labor contracted with several organizations to provide technical assistance to states and local Workforce Development Boards to foster more widespread adoption of sector strategies in particular.

In addition to the explicit promotion of sectoral strategies and career pathways, key provisions of WIOA that will significantly benefit the strengthening and expansion of these strategies include the following:

- The requirement that state WIOA plans include a description of states' vision for meeting the skilled workforce needs of employers and, similarly, a requirement that local workforce development boards' plans address "how they will better coordinate workforce development programs and economic development"[2]

- Expansion of the allowable uses of governors' 15 percent funds "to support and encourage innovative and evidence-based approaches to workforce development," including providing support to local areas "by providing information on and support for the effective development, convening, and implementation of industry or sector partnerships"[3]

- Combining what had been core and intensive services under WIA Title I into a single career services category, in which career pathways and sector-based training programs are encouraged

- The requirement that workforce boards promote proven promising practices, including the establishment of industry or sector partnerships

- Promotion of enhanced integrated planning across partners

- Promotion of integrated or contextualized Adult Basic Education, English as a Second Language, and occupational training

It is worth noting that the onus for systematic efforts to implement these strategies rests with the nation's governors. If they do not take the responsibility of investing in and guiding their implementation, it is unclear whether local workforce development boards will. The leading boards, such as the ones profiled here, almost always will do so.

EMERGING PRACTICE IN WORKFORCE
INVESTMENT BOARDS

Since receiving an explicit push forward with WIOA's enactment in 2014, along with the renewed resources in the form of governors' discretionary funds, sectoral and career pathway strategies have continued to expand. As part of a research project for the Annie E. Casey Foundation, we identified a handful of local workforce innovation boards (WIBs) that were thought to be relative stand-outs in designing and implementing sectoral and career pathway strategies:

- Opportunity, Inc. (Hampton Roads, Virginia)
- South Central Pennsylvania Works (Harrisburg, Pennsylvania)
- Arizona@Work for Mohave and LaPaz Counties (Kingman, Arizona)
- Larimer County Workforce Development Board (Ft. Collins, Colorado)
- New York City Workforce Development Board (New York)
- The Workforce Development Board (Portland, Oregon)

Each of these WIBs is profiled in greater detail in Appendix 2A, but some common themes are clear. First, most began shifting toward sector-based and career pathway strategies well before federal legislation pushed them in this direction, and the shift appears to have been part of an evolutionary process geared to better serving both job seekers and employers. Second, all of the WIBs feature continuous improvement and an intense data-driven focus. Third, all have substantial employer engagement in key sectors they have prioritized for their strategies, with health care being a primary one. This is not surprising, given the growth and long-term employment potential in that sector. Fourth, it is noteworthy that, in addition to federal resources, strong state commitment and support have played a role in bolstering these strategies in states like Colorado, Oregon, New York, and Pennsylvania. Their governors have taken the WIOA mandates to heart.

OPPORTUNITIES FOR EXPANSION

Entrepreneurial Financing

The current level of public funding still lags far behind the level needed to create a workforce development system that ensures that anyone who wants to advance in the labor market has the skills to do so. However, most successful sector strategies have demonstrated notable innovation in piecing together funding to support their work, and a key to successfully funding sector strategies is a thorough understanding of the range of funding streams that can be creatively leveraged. For example, leveraging state resources to support local sector partnerships enabled South Central Pennsylvania Works (SCPa Works) to capitalize on major Industry Partnership funding made available through the state of Pennsylvania in the mid- to late 2000s, with which it built robust sector partnerships in transportation/logistics, health care, and advanced manufacturing.

Many sector partnerships have looked outside traditional public funding sources to bring in investments from private philanthropy. For example, New York City's efforts have been advanced by the work of the New York City Workforce Funders, a collaborative of more than 60 funders that includes the New York Community Trust, the Rockefeller Foundation, the JPMorgan Chase Foundation, the Taconic Foundation, the W.T. Grant Foundation, and the United Way of New York City.[4] Since it began in 2001, the Workforce Funders have raised almost $10 million to support workforce initiatives in New York City over and above federal and state funding. Support from the Workforce Funders allows the city to leverage additional resources and to engage in intermediary activities that would be hard to fund under traditional public workforce funding streams.

Finally, a growing number of partnerships are documenting their "value proposition" for industry, making the case, through rigorous return on investment analyses, that the service they provide merits investment from industry.

Driving New Approaches to Service Delivery and Cultivating Systems Change

As sector strategies have expanded and matured, many of the more successful ones have come to view their work less as an innovative approach to a long-standing problem, and more as an opportunity to think holistically about how the workforce system might be entirely remodeled to fit the needs of the twenty-first-century labor market. The phrase "not business as usual" is heard often in conversations with stakeholders in sector strategies. Instead of a focus on placement, the focus is on training to meet skills in high demand; instead of relationships between individual business services representatives and employers, groups of employers in a given industry identify common skill needs and communicate these to the system; instead of relationships with postsecondary education institutions that were somewhat disconnected and typically ad hoc, postsecondary education is generally a key partner in the sector partnership; and instead of operating in parallel silos, they have worked to incorporate economic development agencies and actors into their partnerships. For each of the themes included in this list, sector strategies represent a significant change in the way the public system operates.

STATE INVESTMENTS IN SUPPORT OF SECTORAL STRATEGIES

Commonwealth Corporation: The Commonwealth Corporation in Massachusetts may well be the earliest of sectoral strategy initiatives, having gotten into the field in the early 1980s. As a quasi-public entity, they provide an excellent example of consistent bipartisan state support for sector strategies that could be replicated in other states.

Washington State Skills Panels: Washington embedded support for sectoral strategies in state policy starting in 1990 and has continued to foster sectorally based skills panels in regions across the state to the present. Washington's skills panels encompass a wide variety of industry sectors, ranging from the wine industry in Walla Walla in the southwestern corner of the state to interactive media in Seattle to advanced manufacturing and clean energy in a multistate region. The second generation of its skills panels was launched as the High Skills, High Wages Fund in 2008.

Pennsylvania: Drawing on resources in its general fund, the state of Pennsylvania has invested in over 90 industry partnerships since 2005 (Woolsey and Groves 2013). In addition, state law has codified industry partnerships as a core element of the state's workforce development strategy. While funding levels have varied from year to year, Pennsylvania provided $1.7 million in grants to 20 sector partnerships in 2014 (DeRenzis and Wilson 2015). The state of Pennsylvania reports that industry itself has contributed more than $9 million in private funds and over $30 million in in-kind contributions to support training and other initiatives launched under the auspices of state-sponsored industry partnerships (PA Workforce Development Association, n.d.).

Texas Initiatives: Texas has supported sectoral and broader cluster-based strategies through executive and legislative initiatives for over a decade, only in part due to the urging of the Industrial Areas Foundation and its affiliates. The Texas workforce system has emphasized training for jobs in growth occupations and industry sectors at least since passage of state workforce reform legislation in mid-1995; it continued such a focus with the governor's 2005 Texas Industry Cluster Initiative, which stressed support for economic and workforce development in Advanced Technologies and Manufacturing, Aerospace and Defense, Biotechnology and Life Sciences, Information and Computer Technology, Petroleum Refining and Chemical Products, and Energy. It is also noteworthy that the Texas Association of Workforce Boards (2014) recently put forth a set of recommendations supporting career pathways models for education and workforce development in the state.

In addition, many states have training funds that have been created from Unemployment Insurance (UI) tax diversions or in some cases state general revenues (see King and Smith 2006). These may provide a mechanism for scaling sectoral strategies as well.

Leveraging Data to Inform Strategy, Drive Performance, Ensure Sustainability

Access to a broad range of economic and administrative data can be leveraged to help sector partnerships by clarifying where and how to direct their focus and resources, managing performance and driving continuous improvement, and establishing the base of evidence needed to justify further investments and to sustain successful efforts.

Whereas decisions about which occupational skills were in highest demand previously tended to rely solely on conversations with employers—which are still vital activities—innovative programs add to these conversations a careful study of labor market information, the inclusion of input from regional economic development agencies, and other strategies. For example, SCPa Works (previously the South Central Workforce Investment Board), representing a broad swath of southern Pennsylvania, including Harrisburg, employs a multifaceted approach to collect, analyze, and use critical data to make decisions around employer engagement, as well as service design and delivery. SCPa Works operates several sector-based programs, including those in advanced materials and diversified manufacturing, health care, information and communication services, and logistics and transportation. For quantitative data, SCPa Works looks at traditional labor market information (LMI) from the state of Pennsylvania regarding in-demand occupations, wages, market penetration, and other key factors. SCPa Works also collects some economic development data derived from a proprietary tool, IMPLAN®. This information is verified with qualitative data collected through direct engagement with employers at industry partnership meetings, and through input from Business Service Representatives.

The move toward identifying evidence of effectiveness based on rigorous evaluation of data has become part of standard operating procedures within the Department of Labor and among many major philanthropic funders over the past decade, and for good reason. Greater capacity to collect and report program data, improved methods for analyzing quantitative data, and the desire to scale up effective programs have placed a premium on the use of data to inform decision making and investments.

CHALLENGES TO SUSTAINING, EXPANDING, AND REPLICATING STRATEGIES

Advancing the adoption of sectoral and career pathway strategies is fraught with challenges. Those interested in sustaining, expanding, and/or replicating sector strategies will need to clear several hurdles on their way to displacing "business as usual" in the workforce development field.

Scarcity of Resources

The biggest challenge is simply the lack of adequate resources. Because sector strategies are such a departure from business as usual, securing funding is not easy and, as previously noted, often requires creativity and innovation. Federal, state, and local funding for workforce development programs has seen steady erosion over the past few decades. With the exception of American Recovery and Reinvestment Act investments in 2009 and the expansion of Pell Grants, federal funding for employment and training programs has remained essentially flat and, since 2000, has declined somewhat from already poor funding levels (Wandner 2015). Until very recently, state and local funding has fared little better than federal support for workforce development programs.

Limitations Imposed by Program Requirements and Funding Silos

Related to the overall level of funding is the persistence of funding silos among programs created to serve very similar, if not the same, populations, despite ongoing and strenuous efforts to bring them into closer alignment. Many of the key components, activities, or services that support effective models may simply not be permitted under particular programs or funding streams, or may be difficult to support and implement across funding streams and platforms. Perhaps the most obvious challenge facing those who are implementing sector strategies is to align funding and coordinate activity between the workforce development and postsecondary education systems. Long considered one of several venues for skills training, including apprenticeships and on-the-job training, postsecondary institutions have become the venues of choice for workforce development practice in general and, more recently, sector-based programs and career pathways in particular.

Similarly, while more intensive, longer-term training is a component of sector strategies, Temporary Assistance for Needy Families (TANF) and Supplemental Nutrition Assistance Program Employment and Training (SNAP E&T) programs may not readily allow them, despite the presence of a large population in need and growing evidence of the strategies' effectiveness.

In addition, the metrics by which a career pathways or sector-based program may measure success—such as completion of industry-recognized credential, advancement in the labor market, or earnings gains—often work at cross-purposes with the metrics typically used to measure whether or not a workforce development program is successful—placement, earnings gains, and retention.

Competing State and Local Priorities

State or local policy and political priorities may also inhibit expansion of these models, federal provisions notwithstanding. For example, a continuing preference for work-first, labor force attachment approaches on the part of policymakers and administrators can be particularly challenging. The impact of state and local policymaker influence can be seen in the wide variation from state to state in the share of WIA expenditures on skills training (Barnow and King 2005; Mikelson and Nightingale 2004).

Even among policymakers who are generally supportive of demand-driven, skill development–centered approaches, pressure from key constituencies to demonstrate rapid progress in addressing local unemployment issues, economic inequalities, and/or employer skill needs can lead agency officials and other appointees to attempt to closely control sector partnership priorities and activities, thus undermining the employer-driven approach that undergirds the success of leading sector strategies.

Varying Community and Technical College Priorities

Community and technical colleges also exhibit a wide range of priorities and focus. Some college leaders are eager partners in workforce training initiatives and have strong connections with employers and industry associations. For example, Austin Community College in Texas has taken over a nearly abandoned shopping mall and implemented a "career expressway" there in partnership with Capital IDEA, a local sector-based workforce development program, and at the same time organized its entire set of academic offerings into career pathways. Austin Community College's approach is a break from the more traditional approach taken by community colleges, which are focused largely on performing the traditional academic transfer function to four-year institutions of higher education. As long as this more traditional transfer function holds sway, community colleges may be reluctant to adopt sector-based approaches.

Remaining Relevant to Employers and Industries

Sector strategies are effective only when there is significant employer engagement. As noted above, employer engagement can take many forms, including providing input on training curricula, donating machinery on which to train, providing subject matter experts to assist with instruction, funding worker training, hiring, or some combination of these.

However, gaining and maintaining employer engagement is subject to a number of sometimes uncontrollable factors, not least of which is demand for skills in the targeted industry. The tight labor markets of the late 1990s and early 2000s made for relatively high levels of employer engagement and led to the creation of several particularly innovative workforce development programs (see, for example, Barnow and Hobbie [2013]). With the onset of the Great Recession in late 2007 and early 2008 and the sharply increasing unemployment rates across the board, many sector strategies began to experience difficulties in maintaining employer interest. Larger numbers of skilled workers looking for employment, coupled with the contraction of the overall economy, led to a waning interest in sector-based programs among employers—it made better economic sense to simply place an ad, to which a number of already-skilled workers would apply, or to hold off on hiring altogether until the economy rebounded. A return to tight labor markets in most of the country means that, once again, conditions are optimal for engaging employers in sector strategies.

The cyclical nature of the economy and employer engagement has been, and will continue to be, a limiting factor in sector strategies' ability to significantly influence the larger workforce development system, unless the approach is systematically adopted as the organizing framework for public investment in workforce development.

Poor Participant Supports

Even when sector partnerships are appropriately funded, implementing support services can be difficult. Integrating the provision of services into sector-based education and training requires coordination between staff who understand the needs brought by the population being served and a postsecondary faculty who may object to the interruption to routine that the provision of these services can represent. Serving, for example, a low-skilled population, the long-term unemployed, or workers with limited English proficiency underscores the importance of bringing the right mix of players to the partnership, particularly community-based organizations and agencies with experience with these populations.

Implementation Barriers

Finally, and somewhat more granular in nature, the following challenges are specific to the day-to-day mechanics of scaling up sector strategies:

- Despite the emerging clarity around a definition of sector strategies, there is still wide variance across the workforce system in the levels of understanding of the basic concepts.

- Even when the concept underpinning a sector approach is reasonably well understood, the skills and capacity to implement it often lag. For example, questions often arise around identifying employer champions, facilitating and sustaining a partnership, and using data effectively.

- Integrating sector strategies into existing state and local strategies also raises questions. Work must be done to clarify that sector strategies are not simply one more program to manage at the local level.

- Hitting the "sweet spot" by identifying skills and occupations that address both employer needs and the needs of the target populations of workers (i.e., those that the public system is funded to serve) represents a significant challenge and is often seen as a deterrent for replicating sector strategies.

The Evidence for Sectoral and Career Pathway Strategies

Before concluding, it is important to point out that the evidence base for the effectiveness of sector-based and career pathway strategies continues to build. An assessment of the more rigorous evaluation studies of these strategies (King 2014) found that, among other effects, they have

- had large, statistically significant effects on program participation, completion, and certification (when measured);

- significantly boosted employment from 2 to 7.5 years postparticipation in many cases and led to increased employment in the sectors targeted, even when the overall employment rate did not increase; and

- produced statistically significant earnings gains of 12–30 percent over 2–7.5 years postparticipation, typically resulting from both increased duration and hours of work as well as higher wages.

Several rigorous evaluations have been since released that bolster those conclusions. MDRC conducted an experimental evaluation of the WorkAdvance Demonstration that ran from 2011 to 2013 in New York (two sites), Ohio, and Oklahoma with support from the Social Innovation Fund.[5] (Note that only the Northeast Ohio site prioritized health care as a sector.) Hendra et al. (2016) reported on impacts at a little more than two years postrandom assignment, finding that the program

- led to large increases in participation in all services, as well as in training completion and credential acquisition;

- increased earnings, with results varying with the providers' experience in running sector-based programs and the extent to which services offered were demand driven; and

- increased earnings among the long-term unemployed.

The "extent to which WorkAdvance increased employment in targeted sector jobs was the critical factor in explaining the pattern of impacts across the sites. At all the sites, jobs in the targeted sector were generally of higher quality than jobs outside the targeted sector." Moreover, in a result that resonates with many of the HPOG UP site programs, Hendra et al. (2016, p. ES-13) found that "the Per Scholas program increased income, reduced material hardship, reduced public assistance usage, and increased overall life satisfaction. It is unusual to see such a consistent pattern of impacts across so many domains. At the other sites, only a few impacts on such measures are statistically significant."

Schaberg (2017) subsequently reexamined the WorkAdvance impacts fully three years postassignment in an effort to determine whether career advancement, as measured by increased earnings, was taking place over time as was intended. She found that earnings impacts still showed considerable cross-site variation and that year-three impacts

- remained strong and continued to increase but only for the most seasoned training provider (Per Scholas in New York City);

- faded but remained significant and positive in Northeast Ohio and Oklahoma, especially for the cohort entering the more "mature" version of the program later in the year; and

- failed to materialize in the remaining New York site.

These results generally offer a somewhat cautionary tale about what to expect from these strategies.

Finally, Elliott and Roder (2017) completed a long-term (six-year) experimental evaluation of Project QUEST, one of the pioneering projects cited earlier. They recently (Roder and Elliott 2019) extended the evaluation to encompass a nine-year period. They found the following:

- Large, statistically significant impacts on earnings over the follow-up period with earnings gains continuing to grow over time: annual gains exceeded $5,000 in the ninth year.

- Participants worked more consistently and earned higher hourly wages than those in the control group.

- Program participants' earnings grew from an average of $11,722 to $33,644 over the course of the evaluation. Those who completed the program earned an average of $46,580 in the final year of the study, a level of earnings that translated into economic self-sufficiency in San Antonio.

- Those over 34 years of age and those with children experienced the greatest benefits from participation.

- Almost all (96 percent) QUEST participants were still living in Texas; 85 percent remained in the San Antonio area six years postenrollment.

We must be mindful of the fact that the sector-based, career pathway programs that have been evaluated to date likely represent the best-case scenario in terms of fidelity to the intervention's model, consistent and comprehensive data collection, rigor of the evaluation design and time span for measuring the outcomes of greatest interest, as well the education and labor market impacts themselves. While policymakers and the research community anxiously await the impact findings from the National HPOG Impact Evaluation—36-month impacts and 72-month impacts are now scheduled for release in 2019 and 2021, respectively—it may be unrealistic to hope that its results will fully validate those of prior program evaluations. However, we can certainly expect to learn much from a wider, more representative assessment of these strategies in the health care sector.

CONCLUDING OBSERVATIONS AND RECOMMENDATIONS

There is a significant and growing body of solid practice in the sector-based and career pathway strategies, and numerous recommendations for scaling up the field and improving practice can be offered. Our recommendations are categorized according to the four themes outlined above: engaging industry; entrepreneurial financing; new approaches to service delivery; and leveraging data for decision making, performance management, and sustainability.

STRONG INDUSTRY ENGAGEMENT

The term *industry engagement* has evolved considerably over the past two decades and has now come to mean something much more than simply irregular contact with employers around skill needs. Successful sector strategies now not only engage industry but also place core groups of industry employers at the head of their efforts to address the intersection between industry's need for skills and workers' need for opportunities to earn family-supporting incomes. Three main lessons emerge from their experience:

1) Initially engage a core group of sector strategies champions and allow them to set the agenda for the partnership and, crucially, to recruit additional employers themselves. Many workforce development boards already do this effectively, particularly Worksystems, Inc., in Portland, Oregon, and the Lancaster County workforce board (profiled in Appendix 2A).

2) Involve employer representatives with a deep understanding of the occupation on which training will focus, as well as senior level management, and on a continuous rather than an ad hoc basis. This is critical to keeping employers effectively engaged in the partnerships. The New York Alliance for Careers in Healthcare—an effort jointly sponsored by the NYC Department of Small Business Services and the NYC Workforce Funders—is a good example of this practice.

3) Use peer-to-peer mentoring and coaching to link high-performing sector leaders with employers new to the strategy.

FINANCING

Successful sector strategies have demonstrated notable innovation in piecing together funding to support their work. A key value workforce boards can offer to sector partnerships is their thorough understanding of the range of funding streams that can be creatively leveraged. Examples of promising strategies include

- blending and braiding resources from a variety of funding streams, including local, state, and federal programs (e.g., WIOA, TANF, and SNAP Employment and Training);
- leveraging public and business investments to secure flexible, aligned funding from philanthropic partners; and
- documenting impact to build the case for industry investment.

SYSTEMS CHANGE

Delivering services within the context of a sector strategy involves a somewhat different set of skills than administering a traditional employment and training program. Because employer commitment to an effective sector partnership is, by definition, central to the effort, and because, in the more successful sector partnerships, workers benefit from participation in education and training that is part of a career pathway, services provided through a sector strategy are necessarily more involved than programs focused primarily on placement or short-term training. Designing a service delivery for a sector strategy that serves both workers—at multiple education and skill levels—and industry partners could be aided by the following actions:

- Generate support and funding from state level agencies, particularly given the tendency for many of the more successful sector programs to develop in the context of a supportive state policy and funding environment.
- Cultivate strong relationships with agencies that can provide the types of support services most likely to be required by participants while engaged in the training, including assistance with child care, transportation, utilities, and counseling.
- Explicitly incorporate career pathways as the vehicle for delivering training at multiple levels. Doing so may help ensure employers that there is a workforce being trained to meet short- and long-term skill needs, as well as assist workers to build skills, add to experience gained on the job, and advance in their careers.

- Take advantage of WIOA and the substantial change that it represents to provide more guidance on what comprehensive sector-based and career pathway strategies are and can accomplish.

- Support additional research that drills down into the mechanics behind the success experienced by the sector strategies highlighted in this guide.

One of the more frequently noted difficulties faced by sector partnerships is developing an organizational culture that is supportive of a sector approach. Breaking from business as usual involves learning an entirely new lexicon for, and perspective on, the actual work of preparing a workforce to meet the skill needs of employers. Where sector strategies have been successful, they have also

- invested in capacity development for staff through providing them with opportunities to attend industry-related professional development events;

- provided training to help administrators, including workforce board chairs and directors in particular, understand what sector strategies are and how they should be implemented; and

- incorporated an economic development perspective into their activities, including continuous efforts to anticipate industry needs and potential areas for regional economic growth.

IMPROVED DATA UTILIZATION

The Department of Labor, the funding community, and, increasingly, industry, have made a strong case for the better use of data for the purposes of improving outcomes. However, the practice often falls short at the implementation level for a number of reasons, namely, the capacity to collect, report, and analyze data in a way that is useful for sector strategies. This could be addressed at least partially through the following:

- Include among the sector partners an organization, academic or otherwise qualified, for which the primary role is to collect and analyze LMI, economic development data, postsecondary education data, and all other data relevant to the success of the partnership.

- Ensure the collection of data in such a way that it can be analyzed as part of a rigorous experimental or quasi-experimental evaluation.

- Take advantage of the opportunity afforded by workforce boards and their ability, among other vital roles, to access UI wage data for the purposes of following sector strategy participants into the labor market.

- Achieve long-term sustainability by consistently collecting and reporting data on outcomes and implementation, measuring program impact, and using these findings to make the value proposition to investors; leveraging the experience and guidance of existing national networks, such as the NFWS, NNSP, and the Aspen Institute; and dedicating staff to staying abreast of emerging industry needs, as well as emerging industry sectors, and positioning the partnership to meet these needs.

In conclusion, sector partnerships offer valuable opportunities to move traditional workforce development programs from program administration and oversight to taking more strategic roles in building regional talent pipelines, addressing skill gaps, and creating meaningful career pathways for a range of workers in important regional industries. Continued efforts to replicate promising practices across more boards and to develop evidence of their effectiveness will be critical to sustaining public financing and workforce policies that are supportive of sector strategies.

Needless to say, these observations and recommendations should resonate well with HPOG, which is the embodiment of a sector-based career pathway strategy, and one that has taken full advantage of program/academic partnerships.

Notes

1. Fein (2012) provides an excellent framework for understanding career pathways and their expected outcomes.
2. See https://doleta.gov/wioa/Docs/WIOA_FAQs_Acc.pdf (accessed August 13, 2019).

3. The tool kit published by the National Skills Coalition in 2005 outlines governors' responsibilities in detail, including supporting sector and career pathway strategies. See DeRenzis and Wilson (2015).

4. For more information, visit the New York City Workforce Funders website at http://www.nycommunitytrust.org/AboutTheTrust/CollaborativeFunds/NYC WorkforceDevelopmentFund/AbouttheNewYorkCityWorkforceFunders/tabid/ 661/Default.aspx (accessed October 1, 2019).

5. Tulsa Community WorkAdvance, a subsidiary of Madison Strategies in New York City, has become the key workforce partner of the Community Action Project of Tulsa County in its Career*Advance*® Program under HPOG 2.0; for more information, see the chapter by Sommer et al. in this volume.

Appendix 2A

Sector Strategy Case Studies

OPPORTUNITY, INC. (HAMPTON ROADS, VIRGINIA)

Opportunity, Inc. (OI), the workforce board for the Hampton Roads, Virginia, region, has been working to align workforce development and economic development for the past 15 years. Its sector work was recently revived, focusing on information technology (IT), advanced manufacturing, parts and logistics, and health care. It has built out strands of work that include outreach to youth, improved coordination with economic development, and a strengthened focus on serving incumbent workers.

In 2000, OI made a decision to move beyond a "program mentality" toward becoming a more economic development–oriented WIB. This move involved, in part, adopting a sector strategy with the health care, advanced manufacturing, parts and logistics, and IT industries. These initial efforts slowed considerably in the late 2000s with the onset of the recession.

More recently, OI has created a vice president for workforce innovation position to work directly with employers and to serve as the coordinator between OI and the city's economic development department. Business services representatives from OI meet with individual employers to determine their needs and how best to meet them. OI meets one-on-one with representatives from economic development, and with community college stakeholders, rather than convening these stakeholders in larger, multiparty meetings, believing that these one-on-one meetings provide better opportunities for strategically planning how OI will best serve them and the workforce.

OI has moved away from the role of convener and instead sought out employer associations and other organizations that already regularly convene their members, then worked to get on their agendas. OI views its participation in these meetings as opportunities to sell what it can offer—for example, layoff aversion strategies or sector-based training for incumbent workers. Participation in meetings is simplified by virtue of the fact that many of these employers are already members of the workforce board and therefore have existing working relationships with OI.

Data-Informed Decision Making

Labor market information (LMI) is used to focus the board's training investments, but OI staff also take into consideration program completion and outcomes data to inform program design. OI views LMI as not only a planning tool but also a service that it offers to business and the community. For example, the OI website invites the public to view their LMI researchers as a resource.

Industry Engagement

In recent years, however, OI's sector work has been revived with an "industry-focused" ethos. This reengagement with sector work began with the advanced manufacturing industry, which was a driving force behind OI's work with local community colleges and K–12 systems to create mechatronics training programs, as well as manufacturing-oriented dual-credit programs in high schools. OI credits industry champions and the considerable time and attention they devote to the partnerships between industry and education for its early successes in getting traction.

At present, OI estimates that there are "hundreds" of employers engaged in its various sector strategies, with engagement ranging from simply "understanding that OI is there to help" to, at the upper end of the engagement scale, providing OI-supported on-the-job training (OJT) to incumbent workers. In addition, when OI is unable to meet an employer's need, it typically is able to refer the employer to other organizations that can assist, considering this service an essential part of its sector work.

Sustainability and Continuous Improvement

At this stage of OI's efforts to revive the sector approach, sustainability is focused primarily on ensuring that industry partners' needs are met. OI notes that a key to its success is adopting a more distributive model that makes strategic use of existing resources in the community (e.g., industry associations) and avoids attempting to be all things to all employers.

SOUTH CENTRAL PENNSYLVANIA WORKS (HARRISBURG, PENNSYLVANIA)

South Central Pennsylvania Works (SCPa Works) is the workforce board for an eight-county region with about 1.4 million people and 700,000 workers.[1]

SCPa Works has a history of strong sector-based business engagement and service delivery. The board capitalized on major industry partnership funding made available through the state of Pennsylvania in the mid to late 2000s to build robust sector partnerships in transportation/logistics, health care, and advanced manufacturing, which includes major area employers like Hershey's. Those partnerships continue to thrive and provide training essential to the industries' growth. However, changes in capacity, state funding, and focus over the past few years have limited SCPa Works' continuous expansion and innovation in sector partnerships.[2] Nevertheless, new leadership and a sharper focus have brought a renewed commitment to engage, partner, and serve the employer community in a way that makes more sense to business and will help the regional economy grow.

Key Partners/Industries

Twelve key industries employ 83 percent of Pennsylvania's workforce. The region covered by the South Central Workforce Board includes the three industries noted above, as well as food processing and wood product development. Manufacturing in particular is strongly embedded in the region's economy, history, and culture. SCPa Works is in the process of restructuring its board to ensure maximum input and engagement from those key industries.

Partner Roles

SCPa Works is focused on collaboration with its strategic partners to advance sector partnerships. SCWIB participates in a regional economic development consortium, and leadership from local economic development is currently on the workforce board. In fact, SCPa Works and its partners have a shared focus on being "networked" organizations, which means they intentionally strive to share board members and fully engage as partners in key efforts in the region. For example, SCPa Works has identified key human services representatives for their board who will help support the development of cross-organization strategies that streamline employer engagement while leveraging capacity and organizational strengths.

Data-Informed Decision Making

SCPa Works employs a multifaceted approach to collect, analyze, and use critical data to make decisions around employer engagement, as well as service design and delivery. For quantitative data, SCWIB looks at traditional LMI from the state of Pennsylvania regarding in-demand occupations, wages, market penetration, and other key factors. It also collects economic development data derived from a tool called IMPLAN®. This information is verified with qualitative data collected through direct engagement with employers at industry partnership meetings and input from business service representatives.

The workforce board is continuously looking for additional methods for collecting quality data. Future efforts will likely include surveys (both a survey of general business trends as well as a detailed inquiry by sector), engagement with a contracting firm to do an in-depth analysis of the key jobs in each sector and the tie between those jobs and regional economic impact, and a potential partnership with other workforce boards in the state to build up research and analysis expertise through the use of data products provided by such groups as EMSI or Burning Glass.

A director of strategic partnerships position was created to work with an enhanced state team developing employer engagement and sector penetration measures and using data to drive its allocation of resources. This type of hard, data-driven conversation about service strategy has not previously happened at SCPa Works. Economic development data, including industry location quotients, are part of their data analysis as well.

SCPa Works produces various products to share data with employers and other partners, but it never does so without first asking employers what data they need and how to package it for maximum usability.

Industry Engagement

Although SCPa Works is using WIOA to bring partners to the table, its director acknowledges that it is going to take time to further expand their existing sector partnerships and build new ones. SCPa Works pushes a key message that employers across industries are all part of an interdependent talent ecosystem that depends on peer firms to develop talent that will move up and across career pathways and employers over time. As a result, employers are encouraged to partner, by sector, through skill development to build a pipeline of talent that benefits all.

The main role SCPa Works envisions for its employer industry partners is clearly articulating their needs to help focus the implementation process. If employers can identify their "pain points," SCPa Works can offer to relieve them through an array of suggested supply- and demand-side workforce strategies.

Peer discussions among employers about staffing and related human resources issues are key to this approach. For example, it became clear during a health care roundtable conversation that employers did not want more training for RNs but instead needed better training for RN supervisors.

Sector-Based Service Delivery

SCPa Works is realigning its business services to reflect several key priorities:

- Operating the workforce system at the speed of business
- Using information from sector partnerships to drive how funding is allocated and services are delivered
- Capturing and articulating the workforce system's impact on business

The organizational structure is driven by knowledge of sectors and solution development based on identified employer needs. SCPa Works also counts a strong financial and administrative team as a key component of its strategy for serving employers. Developing highly competent staff in those areas ensures compliance issues are adequately addressed, which then frees leadership and service delivery staff to focus on strategic, sector-based priorities. SCPa Works also addresses program and financial compliance on the back end, which leaves those complex and potentially off-putting elements out of the conversation with business.

By building peer groups of employers across sectors, SCPa Works has established a forum for peer problem solving that often runs into areas other than workforce development, including infrastructure, tax credits, and immigration issues. SCPa Works then shares the information back to its partners to identify solutions for the identified challenges. This resource for business helps build trust, which is critical to gathering the input needed to devise effective training and other services provided by the workforce system and its partners.

Sustainability and Continuous Improvement

SCPa Works recognizes meaningful outcome measurement as a critical management tool to drive continuous improvement and is interested in adopting new business services measures. It has adopted market penetration as a key measure, growth in wages over time, and measures that answer the question of how the workforce system is addressing industry workforce needs (e.g., retention, upskilling to fill voids through retirement, attrition, and business expansion).

ARIZONA@WORK FOR MOHAVE AND LAPAZ COUNTIES (KINGMAN, ARIZONA)

Sector-based work in Kingman began in 2008, when the Arizona Commerce Authority, which serves as the state's economic development agency, convened a "sector academy" to determine how the state's workforce boards could develop and sustain sector partnerships. The sector academy identified industry champions, established common objectives, and selected industries that were vital to each workforce board's region (using location quotients) on which to focus their efforts. In addition, teams composed of representatives from the workforce boards, economic development, and education were formed.

The Mohave and LaPaz County workforce development staff, serving Kingman and the surrounding region, selected manufacturing as a priority sector, and members from the regional workforce investment board, Arizona@ Work, were selected from the targeted industries. Manufacturing industry partners were convened by a staffer from Mohave County Workforce Development who was tasked with creating an internal sector-strategies team, as well as serving as lead advocate and the primary point of contact between regional manufacturing employers and the county. Also critical to the successful launch of the manufacturing sector initiative in Kingman was the role played by Collaborative Economics, a consulting firm with a deep understanding of sector strategies, which enabled them to also recruit firms to the partnership.

Mohave Workforce Connections held the inaugural convening of regional manufacturing employers and other stakeholders in fall of 2011, and after a series of monthly meetings among these partners, the Kingman and Mohave Manufacturing Association (KAMMA) sector partnership was formed. According to those we interviewed, the initial conversations among the partners were less about discussing workforce development issues, and more about how to become a manufacturing and logistics hub for Northwest Arizona.

Monthly meetings, the distribution of meeting minutes, agenda setting, marketing, and communication were essential components to getting the sector strategy off the ground. Once a working relationship between Mohave Workforce Connections staff and the employer partners was established, work toward creating new curricula and recruiting and training workers began in earnest.

Mohave Workforce Connections (now Arizona@Work for Mohave and LaPaz Counties) provided administrative support to KAMMA, while KAMMA staff worked directly with employers. KAMMA is now an independent 501(c)6 employer association with over 50 paying employer members in addition to the

Mohave County workforce development, economic development, and social services offices. Moreover, KAMMA is now able to act as an advocate locally and at the state level in the interests of manufacturers, including, for example, advocating for the construction of an interchange on Interstate 40 to connect to an industrial park, as well as for the establishment of a foreign trade subzone in the region.

Early Wins

KAMMA's partnership with Mohave Community College (MCC) as its primary training provider produced early wins, including a curriculum for Manufacturing Certified Production Technicians. KAMMA and MCC have also created a "mobile lab" that travels throughout the region in order to provide as many workers as possible with training.

In addition, one of KAMMA's leading employers, Laron, Inc., has opened its apprenticeship program up to workers from competing firms, with the understanding that workers will participate in Laron's class and lab work, and then return to their home firms for OJT. Laron, Inc. signs an agreement with the home firms, agreeing not to compete for those workers from other firms trained through its apprenticeship program for a number of years postapprenticeship.

Data

Arizona@Work Mohave/LaPaz has recently completed a regional workforce development plan, based on its review of current LMI data, with assistance from MCC, and it also uses LMI to target occupations on which to focus investments. It views LMI as a cornerstone of all of its workforce development work in the region.

Employer Engagement

Employer engagement in KAMMA spans the spectrum, from occasionally engaging with KAMMA's service providers, to providing subject matter experts to assist with training, to contributing to curricula development, to, as noted above in the Laron, Inc. example, providing training on-site and, of course, hiring. New sectors, including hospitality and tourism, are currently being explored as potential sector partnerships.

LARIMER COUNTY WORKFORCE DEVELOPMENT BOARD (FT. COLLINS, COLORADO)

Colorado has long been home to a relatively integrated workforce policy framework that stresses strong state direction, business engagement, and local delivery.[3] It has also been actively implementing sector partnerships and career pathways for almost a decade. After participating in the National Governors Association's Policy Academy in 2007, it moved deliberately to tailor a sector strategy for the state and implement it—complete with its own tool kits and targeted technical assistance—over several years.[4]

Key developments include, among others:

- Creation of a *Sector Strategies Steering Committee* of industry leaders and representatives of workforce, education, and economic development agencies, followed by labor market analyses and state start-up grants to support local sector partnerships. This committee was subsequently established as a regular subcommittee of the Colorado Workforce Development Council (CWDC).

- Convening State Sector Partnership Academies (Sector Summits) in 2009, 2013, and 2014 to provide professional development and peer-learning opportunities for the local partnerships.

- Publishing the *Colorado Blueprint 1.0* in late 2011 followed by *Blueprint 2.0* in 2015 to guide the state's economic growth. Objective V of the *Blueprint* is "To Educate and Train the Workforce of the Future." The *Blueprint 1.0* was organized around 14 key industries, while *Blueprint 2.0* continued to emphasize these industries with an increased focus on rural areas of the state.[5]

- The Colorado Legislature enacted a series of bills in recent years supporting sector partnerships and career pathways.
  - House Bill 1165 (2013) created a career pathway in and driven by the manufacturing sector partnership.
  - Senate Bill 205 (2014) codified sector partnerships as a component of the state workforce system.
  - House Bill 1274 (2015) required Colorado to develop career pathways in construction, IT, and health care that engage employers through sector partnerships.

- In May 2014, CWDC published an online tool kit, Creating Career Pathways in Colorado, to guide creation of career pathways within sector partnerships (Collaborative Economics & The Woolsey Group 2014).

Colorado views sector partnerships as "the way we do business with business" in the state—as a partner, not just a customer—and has offered substantial resources and technical assistance in the form of guides, tool kits, and one-on-one coaching to make this a reality. All these efforts over the past decade have eased Colorado's implementation of the Workforce Innovation and Opportunity Act (WIOA) with its mandate for sector partnerships and emphasis on career pathways. Colorado currently features some 21 "active or emerging" industry partnerships with more in development.[6]

It is also worth noting not only that Colorado's workforce system partners actively with the Colorado Department of Economic Development and its education agencies, but that the Colorado Department of Labor and Employment has responsibility for funding streams ranging from WIOA, Wagner-Peyser Employment Services (ES), and Unemployment Insurance to Trade Adjustment Assistance, Veterans Employment and Training, and Migrant and Seasonal Farm Worker programs.

Larimer County Workforce Development Board

The Larimer County Workforce Development Board is located in far North Central Colorado and is based in Ft. Collins.[7] The board's area spans both Larimer and Weld Counties. In 2014, the board served over 1,400 employers and 19,000 job seekers. Given Colorado's funding model, with workforce program allocations going directly to local workforce centers, staffing at the workforce board is kept lean.

Larimer County's involvement in sector partnerships and career pathway strategies follows the path of Colorado's as a state, starting with the adoption of these strategies as far back as 2009. However, their engagement in sector partnerships began to coalesce as a result of the first CWDC, which sponsored a sector summit in 2013. Local leaders met with state Colorado Department of Labor and Employment and other officials in a two-day study of labor market data and conditions, facilitated by state consultants (Melville and Woolsey with the Woolsey Group) to determine which sectors offered robust growth, high wages, and career advancement opportunities. The board also held a prep meeting to get ready for the summit with workforce, economic development, business, academic, and other groups.

Larimer County Sector Partnerships

At present, Larimer is focusing on their sector partnerships in manufacturing and health care, each of which receives $30,000 in support from CWDC to staff and manage the partnerships and convene meetings. Business leads each partnership, with the Larimer County workforce board in a supporting role. They have established a Committee to Coordinate the Partners featuring single points of contact and are moving forward on creating a portal for partnership information sharing. CWDC announced new state funding to support and implement sector partnerships in spring 2016.

Each of the Larimer County partnerships has taken its own approach to the work in their industry, as noted below. The private sector is driving the partnership in both.

Health care

The Healthcare Partnership, the less formal of the two partnerships, has formed four committees to carry out its work, as follows:

- The Exploring the Healthcare Pipeline focuses on exposing youth to the broad range of career opportunities in health care (e.g., IT, marketing) in addition to nursing and other more traditional frontline, health-related positions.
- The Curriculum Development Committee is focused on creating educational curricula in health care.
- The Behavioral Health Committee is looking at needs and talent development in behavioral health.
- The Healthcare Policy Committee focuses on larger policy issues, including federal law and regulations (e.g., HIPPA, patient release to long-term care, drug policy, tax policy as it affects the health care pipeline).

As noted, the Healthcare Partnership operates relatively informally, without an elected board of directors or formal votes for actions.

Manufacturing

From the beginning, the Manufacturing Partnership opted for a more formal approach, complete with a board of directors, a charter, regularly scheduled meetings, and recorded votes. Only private sector members have an official vote in their proceedings; others (e.g., workforce, education, economic development) have a voice but no vote. Area manufacturers range from auto and electronics assembly to aerospace, breweries, RVs (Winnebago), food and beverage distribution, and small "job shops." The partnership formed three committees to carry out their work:

1) The Manufacturing Rocks Committee is essentially a youth career exposure committee for manufacturing.

2) The Higher Education Curriculum Committee examines two- and four-year curricula for relevance to labor market needs, which has, as an ancillary benefit, led to greater engagement on the part of colleges' industry advisory boards. It has also led to teacher internships inside manufacturing workplaces. Ames Community College, Front Range Community College, and Colorado State University (Ft. Collins) have actively participated.

3) The Manufacturing Networks Committee has responded to the expressed needs of area manufacturers who wanted to learn from each other. With a special focus on supply chains, the committee has established peer-to-peer learning networks and built greater industry cohesion.

Lessons Learned

Lessons learned to date include the following:

- Each sector is unique and needs to determine its own needs and its own path forward. The simplicity of focusing on job X with certification Y in manufacturing may not translate to health care, a highly regulated sector with strict licensing and credentialing standards.

- Partnerships are more effective when employers are in leadership positions and when they focus on specific actions they can take to move forward. "It has to be about implementation, not just talk" to get and keep employers engaged.

- Starting with an economic development rather than a more traditional workforce development focus led to early sector partnership success. More attention was being paid to adding value for industry. It wasn't just another workforce initiative but was, rather, part of a larger, more holistic effort with real returns for business.

- It is also important that the sector partnerships operate with appropriately shared responsibility. Larimer County workforce functions as the secretariat and provides logistical support to the partnerships, while the private sector focuses on visioning and strategy.

NEW YORK CITY WORKFORCE DEVELOPMENT BOARD (NEW YORK CITY, NEW YORK)

The New York City workforce development area spans all of New York's five boroughs and, due to its unique complexity and size, is expected to operate as a stand-alone board region under the Workforce Innovation and Opportunity Act (WIOA) as well.[8] Workforce programs operate under the Office of Workforce Development, which was created within Mayor Bill de Blasio's office in 2014, replacing the Office of Human Capital Development that former Mayor Michael Bloomberg established in 2012.

New York has been engaged in a highly collaborative effort since the early 2000s as it sought to shift from a traditional work-first, job placement approach to a sector-based career pathways model focused on ensuring employer needs are met while connecting New York residents to quality jobs with opportunities for career advancement. It served as a Workforce Intermediary Project Pilot site starting in 2003 with support from the New York City Workforce Funders, a collaborative of more than 60 funders that includes the New York Community Trust, Rockefeller Foundation, the JPMorgan Chase Foundation, the Taconic Foundation, the W.T. Grant Foundation, and the United Way of New York City, among others.[9] Since it began in 2001, the Workforce Funders have raised almost $10 million to support workforce initiatives in New York City over and above federal and state funding. Support from the Workforce Funders also allows the city to leverage additional resources and to engage in intermediary activities that would be hard to fund under traditional public workforce funding streams.

In 2004, the commissioner of Small Business Services (the city agency then charged with implementation of the Workforce Investment Act's Adult and Dislocated Worker programs) met with local foundations to explore strategies for moving the model forward. Out of that discussion came the first New York City sectors initiative. The pilot focused on the biotech and health care industries. The success of the effort spurred additional investment into sector-based service design.

New York City's commitment to a sector-based approach was reinforced through a grant from the National Fund for Workforce Solutions, then managed by Boston-based Jobs for the Future to engage in capacity building to strengthen the effort among partners locally. The Sectors Strategies Practicum, led by the Aspen Institute and Public/Private Ventures,[10] resulted in a sectors collaborative that has engaged all of the city's workforce development assets to further their common mission. This effort, which emerged from the broadly representative New York City Task Force appointed by the mayor, is now referred to as New York City's *Career Pathway* model.[11] *Career Pathways* has three main pillars:

1) Building skills employers seek

2) Improving job quality

3) Increasing system and policy coordination

The model features a career pathways approach situated within strong industry sector partnerships. They are also explicitly data driven with a data collection and measurement strategy developed for the city by the Aspen Institute. New York City WKDEV accesses quantitative labor market information (LMI) data through the state LMI office as well as a service with the City University of New York (CUNY). It also has a contract with CUNY to analyze and verify these data through the collection of qualitative data via surveys and focus groups with local employers. In addition, partners also factor in local policy changes or initiatives, which, given the magnitude of the city, can drive workforce needs for a particular industry.

New York City's Sector Partnerships

The city partnered with the local National Fund for Workforce Solutions site to establish the New York Alliance for Careers in Healthcare (NYACH), an intermediary organization that works closely with local health care industry/ trade associations and unions to identify and respond to employer and worker needs. A second industry partnership, the Tech Talent Pipeline, was also created to focus on the IT sector. NYACH and Tech Talent Pipeline are housed at Small Business Services and integrated into the fabric of the agency's service design and delivery. These partnerships serve as the industry engagement arm of the agency charged with driving system change across the workforce and education systems.

- **Health care**. NYACH collaborates with CUNY to ensure that curricula reflect health care employers' most pressing needs, while also working with area employers to address issues, such as supervision and scheduling, which can negatively affect retention and movement up the career ladder. A registered nurse with close ties to area health care employers and a deep understanding of the industry leads NYACH.

- **IT.** Because IT lacks strong industry associations or unions and has few standardized certifications or career pathways, the Talent Tech Pipeline focuses on identifying specific needs around key competencies such as mobile application development and the need to find quality providers who can create employer-driven curricula in that area.

Contractor-employed business service representatives (BSRs) also interface with employers, and as a result of their connections with NYACH and Talent Tech Pipeline they are more knowledgeable about the skills and competencies needed in those industries. To drive effective BSR outreach to employers, Small Business Services conducts research to identify jobs that require less than a college degree and provides a list of those employers within the defined sales territory to each BSR. The BSR then follows a business development plan that includes activities such as cold calling, attendance at industry events, networking, and relationship building. All activities are designed to strategically build a brand that employers will ultimately trust to save them money.

The city's early success with a sector focus led to the establishment of sector-specific career centers, starting with a focus on transportation, manufacturing, and health care with an ultimate merger of transportation and manufacturing into the Industrial and Transportation Career Center. These centers focus on two to three sectors, with staff developing expertise in them. Most staff work as account managers who are assigned sales territory to prevent duplicative calls on employers. Industry partnerships focus on serving job seekers by forging connections with local support service organizations to provide the wrap-around services required to ensure job seekers are work ready.

The strong emphasis on job quality pushes the NYC Workforce Board staff past the boundaries of traditional workforce development into areas that affect both employer and jobseeker outcomes. These services are also a key component of the Small Business Services office. Industry partnerships provide a valuable forum for addressing employer needs beyond training and skill development.

Challenges and Lessons Learned

One of the biggest challenges NYC has faced in implementing this comprehensive Career Pathways model according to WKDEV staff has been an old one: every agency has its own interests, is tasked to do a particular set of activities and deliver a specific set of services to certain groups, and has program metrics it is held accountable for. Aligning these agencies, many of which answer to a different deputy mayor, around Career Pathways with all of its components and expectations is a tall order and will take time. Lessons learned to date include the following:

- **Leadership and messaging.** Both carrots and sticks are required to reinforce Career Pathways. In New York City, Career Pathways has benefited from considerable bipartisan political leadership spanning several administrations (Bloomberg, de Blasio) since at least 2003. Mayor de Blasio as a vocal and visible champion for the model has helped a great deal. All of the relevant deputy mayors must also be on board so they can serve as the enforcers when necessary. Agencies now understand the expectation that collaboration is the norm, not operating within their silos. Messaging and a well thought-out communications strategy are also key to affirming the value proposition of Career Pathways to participants, to businesses/employers, to policymakers, to program leaders, and to the wider public.

- **Sustained investment.** High levels of continued investment—public and private/philanthropic—with accompanying flexibility are essential to implementing and sustaining Career Pathways into the future.

- **Leveraging expertise.** Career Pathways has benefited from considerable thought leadership by leading sector experts such as the Aspen Institute's Workforce Strategies Initiative and the (now defunct) Public/Private Ventures.

- **Systems change orientation.** The focus on both programmatic and systems change is also important. Providing more quality job training will not be sufficient in and of itself. Systems change is necessary as well.

WIOA Effects

The city of New York is working closely with the Department of Youth and Community Development (youth services) and the Department of Small Business Services (adult services) to implement WIOA. The board engages leaders from the private sector, labor unions, community-based organizations, educational institutions, and government agencies to guide and inform the city's workforce development policies and services, including its sector partnerships and career pathway strategies. Given the work New York has done in both of these areas, WIOA's implementation appears not to have affected New York City's sector partnership and career pathway approach very much if at all.

THE WORKFORCE DEVELOPMENT BOARD (PORTLAND, OREGON)

The Workforce Development Board is a public/private partnership representing the city of Portland and Multnomah and Washington counties. Among its many successes, this workforce board led development of a Community Workforce Agreement as part of the Clean Energy Works Portland (CEWP) pilot, which ultimately provided the proof of concept for the statewide Clean

Energy Works Oregon. CEWP had excellent outcomes, owing to an agreement that required workforce development programs to provide industry-recognized credentials and energy efficiency contractors to meet standards for job quality and diverse hiring. The board is also engaged in regional manufacturing sector work in a cooperative effort with the adjoining Southwest Washington Workforce Investment Council.

Portland started its close work with industry in 1998–1999 as part of its Career Pathways work. That initiative was rooted in trying to transmit skills more quickly than traditional degree programs, which often required workers to remove themselves from the labor market for two to four years. Career Pathways efforts focus on the health care and manufacturing industries, two of the larger, better paying industries in the region. These industries also used well-defined, progressive credentials for hiring that work well in career pathways programs.

For several years, the workforce board continued investing its funds in helping redesign and refine curricula for the two industries. Over time (between 2003 and 2004), the industries moved from guiding the workforce discussion to becoming more advisory in nature. The Career Pathways work remained relatively expensive and still required worker disengagement from the labor market, although for less time (from six months to a year). As the Pathways initiative became more institutionalized, the workforce board became more of a funding mechanism than a driver.

Data-Informed Decision Making

The Portland board decided early on that sound data analysis was critical to the success of their sector efforts, and it chose to support four state-funded labor market analysts in the board offices. These analysts are trained in the use of the state's multiple LMI tools, including tools that identify employers by industry and those that provide information on industry trends. Their analysis is communicated via annual *State of the Workforce* reports, which identify, among other things, major employers and their size, earnings trends, demographic trends, and employment trends by major industry.

Industry Engagement

The Portland board's industry engagement efforts begin with research. Board staff consider 12 data elements, focusing primarily on the number of jobs, current and projected openings, growth rate, demographics of labor force, and wages. Working with supportive employers, board staff review the data for accuracy and will move forward only with employer approval.

A change in past approaches to engage industry includes inviting employers to meet in a neutral setting, with no assumptions about what is needed to
address employer needs. These meetings are less about inviting employers to
participate in a career pathways or sector project, and more about understanding current and projected education and skill needs, identifying those employers willing to push the agenda forward. These employers are also tasked with
convening additional employers. Other partners, from the education or service
provider communities, are invited to attend these discussions, but typically
only after a critical mass of committed employers has taken shape.

Sustainability and Continuous Improvement

Continuous improvement in and sustainability of its sector-based work
are priorities for the board. A key element of its sustainability and continuous
improvement work has been its ongoing work to coordinate its sectors work
across a three-board region, including Workforce Southwest Washington representing Clark, Cowlitz, and Wahkiakum Counties, which, along with Clacka-
mas Workforce Partnership and the Portland Workforce Development Board
form the Columbia-Willamette Workforce Collaborative. The three boards
have a shared committee overseeing their sector work, and each board appoints
leadership to disseminate information to their respective staffs. Despite being,
at times, more difficult and complex to implement, the coordination of the
three boards permits the public workforce system to better serve its industry
partners by recognizing that the workforce needed for these industries is drawn
from throughout the region and not simply from within their board areas. The
Portland board anticipates that the WIOA regional collaboration requirements
will make this current arrangement among the three boards stronger.

Appendix Notes

1. This profile is based on interviews conducted by the authors with former board
   director Scott Sheely in May 2015 and current director Kevin Perkey in May 2015
   and April 2016.
2. State support for industry partnerships has been reduced from a high of $15 mil-
   lion to just $1–$1.5 million annually, although Governor Wolfe wants to restore it
   to around $10 million.
3. For more information, see DeRenzis and Wilson (2015) and *Colorado Workforce
   Investment Act Annual Reports for PY2013 & PY2014* (n.d.).
4. This description draws on DeRenzis and Wilson (2015, pp. 14–15).
5. See http://choosecolorado.com/programs-initiatives/colorado-blueprint/ (accessed
   February 27, 2019).

6. Email exchange with Lauren E. Victor, PhD, Talent Development Research and Policy Analyst, Colorado Workforce Development Council and Colorado Department of Higher Education.

7. This description is based largely on a telephone interview with Mr. Jacob Castillo, Larimer County Workforce Board liaison, conducted by Christopher King of the University of Texas at Austin's Ray Marshall Center on April 22, 2016. It has been supplemented by document reviews and online information.

8. This discussion draws on numerous documents, including, among others, New York City Workforce Development Board (2015). It expands upon an earlier New York City workforce board case study prepared by the Ray Marshall Center for the Study of Human Resources and colleagues and an extended interview conducted with board director Chris Neale and board coordinator Reynold Graham by Christopher King on May 11, 2016.

9. See http://www.nycommunitytrust.org/AboutTheTrust/CollaborativeFunds/NYC WorkforceDevelopmentFund/AbouttheNewYorkCityWorkforceFunders/tabid/661/Default.aspx (accessed February 27, 2019).

10. Public/Private Ventures ceased operations several years ago. P/PV's projects have been picked up by the Aspen Institute, the Corporation for a Skilled Workforce, and others.

11. The following reports provide details on the Career Pathway Model effort: Jobs for New Yorkers Task Force (2014), City of New York (2015), and Gasper and Henderson (2014).

References

Barnow, Burt S., and Richard Hobbie, eds. 2013. *The American Recovery and Reinvestment Act: The Role of Workforce Programs.* Kalamazoo, MI: W.E. Upjohn Institute for Employment Research.

Barnow, Burt S., and Christopher T. King. 2005. *The Workforce Investment Act in Eight States.* Albany, NY: Nelson A. Rockefeller Institute of Government. http://doleta.gov/reports/searcheta/occ (accessed November 19, 2014).

Career Pathway Model Effort: Jobs for New Yorkers Task Force. 2014. *Career Pathways: One City Working Together.* New York: Jobs for New Yorkers Task Force.

City of New York. 2015. *Career Pathways: Progress Update.* New York: NCY.

Collaborative Economics & The Woolsey Group. 2014. *Creating Career Pathways in Colorado: A Step-by-Step Guide.* Denver, CO: CWDC. https://www.dol.gov/sites/default/files/documents/nationaldialogue/colorado careerpathwaysguide.pdf (accessed February 27, 2019).

Colorado Workforce Investment Act Annual Reports for PY2013 & PY2014. N.d. Denver, CO: Colorado Workforce Development Council, Colorado

Department of Labor and Employment, & Colorado Workforce Centers. https://www.colorado.gov/pacific/cwdc/news/colorado-workforce -investment-act-annual-report (accessed February 27, 2019).

Conway, Maureen, Amy Blair, Stephen L. Dawson, and Linda Dworak-Munoz. 2007. *Sectoral Strategies for Low Income Workers: Lessons from the Field.* Washington, DC: Aspen Institute, Workforce Strategies Initiative.

Conway, Maureen, and Robert P. Giloth, eds. 2014. *Connecting People to Work: Workforce Intermediaries and Sector Strategies.* New York: American Assembly Press.

DeRenzis, Brooke, and Bryan Wilson. 2015. *Skills in the States: Sector Partnership Policy Toolkit.* Washington, DC: National Skills Coalition. http:// www.nationalskillscoalition.org/resources/publications/file/Final-Sector -Partnership-Policy-Toolkit-1.pdf (accessed February 27, 2019).

Elliott, Mark, and Anne Roder. 2017. *Escalating Gains: Project QUEST'S Sectoral Strategy Pays Off.* New York: Economic Mobility Corporation. https://economicmobilitycorp.org/wp-content/uploads/2018/01/Escalating -Gains_WEB.pdf (accessed November 16, 2018).

Fein, David J. 2012. *Career Pathways as a Framework for Program Design and Evaluation: A Working Paper from the Pathways for Advancing Careers and Education (PACE) Project.* OPRE Report No. 2012-30. Washington, DC: Office of Planning, Research, and Evaluation, Administration for Children and Families, U.S. Department of Health and Human Services.

Gasper, Joseph, and Kathryn Henderson. 2014. *Sector-Focused Career Centers Evaluation: Effects on Employment and Earnings after One Year.* Rockville, MD: Westat, NYC Center for Economic Opportunity Independent Evaluation.

Giloth, Robert P. 2004. *Workforce Intermediaries for the Twenty-First Century.* Philadelphia: Temple University Press.

Glover, Robert W., and Christopher T. King. 2010. "The Promise of Sectoral Approaches to Workforce Development: Towards More Effective, Active Labor Market Policies in the United States." In *Human Resource Economics: Essays in Honor of Vernon M. Briggs, Jr.,* Charles J. Whalen, ed. Kalamazoo, MI: W.E. Upjohn Institute for Employment Research, pp. 215–251.

Hebert, Scott, and Tom Waldron. 2007. *Strengthening Workforce Policy: Applying the Lessons of the JOBS Initiative to Five Key Challenges.* Baltimore, MD: Annie E. Casey Foundation.

Hendra, Richard, David H. Greenberg, Gayle Hamilton, Ari Oppenheim, Alexandra Pennington, Kelsey Schaberg, and Betsy L. Tessler. 2016. *Encouraging Evidence on a Sector-Focused Advancement Strategy: Two-Year Impacts from the WorkAdvance Demonstration.* New York: MDRC.

King, Christopher T. 2014. "Sectoral Workforce and Related Strategies: What

We Know . . . and What We Need to Know." In *Connecting People to Work: Workforce Intermediaries and Sector Strategies*, Maureen Conway and Robert P. Giloth, eds. New York: American Assembly Press, pp. 209–238.

King, Christopher T., and Heath J. Prince. 2015. "Moving Sectoral and Career Pathway Programs from Promise to Scale," In *Transforming U.S. Workforce Development Policies for the 21st Century,* Carl Van Horn, Tammy Edwards, and Todd Greene, eds. Kalamazoo, MI: W.E. Upjohn Institute for Employment Research, pp. 195–229.

King, Christopher T., and Tara Carter Smith. 2007. "State Unemployment Insurance-supported Training Funds." In *Strategies for Financing Workforce Intermediaries: Working Papers*, Heath Prince, ed. Boston, MA: Jobs for the Future/National Fund for Workforce Solutions, pp. 69–122.

Martinson, Karin, and Karen Gardiner. 2014. *Improving the Economic Prospects of Low-Income Individuals through Career Pathways Programs: The Pathways for Advancing Careers and Education Evaluation.* OPRE Report No. 2014-17. Washington, DC: Office of Planning, Research, and Evaluation.

Mikelson, Kelly S., and Demetra Smith Nightingale. 2004. *Estimating Public and Private Expenditures on Occupational Training in the United States.* Washington, DC: U.S. Department of Labor.

New York City Workforce Development Board. 2015. *Quarterly Meeting Minutes.* September 17. New York: New York City Workforce Development Board.

PA Workforce Development Association. n.d. "Industry Partnerships." https://www.pawork.org/about-us/industry-partnership (accessed October 1, 2019).

Prince, Heath, Chris King, and Sarah Oldmixon. 2017. *Promoting the Adoption of Sector Strategies by Workforce Development Boards under the Workforce Innovation and Opportunity Act.* Prepared for the Annie E. Casey Foundation. Austin: Ray Marshall Center for the Study of Human Resources, University of Texas at Austin.

Roder, Anne, and Mark Elliott. 2011. *A Promising Start: Year Up's Initial Impacts on Low-Income Young Adults' Careers.* New York: Economic Mobility Corporation.

———. 2014. *Sustained Gains: Year Up's Continued Impacts on Young Adults' Earnings.* New York: Economic Mobility Corporation.

———. 2019. *Nine-Year Gains: Project QUEST's Continuing Impact.* New York: Economic Mobility Corporation.

Schaberg, Kelsey. 2017. *Can Sector Strategies Promote Longer-Term Effects? Three-Year Results from the WorkAdvance Demonstration.* New York: MDRC.

Smith, Tara, Kristen Christensen, Daniel G. Schroeder, and Christopher T. King. 2012. "Local Investments in Workforce Development Evaluation: Travis County-Funded 2009/10 Participants, Plus Longer-Term Outcomes for Capital IDEA." Austin, TX: Ray Marshall Center for the Study of Human Resources, Lyndon B. Johnson School of Public Affairs, University of Texas at Austin.

Smith, Tara Carter, Christopher T. King, and Daniel G. Schroeder. 2012. *Local Investments in Workforce Development: 2012 Evaluation Update.* Austin: Ray Marshall Center for the Study of Human Resources, Lyndon B. Johnson School of Public Affairs, University of Texas at Austin.

Texas Association of Workforce Boards. 2014. "The Workforce in Texas: Aligning Education to Meet the Needs of Texas Employers." Dallas: Texas Association of Workforce Boards.

Wandner, Stephen A. 2015. "The Future of the Public Workforce System in a Time of Dwindling Resources." In *Transforming U.S. Workforce Development Policies for the 21st Century*, Carl Van Horn, Tammy Edwards, and Todd Greene, eds. Kalamazoo, MI: W.E. Upjohn Institute for Employment Research, pp. 129–166.

Woolsey, Lindsey, and Garrett Groves. 2013. *State Sector Strategies Coming of Age: Implications for State Workforce Policymakers.* Washington, DC: National Governors Association Center for Best Practices.

3

Pairing Program Administration with Evaluation to Build Evidence

The Health Profession Opportunity Grants Program and Federal Evaluation Portfolio

Hilary Bruck
Amelia Popham
Kim Stupica-Dobbs
*Administration for Children and Families,
U.S. Department of Health and Human Services*

The programs funded by the Health Profession Opportunity Grants (HPOG) are based on a career pathways framework of postsecondary education, which posits that instruction should be organized as a series of manageable and well-articulated steps, accompanied by strong supports and connections to employment (Fein 2012).

The Office of Family Assistance (OFA) within the Administration for Children and Families (ACF) administers the HPOG program. ACF is one of 11 operating divisions of the U.S. Department of Health and Human Services and is composed of 21 offices, each of which supports a variety of initiatives that further the ACF mission "to foster health and well-being by providing federal leadership, partnership and resources for the compassionate and effective delivery of human services" (ACF 2016a). This mission and OFA's history of administering federal grant programs that foster family economic security and stability, including the Temporary Assistance for Needy Families (TANF) program, rendered OFA a good fit for managing the HPOG program.

The HPOG program was authorized as a demonstration program with a mandated federal evaluation to assess the success of the initiative. The ACF Office of Planning, Research, and Evaluation (OPRE) leads these evaluation efforts in close coordination with OFA. OPRE's primary duty is to study ACF programs and the populations they serve through rigorous research and evaluation projects. OPRE has a strong history of sponsoring rigorous research on the effectiveness of employment and training strategies for low-income populations. The HPOG research and evaluation studies have become a key component of this expansive and ongoing portfolio of work.

When HPOG was authorized in 2010, the career pathways framework was gaining attention as a promising strategy to promote education, training, and workforce advancement among low-income or low-skilled individuals. At that time, the framework was relatively new, and its effectiveness had not been rigorously evaluated. However, OPRE was in the initial stages of its Pathways for Advancing Careers and Education (PACE) project, a multisite, random-assignment evaluation of programs following the career pathways framework. HPOG provided OPRE with an opportunity to build on this portfolio of research and evaluation around the career pathways approach. HPOG expanded PACE by adding three sites to the six already participating in the evaluation. It also enabled OPRE to design and implement a comprehensive, multipronged research and evaluation portfolio specific to HPOG. With this broad portfolio of studies, OPRE has become a national leader in the rigorous evaluation of postsecondary career pathways programs (ACF 2016b).

In April 2012, the U.S. Departments of Labor, Education, and Health and Human Services formed a federal partnership and issued a letter of joint commitment to promote the use of career pathways and the coordination of activities in this area across agencies. In 2016, an updated letter was circulated that indicated the federal partnership had grown to include the White House National Economic Council, the Office of Management and Budget, and 10 additional federal agencies. The HPOG program, including OPRE's rigorous evaluation of it, is one of a handful of initiatives highlighted in the letter. This underscores both the relevance and significance of HPOG and OPRE's robust career pathways research and evaluation portfolio. The knowledge developed under and evidence generated by HPOG and the portfolio stand to inform and advance the broader research, practice, and policy fields.

The HPOG University Partnership Research Grants (HPOG UP) are a notable component of this portfolio. The grants complement the national implementation and impact evaluations of HPOG by supporting university-led studies tailored to and developed in partnership with individual HPOG programs. This partnership is intended to build the research capacity of the local program partners and increase the utility and effectiveness of the applied research work.

This chapter provides context for the funding of the HPOG UP studies by presenting an overview of the HPOG program—its administration, goals, and strategy—and the federal research and evaluation portfolio within which the studies reside. The chapter also discusses the broader goals of the HPOG research and evaluation portfolio and offers reflections on lessons learned from its implementation thus far. This discussion might be useful for practitioners engaged in administering programs with an evaluation component, as well as researchers and federal staff evaluating career pathways programs or conducting other large-scale, federal evaluation efforts.

THE HPOG PROGRAM

Authorization and Administration

The Affordable Care Act authorized funds to develop demonstration projects that provide TANF recipients and other eligible low-income individuals with the "opportunity to obtain education and training for occupations in the health care field that pay well and are expected to either experience labor shortages or be in high demand." The Bipartisan Budget Act of 2018 extended the HPOG program through fiscal year 2019, allowing the programs to operate through September 29, 2020, and complete the five-year grant cycle. HPOG's appropriation has been $85 million per year, with $10 million of this amount set aside for evaluation activities.

OFA administers federal grant programs that foster family economic security and stability, including the TANF program, the Tribal TANF program, Native Employment Works, Healthy Marriage and Responsible Fatherhood grants, Tribal TANF-Child Welfare Coordination grants, and HPOG.

In administering the HPOG discretionary grant program, OFA awards the grants, monitors grantee program progress, provides programmatic technical assistance directly and through contractors, and coordinates with other ACF offices to ensure HPOG is meeting its intended purpose. Additionally, OFA shares lessons learned through HPOG, such as how TANF agencies can partner more strongly with sector training programs, with other OFA grantees, and with stakeholders.

In September 2010, OFA awarded the first round of five-year HPOG grants, referred to as HPOG 1.0. OFA awarded approximately $67 million in funding, distributed each year, to 32 organizations located across 23 states. There was significant variation among the HPOG grantees in their location, program size, and organizational characteristics. Grantees were located across the country: 9 in the Northeast, 6 in the South, 11 in the Midwest, and 6 in the West. Grantees included 2 community-based organizations, 4 state government agencies, 9 workforce system agencies, 12 higher education institutions, and 5 tribal organizations (of which 4 were tribal community colleges and 1 was a nonprofit tribal social service organization).

In part because grantees had different participant enrollment goals, the amount of funding for HPOG 1.0 grants also varied. During the first year of funding, HPOG 1.0 grants ranged between $1 million and $5 million, with most grantees (18 of 32) receiving awards between $1 and $2 million. Another 9 were awarded between $2 and $3 million, and 5 had grants between $3 and $5 million. After the first year, annual amounts received by each grantee varied somewhat based on program needs. Over the course of its five-year grant period, HPOG 1.0 served 38,891 individuals, of whom 36,548 enrolled in HPOG programs implemented by nontribal grantees, and 2,343 enrolled in HPOG programs implemented by tribal grantees.[1]

In September 2015, OFA awarded a second round of grants, known as HPOG 2.0. These grant awards went to 32 organizations across 21 states, with approximately $72 million disbursed each year. A little more than half of the HPOG 2.0 grantees (17 of 32) had previously received funding through HPOG 1.0; the rest were new grantees. Grantees are located across the country: 9 in the Northeast, 7 in the South, 9 in the Midwest, and 7 in the West. Grantees include 10 higher education institutions, 5 tribal organizations, 7 workforce system agencies, 4 state government agencies, and 6 community-based organizations. Grants range from approximately $1 million to $3 million annually.

HPOG Program Intent and Strategy

The HPOG program addresses two related issues: the shortfall in the supply of qualified health care professionals in the face of expanding demand, and the increasing requirement for a postsecondary education in order to secure a job with a living wage for families. Low-income individuals, including TANF recipients and recipients of other public benefits, often face significant barriers in obtaining the skills, education, and training needed for jobs that provide self-sufficiency and family-sustaining wages.

HPOG thus is structured to meet the dual goals of demonstrating new ways to increase the supply of health care workers while creating vocational opportunities for low-income, low-skilled adults. This is achievable in part because the health care industry has great flexibility. Multiple points of entry exist for low-skilled individuals to find jobs after attaining short-term training credentials. They then can move up the career ladder through additional education and work experience.

More specifically, HPOG aims to

- prepare participants for employment in the health care sector in positions that pay well and are expected to either experience labor shortages or be in high demand;
- target skills and competencies demanded by the health care industry;
- support career pathways, such as an articulated career ladder;
- result in employer- or industry-recognized, portable educational credentials (which can include a license, third-party certification, postsecondary educational certificate or degree, or Registered Apprenticeship certificate);
- combine support services with education and training services to help participants overcome barriers to employment; and
- provide training services at times and locations that are easily accessible for targeted populations (ACF 2010, 2015).

Of these objectives, those pertaining to career pathways, combining support services with training, and connections to employment are most fundamental to the HPOG strategy, distinguishing it from more traditional workforce development strategies.

The HPOG 1.0 Funding Opportunity Announcement (FOA)[2] required HPOG programs to "support career pathways" and to include activities that "support participants' advancement along a defined career pathway, such as an articulated career ladder, if such a pathway exists in the health care industry, or that involve developing such pathways where they do not currently exist" (ACF 2010). The FOA for HPOG 2.0 more carefully defined the career pathways model, stating, "Well-defined career pathways include the specific education and employment steps for the career pathway and how those steps are connected and associated with student supports. They show how training connects to specific employer-recognized credentials; what competencies are required for each step; how credentials stack on each other to lead to higher-paying jobs; and how the noncredit training is connected to credit-bearing education." The FOA also described specific strategies for helping participants progress along a career pathway (ACF 2015).

HPOG grantees create career pathways in accordance with the guidance given above and connect participants to occupational training along those pathways that meets employer demand and requirements. Basic skills training is included in these career pathways and the HPOG program, as it is an important strategy in creating on-ramps in the health care field. In many cases the career pathway begins with those basic skills and then progresses to entry-level health care training, such as home health aide or certified nursing assistant. The participant can then be linked to employment and/or the next training along the chosen career pathway. HPOG grantees vary widely in regard to the health care occupational training being offered, but the most common training programs include those for nurse aides, home health aides, licensed and vocational nurses, registered nurses, medical assistants, pharmacy technicians, and phlebotomists.

In addition to its support for career pathways, another distinctive component of the HPOG program is its emphasis on providing support services to participants to help ensure that they successfully complete their training and secure employment in their field. HPOG's authorizing legislation requires HPOG programs to "provide eligible individuals with financial aid, child care, case management, and other supportive services."[3] Almost all HPOG grantees cover at least part of participants' tuition costs, and virtually all employ case managers who work intensively with program participants. In addition, most HPOG grantees offer other supports, such as transportation vouchers or child care assistance. And nearly all grantees provide a wide variety of employment assistance services to help participants secure a job upon training completion.

In many cases, HPOG grantees partner with a wide variety of agencies to provide support services and, more broadly, to design and implement their programs. Partners may assist with recruiting applicants, delivering training and support services, and placing participants with employers.

HPOG's authorizing legislation requires grant applicants to demonstrate that they have consulted and will coordinate with the state TANF program, the local Workforce Investment Board, the state Workforce Investment Board, and the state apprenticeship agency.[4] In addition, the HPOG 1.0 and 2.0 FOAs strongly encouraged applicants to form strategic partnerships with additional organizations that could provide resources or expertise to the project, particularly health care employers (ACF 2010, 2015).

HPOG's connection to employers and employment also distinguishes it from traditional workforce development programs. As noted above, most programs provide participants with employment assistance services, and many partner with health care employers in the design and delivery of services and supports. In addition, HPOG participants are connected to work in various ways—through clinical rotations built into training courses (staffing hospitals or nursing homes, for example); job shadowing during training; working a full- or part-time job while also taking classes; or cycling back and forth between positions in the health sector and their training courses, as they advance up their career ladder. Many HPOG grantees integrate activities such as soft skills training, résumé and interview preparation, and career readiness classes in order to provide employers with qualified candidates to fill positions. HPOG grantees may employ job navigators and/or partner with workforce agencies in order to communicate with employers about in-demand jobs and connect participants directly to those jobs.

Programmatic Training and Technical Assistance

OFA provides extensive programmatic training and technical assistance to HPOG grantees. These efforts aim to support the goals of

HPOG's authorizing legislation by sharing innovative practices, creating a community of learning among grantees, and supporting continuous quality improvement among programs. Training and technical assistance are provided to grantees in several ways. OFA continually assesses and addresses grantees' training needs as they develop and provides ongoing technical assistance. OFA contractors provide additional support where more intensive technical assistance is needed. Modes of programmatic training and technical assistance include the following:

- Providing HPOG grantees with research publications, tool kits, reports, and other materials relevant to their programs.

- Hosting in-person meetings for HPOG grantees, including an annual meeting and a small number of additional in-person meetings, to address grantees' group technical assistance needs and foster collaboration.

- Offering virtual technical assistance through webinars and virtual learning cohorts, which bring small groups of HPOG grantees together with a subject matter expert to work together over several months to improve a specific aspect of their programs.

- Conducting one-on-one technical assistance with HPOG grantees, which can include coaching, expert assistance, on-site training, or assistance connecting to and building partnerships with local employers and other stakeholders.

OFA has used these training and technical assistance methods to assist HPOG grantees in a wide variety of areas such as career pathways, partnerships, and employer engagement. Other topics of programmatic training and technical assistance have included participant recruitment, assessment, support services, case management, instructor engagement, and the future of health care. OFA regularly explores emerging issues relevant to grantees and new methods of delivering training and technical assistance. Thus, the training and technical assistance provided by OFA continues to grow and change according to the needs of its grantees.

THE HPOG RESEARCH AND EVALUATION PORTFOLIO

Given the scope of activities being conducted under the HPOG program, it is evident that there is much to learn from the initiative's implementation. Fortunately, HPOG was authorized as a demonstration program with a mandated federal evaluation. OPRE is utilizing a multipronged research and evaluation portfolio to assess the success of the HPOG program. OPRE studies ACF programs and the populations they serve through rigorous research and evaluation projects, including evaluations of existing programs, evaluations of innovative approaches to helping low-income children and families, research syntheses, and descriptive and exploratory studies. OPRE also works to improve the analysis of data and coordinate performance management for ACF (ACF 2017).

The ACF evaluation policy, published on the OPRE website in 2012 and in the *Federal Register* in 2014 (79 FR 51574), confirms ACF's commitment to conducting evaluations and to using evidence to inform policy and practice. The evaluation policy identifies five evaluation principles: rigor, relevance, transparency, independence, and ethics. The policy discusses how each of these principles guides ACF's evaluations and culture as a learning organization. The five principles, briefly described below, inform not only OPRE's HPOG portfolio but also all of the research and evaluation activities OPRE undertakes.

1) **Rigor.** ACF is committed to using rigorous methods that are appropriate to the evaluation questions and feasible within budget and other constraints. Rigor is not restricted to impact evaluations but is also necessary in implementation evaluations, descriptive studies, and outcome evaluations, among other types of approaches.

2) **Relevance.** ACF evaluations should address legislative requirements and reflect the needs and interests of stakeholders, including Congress and federal, state, tribal, and local partners.

3) **Transparency.** ACF will make information about planned and ongoing evaluations easily accessible and release results regardless of the findings. Reports will present comprehensive results, including favorable, unfavorable, and null findings.

4) **Independence.** Key stakeholders should participate actively in setting evaluation priorities, identifying evaluation questions, and assessing the implications of findings. However, it is important to insulate evaluation functions from undue influence and from both the appearance and the reality of bias. To promote objectivity, ACF protects independence in the design, conduct, and analysis of evaluations.

5) **Ethics.** ACF-sponsored evaluations will be conducted in an ethical manner and safeguard the dignity, rights, safety, and privacy of participants (ACF 2012).

While much of ACF's evaluation activity is overseen by OPRE, sometimes other ACF offices also sponsor evaluations. The evaluation policy describes OPRE's role in working with the other ACF offices to promote quality, coordination, and usefulness of evaluations undertaken across ACF. As discussed later in this chapter, even when OPRE is responsible for overseeing an evaluation, it works closely with other relevant ACF offices in designing and conducting evaluations related to programs administered by those offices.

OPRE includes four divisions: the Division of Economic Independence, the Division of Child and Family Development, the Division of Family Strengthening, and the Division of Data and Improvement. The HPOG research and evaluation portfolio resides within the Division of Economic Independence (DEI), which focuses on welfare, employment, and family self-sufficiency. DEI's research in these areas is designed to expand knowledge about effective programs to promote employment, self-sufficiency, and economic well-being among low-income families. DEI's research focuses on five major areas: TANF, employment and the labor market, education and training, behavioral science, and cross-cutting and other safety net research (ACF 2016b).

When the HPOG program was authorized in 2010, DEI already had a strong history of sponsoring rigorous research on the effectiveness of employment and training strategies for improving employment and earnings for TANF recipients and other low-income individuals. Additionally, DEI was leading the field in evaluating career pathways programs with the launch of its PACE evaluation in 2007.[5] Given that the HPOG program's authorizing legislation mandated a comprehensive federal evaluation, DEI partnered with OFA from the beginning to design and launch the HPOG research and evaluation portfolio.

Portfolio Purpose and Design

As noted, HPOG was authorized as a demonstration program. Generally, the purpose of such programs is to develop and test effective program approaches and models. Accordingly, HPOG's authorizing legislation requires that a federal evaluation be undertaken to assess HPOG's effectiveness. Specifically, the legislation tasks the evaluation with determining whether and how HPOG supports "successful activities for creating opportunities for developing and sustaining, particularly with respect to low-income individuals and other entry-level workers, a health professions workforce that has accessible entry points, that meets high standards for education, training, certification, and professional development, and that provides increased wages and affordable benefits, including health care coverage, that are responsive to the workforce's needs."[6]

By establishing the HPOG program as a demonstration, its authorizing legislation underscored the importance of coupling program operations with evaluation. Further, it signaled to grant applicants that the evaluation is a fundamental component of the HPOG initiative, not an afterthought; hence, grant award is contingent on participation in the evaluation. This enables ACF to delineate evaluation requirements in the HPOG grant FOAs, so that anyone applying for an HPOG grant understands the expectation of participation in federal evaluation activities and what it will likely entail.

By explicitly linking program and evaluation, HPOG's authorizing legislation also set the stage for the way in which OPRE and OFA operate in partnership to administer the program and to design, execute, and apply learning from the evaluation efforts. Through this partnership, OPRE and OFA strive to capitalize on the significant learning opportunity that HPOG affords. The legislative mandate for the evaluation, paired with the resources to carry it out, presents an opportunity for rigorous evaluation of wide scope and rich depth. It is an opportunity to learn whether and how this program model achieves its dual goals of meeting the health care sector's demand for qualified workers and low-income individuals' need to secure jobs that support self-sufficiency. It is an opportunity to promote the use of evidence to inform programmatic decisions at the federal and local levels. And it is an opportunity to advance the broader employment and training research, practice, and policy fields regarding the effectiveness of sector-based, career pathways programs serving low-income populations. The HPOG research and evaluation portfolio endeavors to pursue and achieve these expansive learning goals.

OPRE's and OFA's selection of the primary research questions for the portfolio was driven by the specific Congressional evaluation requirements and ACF priorities. These questions were then supplemented with additional questions to address existing knowledge gaps in the postsecondary education and training research and practice fields. At the same time, OFA considered what information was essential for program performance monitoring and management. OPRE and OFA intentionally coordinated the identification of this information with the evaluation to ensure that the needs of both efforts were met in a manner that also produced useful, accessible information for the grantees at the lowest possible burden to them in terms of participating in these efforts.

The result was a research and evaluation portfolio comprising several individual projects or studies, each with a distinct purpose: to examine HPOG program implementation, systems change, and participant outcomes; to assess impacts; or to support the collection of program administrative data. OPRE designed the projects to employ the most appropriate and rigorous methods to accomplish their specific aims, per the ACF evaluation policy, while also coordinating them to avoid duplicative efforts, maximize the reuse of information, and promote cross-project learning.

There are two phases of the research and evaluation portfolio. The first phase comprises projects and studies specific to the HPOG 1.0 grants, including the HPOG UP grants that are the subject of this publication. The second phase comprises projects and studies specific to the HPOG 2.0 grants. Table 3.1 presents an overview of the components of the HPOG 1.0 portfolio. The components of the HPOG 2.0 portfolio are discussed in the concluding section of this chapter.

Research and evaluation specific to HPOG 1.0

OPRE's research and evaluation portfolio for HPOG 1.0 includes eight projects, each focused on a set of core research questions. Each of the 32 HPOG 1.0 grantees participated in one or more components of the portfolio (see Table 3.1).

Some components of the HPOG 1.0 portfolio ended when or shortly after the HPOG 1.0 grants concluded in 2015, whereas other components are ongoing and seek to assess longer-term outcomes and impacts. Final reports from the National Implementation Evaluation and the Evaluation of Tribal HPOG are available on the OPRE website, and subsequent chapters in this book describe these studies in more detail.[7] The HPOG 1.0 short-term impact report and site-specific short-term impact reports for all nine programs participating in PACE are also available on OPRE's website.[8] Reports on HPOG and PACE intermediate and longer-term impacts are expected in 2019/2020 and 2021, respectively. All these findings will be published on the OPRE website as they become available.

The HPOG UP grants are an important component of OPRE's research and evaluation portfolio. OPRE staff considered the set of grants an opportunity to complement its research and evaluation portfolio by supporting studies tailored to and developed in partnership with individual HPOG programs. The grants required applicants to demonstrate a partnership with one or more of the HPOG programs as an integral part of the research plan development and execution. In this way, the studies could tailor the research questions to specific programs, in contrast to the other portfolio components, which focus largely on research questions applicable to the full set of nontribal or tribal grantees in the HPOG program. OPRE staff viewed the HPOG UP grants as a way to emphasize the importance of developing true working research partnerships with HPOG programs and other relevant entities within the community, thereby increasing the effectiveness of the applied research work. OPRE staff hope that the findings from the HPOG UP studies not only inform the HPOG program partner's program implementation and service delivery but also benefit the education, training, and employment research field more broadly (ACF 2011).

In 2011, OPRE awarded the first round of HPOG UP research grants through a competitive grant review process. The five grants examined specific program components, models, or contexts, such as a two-generation approach or serving special populations, in partnership with one or more HPOG 1.0 programs. Table 3.2 provides an overview of these grants.

Subsequent chapters of this publication describe in depth the studies conducted under these grants and offer insights based on their find-

Table 3.1 Components of the HPOG 1.0 Research and Evaluation Portfolio

Project title	Primary research questions	Participating HPOG 1.0 grantees	Status of reports[a]
HPOG Implementation, Systems and Outcomes Project	• What grantee-, program-, and participant-level data measures are required for ACF performance management and the evaluation?	All 32 HPOG 1.0 grantees	Released: • Literature reviews • Annual reports
HPOG National Implementation Evaluation	• How are HPOG programs implemented? • What changes to the service delivery system are associated with HPOG program implementation? • What individual-level outputs and outcomes occur?	All 27 nontribal HPOG 1.0 grantees	Released: • Design report • Systems change analysis report • Interim implementation & outcomes report • Final implementation & outcomes report
HPOG Impact Study	• What short-term impacts (those assessed 15 mo. after random assignment) did HPOG programs as a group have on participant outcomes? • To what extent did those impacts vary across selected subpopulations? • Which locally adopted program components influenced average impacts? • To what extent did participation in a particular HPOG component(s) change the impact?	23 HPOG 1.0 grantees[b]	Released: • Design report • Analysis plan • Program implementation and short-term impact report

| Pathways for Advancing Careers and Education | • What short-term impacts (*those assessed 15 mo. after random assignment*) did each program have on key indicators of progress in career pathways–relevant training?
• What short-term impacts did each program have on entry to career-track employment and earnings?
• What is the basic design, underlying logic, and institutional and community context of each program?
• To what extent was the intervention delivered as planned? | Three HPOG 1.0 grantees:[c] Pima Community College, San Diego Workforce Partnership, and Workforce Development Council of Seattle-King County | Released:
• Design report
• Analysis plan
• Program profiles
• Participant experience briefs
• Program implementation and short-term impact reports |
| Career Pathways Intermediate Outcomes Study | • What are the intermediate impacts (*those assessed 36 mo. after random assignment*) of the HPOG and PACE programs on their populations of interest?
• How do effects of career pathways programs vary over time, across outcomes or domains, by occupational sector, by program model, and by participant characteristics?
• Do different models, strategies, or components lead to different impacts for participants?
• How can career pathways models be adjusted to promote longer-term outcomes for participants? | Aggregate impacts for all HPOG 1.0 grantees who participated in HPOG Impact and PACE

Site-specific impacts for sub-set of selected HPOG 1.0 grantees | Released:
• Analysis plans for the HPOG and PACE intermediate follow-up study
• Cost-benefit analysis plan

Forthcoming:
• Cost-benefit reports (expected 2019/2020)
• Intermediate impact reports (expected 2019/2020)
• Cross-site synthesis brief (expected 2020) |

(continued)

Table 3.1 (continued)

Project title	Primary research questions	Participating HPOG 1.0 grantees	Status of reports[a]
Career Pathways Long-Term Outcomes Study	• What are the longer-term impacts (*those assessed 72 mo. after random assignment*) of the HPOG and PACE programs on their populations of interest? • How do effects of career pathways programs vary over time, across outcomes or domains, by occupational sector, by program model, and by participant characteristics? • Do different models, strategies, or components lead to different impacts for participants? • How can career pathways models be adjusted to promote longer-term outcomes for participants?	Aggregate impacts for all HPOG 1.0 grantees who participated in HPOG Impact and PACE Site-specific impacts for subset of selected HPOG 1.0 grantees	Forthcoming: • Analysis plans for the HPOG and PACE long-term follow-up study (expected 2020) • Cost-benefit analysis plan (expected 2020) • Cost-benefit reports (expected 2021) • Long-term impact reports (expected 2021)
Evaluation of Tribal HPOG	• What frameworks and relationships did the Tribal HPOG grantees create to implement their programs? • How were training and support services delivered? • What were participant outcomes? • Was health care workforce capacity enhanced in tribal communities?	All five Tribal HPOG 1.0 grantees	Released: • Practice briefs • Interim report • Final report

| HPOG University Partnership Research Grants | • Specific inquiries regarding: developing a diverse workforce; empowerment-based workforce development models; the recruitment and retention of American Indians into professional nursing programs; effects of a two-generation program; and effects of participant networks and community context. | Five HPOG 1.0 grantees | Released:
 • Summary brief |

[a] Most projects also released special topics papers. Additional analyses and reports may be available as funding allows.

[b] Inclusive of data from the three HPOG 1.0 grantees in PACE. Nontribal grantees collecting individual-level data as part of another portfolio project were not required to participate in the Impact Study; all the rest were.

[c] Instituto del Progreso Latino is one of the nine sites in the PACE evaluation and implemented one of the HPOG 1.0 grantee's six HPOG programs. Instituto is not reflected in the count of HPOG 1.0 grantees participating in the PACE evaluation in the table above; however, data collected from Instituto under PACE is included in the HPOG Impact Study's analytic sample.

SOURCE: OPRE (n.d.).

Table 3.2 HPOG UP Research Grants Awarded in 2011

Grantee	Project title	Project summary	HPOG 1.0 program partner
Northwestern University, in partnership with University of Texas at Austin	*CareerAdvance*: A Dual-Generation Program's Effects on Families and Children	Examined two-generation program effects on family, parent, and child outcomes	Community Action Project of Tulsa County, Inc. (Tulsa, OK)
Temple University	Building Capacities/Making Connections: A Multi-Year Study of Human and Social Capital Development through the Health Information Professions Career Pathways Initiative	Examined how participant networks and community contexts facilitate or impede success in workforce development programs	Temple University, Center for Social Policy and Community Development (Philadelphia, PA)
Brandeis University	Study of Employment and Advancement of Racial, Ethnic, and Linguistic Minorities for New Hampshire Health Profession Opportunity Project	Assessed best practices for developing a diverse workforce and related career mobility pipeline	New Hampshire Office of Minority Health and Refugee Affairs (Concord, NH)
Loyola University of Chicago	Evaluation of Empowerment Pathways to Self-Sufficiency in Health Professions Career Development for Low-Income Individuals	Evaluated the extent to which psychological self-sufficiency affects employment placement and outcomes in health professions	Gateway Technical College (Kenosha, WI); Southland Health Care Forum (Chicago Heights, IL); Instituto del Progreso Latino (Chicago, IL)
North Dakota State University	Sustaining Career Pathways for American Indian Health Professionals in North Dakota: Building Apprenticeship and Workforce Options with the Next Steps HPOG Project	Explored the recruitment and retention of American Indians into professional nursing programs	Cankdeska Cikana Community College (Fort Totten, ND)

SOURCE: OPRE (2017).

ings. Additionally, OPRE's website contains a brief that presents an overview of these studies.[9]

Overarching Goals of the Portfolio

As described earlier, through the design of the research and evaluation portfolio, OPRE and OFA intend to capitalize on the expansive learning opportunities that HPOG affords. These opportunities can be viewed as the principal goals of the portfolio—assessing the effectiveness of HPOG; promoting the use of evidence to inform programmatic decisions at the federal and local levels; and advancing the broader employment and training research, practice, and policy fields. Individual elements of the portfolio, and the sum of its parts, contribute in different ways to realizing these goals.

Assessing HPOG's effectiveness

In order to rigorously assess HPOG's effectiveness, the portfolio includes impact evaluations. These evaluations use an experimental design, where eligible individuals are randomized to a treatment group, which is given access to HPOG, or to a control group, which is not given access to HPOG but may access any other services available in the community. Randomization ensures that the two groups have no systematic differences at baseline, making it possible to interpret subsequent differences in average outcomes between the groups as the impact of access to the HPOG intervention, with confidence that this attribution is accurate (Peck et al. 2014).

In addition to answering questions about overall HPOG program effectiveness, the HPOG 1.0 impact study experimentally tested three specific program components, aiming to identify which elements of career pathways programs contribute most to advancing the labor market success of participants. This is the first large-scale impact study of career pathways to test the impact of specific program components (Peck et al. 2014). In this way, the study not only enhances the assessment of HPOG's effectiveness but also advances the research field.

OPRE staff recognized that robust descriptive information was critical for fully understanding HPOG's effectiveness. The portfolio therefore included comprehensive, rigorous evaluations to assess program implementation, systems change, outputs, and outcomes, and projects that support the collection of program administrative data.

Promoting the use of evidence

The HPOG research and evaluation portfolio promotes the use of evidence at both the federal and local levels. It advances the former via OPRE's close coordination with OFA and participation in federal interagency activities, and the latter via activities intended to boost the research capacity of HPOG grantees.

As described above, OPRE and OFA work in partnership to administer the HPOG program and its attendant research and evaluation portfolio. This partnership facilitates the generation and application of evidence to inform OFA's administration of the HPOG program. For example, OPRE and OFA jointly developed the list of required uniform data measures and definitions that are used for both evaluation and performance management purposes. During the development process, OPRE supported OFA in considering the goals and needs of program monitoring and what they wanted to learn through the evaluation, and identifying the types of measures that would reliably meet these purposes. The HPOG 1.0 and 2.0 management information systems that collect the uniform data automatically generate the Performance Progress Reports grantees must submit to OFA on a semiannual and annual basis. This ensures OFA receives comprehensive, reliable information from each grantee in order to monitor program performance. Further, federal staff can access the management information systems to conduct queries or run reports to assess the progress of grantees or respond to an external request for information.[10]

OFA applied what it learned from the HPOG 1.0 research and evaluation portfolio to inform its drafting of the HPOG 2.0 FOA. The program components they determined important to the HPOG approach reflected lessons learned and emerging findings from the HPOG 1.0 evaluation. For example, as described earlier in the chapter, OFA more carefully defined the career pathways model in the HPOG 2.0 FOA, having learned under HPOG 1.0 that many participants completed only one, entry-level training. Additionally, OFA encouraged applicants to consider offering supportive service activities that, based on the existing body of evidence and past performance of HPOG programs, were likely to improve program outcomes. These activities included basic skills education and work readiness activities.

OPRE participates in several interagency work groups to share information about and findings from the HPOG research and evaluation portfolio with fellow federal agencies. These activities are described in more detail later in this chapter, but they are important to note here because they help promote federal agencies' awareness and application of emerging evidence from HPOG to inform their own work.

The portfolio also seeks to build the capacity of local program operators in participating in, understanding the results of, and applying the learning from the HPOG research and evaluation efforts. For example, the federal evaluation teams provide training and technical assistance around evaluation-related issues such as collecting informed consent, configuring intake processes to accommodate random assignment, conducting random assignment, and monitoring sample buildup. Grantees are provided with intensive technical assistance around the use of the HPOG management information systems, such as resources and training sessions regarding collecting and entering data, understanding the data, using the data to track participant progress and service delivery and inform programmatic decisions, and manipulating the data to create products (such as lists, graphs, and charts) to share program progress with stakeholders. Additionally, OPRE and its evaluation contractors attend OFA's annual meeting for grantees to lead sessions on evaluation-related topics. Finally, as described earlier in the chapter, OPRE intentionally funded the HPOG UP research grants to help build the research capacity of programs by requiring that the research grantees partner with an HPOG program to design and execute the study. OPRE staff hope that these capacity-building efforts translate more generally to enhance the grantees' participation in and inform their consumption of other research and evaluation efforts.

Advancing the broader research, practice, and policy fields

The HPOG research and evaluation portfolio also strives to advance the broader employment and training research, practice, and policy fields. Chiefly, it seeks to accomplish this by supporting and executing a comprehensive set of rigorous studies, and disseminating the resulting information and findings.

When HPOG was authorized in 2010, there was only limited evidence on career pathways programs and their effectiveness. OPRE's PACE evaluation was one of the first, large-scale random-assignment evaluations of programs following a career pathways framework. The HPOG research and evaluation portfolio, established three years after PACE launched, expanded the number of impact evaluations under way and integrated a comprehensive set of rigorous descriptive studies. Each study in the HPOG portfolio employs the most rigorous methods applicable to its inquiry, per the ACF evaluation policy.

Many studies in the portfolio are using and/or developing and testing new methods. For example, the HPOG 1.0 National Implementation Evaluation conducted a systems change analysis that represents one of the first efforts to comprehensively evaluate the systems that support career-pathways-based training programs for low-income adults. The exploratory analysis offered lessons for future research as well as policy implications (Bernstein et al. 2016). The HPOG 1.0 Impact Study considered a new method, called Cross-Site Attributional Model Improved by Calibration to Within-Site Individual Randomization Findings, or CAMIC, to reduce bias in analyses that researchers use to understand how a program's structure and implementation leads its impact to vary. The study conducted a simulation of the method, published the results, and encouraged fellow researchers to advance the methodology by applying it to other settings (Bell et al. 2017).

The portfolio also pushes forward the research and practice fields by evolving based on its own experiences and findings. As described earlier in the chapter, there are two phases of the research and evaluation portfolio, with the first phase focused on the HPOG 1.0 grants and the second phase pertaining to the HPOG 2.0 grants. The design and execution of, and emerging findings from, the first phase informed the blueprint for the second phase. For example, the uniform data that grantees are required to collect, data collection protocols and instruments, and analytic methods were all reviewed, reflected on, and sharpened where needed for the HPOG 2.0 efforts, based on the HPOG 1.0 experience. In this way, the portfolio maintains relevance—keyed to the most recent research findings and programmatic experiences—which, in turn, advances OPRE's portfolio and the career pathways research and practice fields more broadly.

The ability to translate and disseminate findings from the HPOG portfolio to relevant stakeholders in a way they can understand and apply the knowledge is critical for informing the broader field. Fortunately, to this end, OPRE has an array of tools at its disposal. Foremost, as described earlier, the ACF evaluation policy upholds the principle of transparency, committing OPRE to making information about evaluations (e.g., questions, methods, designs, time line) easily accessible on the web and other platforms; releasing findings regardless of whether they are positive, negative, or null; and archiving evaluation data for secondary use by interested researchers. When drafting reports and briefs, OPRE evaluation contractors are expected to adhere to the Federal Plain Language Guidelines, which impart strategies for achieving clear communication.[11] OPRE has also supported the development of various resources on dissemination of human services research, including the Value-Added Dissemination Framework, to inform project dissemination activities (Macoubrie and Harrison 2013). Additionally, OPRE employs a full-time dissemination strategist who provides counsel regarding effective dissemination approaches, and prepares information for distribution via the OPRE website and social media.

The HPOG research and evaluation portfolio strives to utilize all these dissemination tools to ensure the knowledge it generates is intentionally and strategically shared. In all its HPOG evaluation contracts, OPRE calls for detailed reporting and publication of evaluation designs, analysis plans, and findings using vehicles tailored to the target audience, including technical reports, special topics papers, and short, visually appealing briefs. OPRE also supports its HPOG evaluation contractors in presenting study information and findings via conference presentations, webinars, blog posts, and social media, among other channels. In addition to the information contained on OPRE's website about the portfolio and its component studies, OPRE also supports one of its contractors in hosting and maintaining a career pathways website, which is intended to compile and disseminate information related to career pathways programs, research, and evaluation in one designated site, with a particular focus on the PACE and HPOG initiatives.[12]

Lastly, coordination with fellow federal agencies is critical to the portfolio's objective of advancing the broader employment and training research, practice, and policy fields. As noted earlier, OPRE participates in a range of federal interagency working groups, through which it shares information from its HPOG research and evaluation portfolio and seeks to coordinate its career pathways work with relevant efforts at other federal agencies. The joint letter expressing federal commitment to support the use of career pathways, described at the beginning of this chapter, led to the formation of the Interagency Working Group on Career Pathways. Staff from more than 10 federal agencies participate in the working group, including OPRE and OFA staff. This group shares information about ongoing work related to career pathways and identifies opportunities for coordination and collaboration across agencies. Given that the joint letter explicitly references HPOG as an example of a career pathways initiative, working group members regularly ask about the status of and findings from the HPOG portfolio, for their general awareness and to inform their own work.

OPRE also leads the Federal Employment, Training, and Education Research and Evaluation Working Group. Launched in 2009, this ongoing working group seeks to promote ongoing exchanges between agencies about their research and evaluations in various stages of development, and explore possibilities for jointly funding and supporting research. Staff from five federal agencies, including the Departments of Health and Human Services, Labor, Education, Agriculture, and Housing and Urban Development, regularly attend meetings. Thus, the working group serves as another vehicle through which OPRE can disseminate information about its HPOG portfolio and identify opportunities for coordinating with other federal agencies in this work.

HPOG RESEARCH AND EVALUATION: CURRENT REFLECTIONS AND FUTURE PATHS

Next Steps for the Portfolio

The research and evaluation portfolio for HPOG 1.0 remains active. Several HPOG 1.0 portfolio components are ongoing to assess intermediate and longer-term outcomes and impacts. This is in keeping with the career pathways theory of change and HPOG program logic model. Career pathways organize postsecondary education and training as a series of manageable steps leading to successively higher credentials and employment opportunities in growing occupations. They are designed to allow entries, exits, and reentries at each step, depending on skill levels and prior training, employment, and changing personal situations. Thus, for participants in career pathways programs, outcomes related to educational progress, employment, and earnings are expected to manifest over a period of time. Similarly, as depicted in Figure 3.1, HPOG's logic model reflects the expectation that receipt of vocational training and support services will lead to vocational skills and industry-recognized credentials, among other outputs; these outputs should then result in educational progress, employment, higher earnings, and other employment-related outcomes over a period of time (Harvill, Moulton, and Peck 2015).

Therefore, OPRE considers the impact findings assessed at 15 months after random assignment as preliminary, or short term. At the outset of the HPOG 1.0 Impact Study, educational progress was designated as the confirmatory outcome at this first follow-up point.[13] OPRE and the evaluation team based this decision on the HPOG logic model described above, theorizing that it may take more than 15 months for participants to make substantial progress toward major postsecondary training credentials and move into and advance in career-track employment. OPRE and the evaluation teams anticipate that employment and earnings-related impacts will more fully emerge by 36 and 72 months after random assignment. Consequently, for these intermediate and long-term studies in OPRE's HPOG evaluation portfolio, earnings will be a confirmatory outcome, in addition to educational progress, and employment and other outcomes will also be assessed. Examining findings at all three points—short-term, intermediate, and long-term—will permit OPRE to thoroughly assess whether and how career pathways programs advance individuals toward self-sufficiency.

At the time of drafting this chapter, the HPOG 2.0 Program is in its fourth year of grants. Given the extension of the HPOG program, the HPOG 2.0 grantees will be able to complete the full five-year grant period, and the corresponding research and evaluation portfolio will continue. As noted earlier in the chapter, the HPOG 2.0 portfolio was informed by and is building off knowledge being generated by the HPOG 1.0 portfolio. Table 3.3 presents a summary of the specific components of the HPOG 2.0 portfolio.

92

Figure 3.1 HPOG Program Logic Model

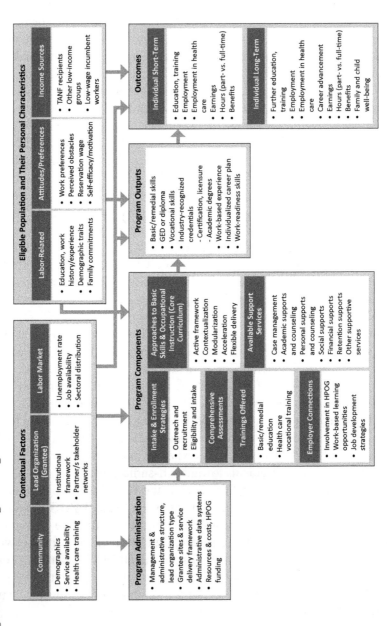

SOURCE: Harvill, Moulton, and Peck (2015).

Table 3.3 Components of the HPOG 2.0 Research and Evaluation Portfolio

Project title	Project purpose	Participating HPOG 2.0 grantees
HPOG 2.0 Evaluation Design and Performance Reporting	• Provide recommendations for the design of an evaluation to assess implementation, outcomes, systems change, and impacts • Design and maintain a management information system to collect data for ACF performance management and evaluation • Provide intensive technical assistance to grantees around the use of the management information system	All 32 HPOG 2.0 grantees
HPOG 2.0 National Evaluation	• Design and conduct an impact study to assess the effectiveness of HPOG 2.0 • Design and conduct a descriptive study that includes implementation, outcomes, and systems change studies • Design and conduct a study to assess the costs and benefits of a standard HPOG 2.0 program • Provide evaluation-related technical assistance to enhance grantees' research capacity	All 27 nontribal HPOG 2.0 grantees
HPOG 2.0 Tribal Evaluation	• Design and conduct a comprehensive implementation and outcome evaluation of the tribal grantees • Provide evaluation-related technical assistance to enhance the tribal grantees' research capacity	All five Tribal HPOG 2.0 grantees
HPOG 2.0 University Partnership Research Grants	• Conduct specific studies in partnership with an HPOG 2.0 program • Support studies pertaining to: career advancement in health care; empowerment-based workforce development models and employer engagement; and effects of a two-generation program	Three HPOG 2.0 grantees *(The WorkPlace, Inc.; Chicago State University; the Community Action Project of Tulsa County)*

SOURCE: OPRE (n.d.).

So, in addition to the status of HPOG reauthorization, next steps for OPRE's career pathways portfolio are also contingent on how the full set of findings from the HPOG 1.0 and 2.0 portfolios develop. From these findings, OPRE hopes to learn about the implementation and short-term, intermediate, and long-term impacts of the career pathways models included in HPOG and PACE. Further, we hope to learn whether the effects vary in systematic ways (over time, across outcomes, by occupation, by program model, or by participant characteristics); whether specific models, strategies, or components lead to different impacts; and whether and how models can be adjusted to promote longer-term outcomes for participants. This comprehensive array of findings will help reveal where there are still gaps in knowledge that merit further research efforts.

OPRE also anticipates coordinating future research efforts with other federal agencies conducting work around career pathways. Specifically, the Workforce Innovation and Opportunity Act requires the U.S. Department of Labor to conduct a study to build on career advancement models and practices in the health care and early education and child care arenas.[14] Findings from OPRE's career pathways portfolio have informed the Department of Labor's assessment of evaluation design options to address critical gaps in knowledge. As both agencies move forward with portfolios of work in this area, they intend to leverage information from and coordinate closely with each other.

Reflections and Lessons Learned

This chapter shows that HPOG is a multifaceted initiative with significant goals, and that its research and evaluation portfolio is equally comprehensive, with wide-ranging learning objectives. Taking a step back to reflect on the HPOG initiative and experience thus far brings to the surface several notable lessons learned.

Importance of legislation

As ACF's evaluation policy states, "For new initiatives and demonstrations in particular, evaluations will be more feasible and useful when planned in concert with the planning of the initiative or demonstration, rather than as an afterthought" (ACF 2012). This alignment is precisely what HPOG's authorizing legislation achieved. By establishing HPOG as a demonstration and mandating and providing specific parameters for an evaluation, the legislation established rigorous evaluation as a fundamental component of the initiative and set the precedent for OPRE's and OFA's partnership in executing both the program and the evaluation. The scope and duration of the HPOG research and evaluation portfolio likely would not be possible without this legislative support. At numerous briefings and convenings, HPOG has been called a model for legislation in terms of pairing programmatic activities with evaluation to support evidence building.

Importance of establishing an evaluation policy

ACF's evaluation policy serves as the underpinning for the HPOG research and evaluation portfolio and has been instrumental to the work. For example, in keeping with the policy's principle of rigor, each study in the portfolio was designed to employ the most rigorous methods appropriate to accomplish their specific aims, and experimental approaches are used where possible to assess causal questions about HPOG's effectiveness. To ensure relevancy, the portfolio's primary research questions were driven by HPOG's authorizing legislation, ACF priorities, and the interests of relevant stakeholders, and the portfolio is coordinated with and informed by OFA's programmatic efforts. To promote transparency, detailed study information and findings are widely disseminated by multiple platforms, and analysis and design plans are published in advance of the study's execution and assessment of findings. Lastly, the portfolio also upholds the evaluation policy's tenets of independence and ethics—all research and evaluation efforts are conducted by external, highly qualified entities, who are awarded the work through competitive grants or contracts, and who comply with regulations governing human subjects research. These are just some of the ways in which the ACF evaluation policy has guided the design, content, and execution of the HPOG research and evaluation portfolio. In addition, the policy serves as an authoritative resource for OPRE to stand on and refer to when providing recommendations for evaluation efforts, around HPOG and more broadly.

The report recently released by the Commission on Evidence-Based Policymaking underscores the importance of having formally established evaluation policies.[15] The commission references the establishment of departmentwide evaluation and research policies that encourage rigor, credibility, independence, and transparency as one way to strengthen the program evaluation function within the federal government, and a step toward expanding evidence building. Further, that the commission's report identifies OPRE as one of a few strong evaluation units currently existing across government reinforces the value and significance of our evaluation policy.

Importance of relationships

Another lesson gleaned from the HPOG portfolio is the importance of relationships—chiefly, those with the program office (i.e., OFA) and the local grantees—to successful evaluation efforts. As the chapter describes in detail, OPRE and OFA maintain a close, collaborative partnership to coordinate the execution of the HPOG program and research and evaluation efforts. This partnership has been crucial for ensuring that these undertakings learn from and inform each other; it strengthens the relevancy of the research and evaluation efforts and applicability of resulting findings. However, in keeping with the ACF evaluation policy's principles of independence and ethics, OPRE staff are careful to actively monitor the nature of the partnership with OFA, and to fund independent entities to conduct the evaluation activities, to protect the evaluation portfolio from undue influence or bias.

As noted, the portfolio also helps local program operators participate in, understand the results of, and apply the learning from the research and evaluation efforts. Intentionally incorporating activities to address this aim not only benefits the grantees, it also benefits the evaluation efforts by supporting grantee buy-in. If the grantees understand how the data and eventual findings can inform and enhance their own work (for example, by providing information to guide program improvements or share with stakeholders to demonstrate progress), their cooperation in and enthusiasm for participating in the evaluation efforts strengthen. This in turn facilitates grantees' collection of high-quality data and smoother operations on the ground in carrying out the evaluation activities. However, it is important to consider the burden placed on grantees in terms of participating in the evaluation and capacity-building efforts. Layering on too many demands can have a negative effect, leading to grantee burnout or frustration. OPRE and OFA therefore strive to balance grantees' information collection activities and evaluation requirements with the practicality of carrying them out. We also consider whether and how the data grantees are asked to collect will be useful to them, so they recognize and capitalize on the value in collecting it, and so the evaluation maintains applicability to program operations on the ground.

This segues to lessons learned from HPOG around the importance of uniform data—how it can affect relationships and how it serves program and evaluation purposes. As described earlier, OPRE and OFA decided to require that the HPOG grantees collect a uniform set of data measures and enter the data into a management information system created exclusively for HPOG. In jointly developing the list of uniform data measures, OPRE and OFA considered what data would meet the needs of OFA for performance monitoring, the HPOG grantees for program management, and OPRE for research and evaluation. We aimed to arrive at a set of measures that would meet this range of needs, could be collected reliably, and whose collection wouldn't overburden the grantees.

Having uniform data across grantees has imparted many benefits. The HPOG 1.0 and 2.0 management information systems were designed to automatically aggregate the data entered by the grantees into the performance progress reports they submit to OFA. This supplies OFA with detailed and reliable information on which to base program performance monitoring. For each grantee, OFA receives data on a range of program activities, including participant enrollment in and completion of health care training by occupation, participation in basic skills activities, receipt of support services, employment, and average wages. This level of information enables much more informed and active monitoring of performance than simple narrative summaries of progress would support. OFA can engage with the grantees on a deeper level to understand program operations and offer support. In terms of benefiting the evaluation, the uniform data measures are defined at the grantee, program, and individual levels, which enables the aggregation and analysis of data in different ways to assess outputs and outcomes meaningfully across grantees, programs, and participant subgroups. It also enables the evaluation to link to administrative data, since the individual-level data include participant social security numbers.

That said, collecting uniform data has not been without challenges. The management information systems developed to support the data collection have been costly. Significant financial resources and time have been required to develop, test, and maintain the systems, and remain in compliance with federal regulations pertaining to data safety and security. Significant resources have also been needed to support the provision of intensive technical assistance to the HPOG grantees around using the systems, ranging from the development of guidance manuals, to establishing a help desk, providing training webinars, and offering one-on-one assistance. While this assistance has strengthened the evaluation team's interaction and relationship with the grantees, it has also stressed it in times when the systems have encountered technical difficulties, or the grantees have struggled with data entry tasks. So, while collecting uniform data via management information systems can be an invaluable tool, one must be prepared for the time, effort, financial resources, and user support required for the effort.

OPRE is particularly mindful of the need to establish positive relationships with the Tribal HPOG grantees and their stakeholders, including tribal leaders, community members, and others. At the onset of the portfolio, OPRE established its expectations that the tribal evaluation team work closely with the tribal grantees to ensure the tribes are comfortable with the evaluation efforts and that the efforts meet not only ACF's needs but also each tribe's needs while respecting tribal sovereignty. OPRE emphasized the importance of establishing relationships that were mutually beneficial and promoted bidirectional learning between the grantees and the evaluation team. Maintaining these relationships requires ongoing engagement and discussions with the tribal grantees throughout the evaluation efforts.

As noted, ACF's evaluation policy states that key stakeholders should actively participate in setting evaluation priorities, identifying evaluation questions, and assessing the implications of findings; at the same time evaluations should maintain transparency and independence and ensure neither the appearance nor the reality of bias. Across both rounds of HPOG, the tribal evaluation team actively engaged with tribal leadership for each awarded Tribal HPOG grantee, as appropriate, and other local stakeholders to ensure that the evaluation efforts were firmly anchored in questions meaningful to the tribes and that assist local service providers in better serving their communities. The evaluation team discussed the goals with the tribal grantees before, during, and after the development of the evaluation design plans. The grantees reviewed the data collection instruments and methods to ensure that information collected is culturally relevant and appropriate. They were also asked to review and offer comments about the interpretation of findings. Ultimately, findings are analyzed and shared objectively; however, the evaluation team also recognizes that data, particularly qualitative data, may be interpreted differently by the evaluation team than a member of the community. Confirming the accuracy of interpretations strengthens the rigor and relevance of the findings.

Importance of dissemination

Lastly, the HPOG research and evaluation portfolio elevates the importance of systematically and strategically integrating plans for dissemination. Any evidence generated by the HPOG portfolio will lie dormant unless it is translated and disseminated to relevant stakeholders in a way they can understand and apply it. Therefore, dissemination planning occurred in tandem with the design of each research and evaluation activity, so that the dissemination goals, strategies, audiences, and products were appropriately matched to effectively communicate the information to be generated. OPRE staff also found it important to be creative with dissemination. Too often studies only produce long, technical reports that are not accessible to many stakeholders. While these types of reports are necessary and valuable to produce, for transparency and for advancing the research field, shorter briefs, blogs, social media posts, webinars, and other methods have been useful for sharing information in innovative ways to reach a wider range of audiences. OPRE and OFA hope this publication will serve as one such innovative way for sharing information on HPOG.

Notes

1. These data were drawn from the Performance Reporting System, the performance management system for HPOG 1.0, by OPRE's evaluation contractor, Abt Associates, on July 18, 2017. Note that of the 36,548 participants enrolled, close to 30,000 consented to participate in the research and evaluation efforts. Therefore, HPOG evaluation reports on the OPRE website reflect varying samples. For more information about the characteristics and outcomes of the HPOG 1.0 participants, see the findings from the National Implementation Evaluation and the Evaluation of Tribal HPOG described in subsequent chapters of this book.
2. ACF issues Funding Opportunity Announcements to announce the availability of funds for specific activities and request applications for these funds.

3. Public Law 111-148, 124 Stat. 119, March 23, 2010, sect. 5507(a), "Demonstration Projects to Provide Low-Income Individuals with Opportunities for Education, Training, and Career Advancement to Address Health Professions Workforce Needs," adding sect. 2008(a) to the Social Security Act, 42 U.S.C. 1397g(a).

4. The HPOG authorizing statute mandates that entities applying for a grant engage in consultation and coordination with a number of organizations (42 U.S.C. 1397g(a) (2)(B)). Specifically, it stipulates that they "shall demonstrate in the application that the entity has consulted with the State agency responsible for administering the State TANF program, the local workforce investment board in the area in which the project is to be conducted (unless the applicant is such board), the State workforce investment board established under section 111 of the Workforce Investment Act of 1998, and the State Apprenticeship Agency recognized under the Act of August 16, 1937 (commonly known as the National Apprenticeship Act) (or if no agency has been recognized in the State, the Office of Apprenticeship of the Department of Labor) and that the project will be carried out in coordination with such entities."

5. For more information on the PACE evaluation, see https://www.acf.hhs.gov/opre/research/project/pathways-for-advancing-careers-and-education (accessed March 1, 2019).

6. Public Law 111-148, 124 Stat. 119, March 23, 2010, sect. 5507(a), "Demonstration Projects to Provide Low-Income Individuals with Opportunities for Education, Training, and Career Advancement to Address Health Professions Workforce Needs," adding sect. 2008(a) to the Social Security Act, 42 U.S.C. 1397g(a).

7. For more information, see the Evaluation Portfolio for the Health Profession Opportunity Grants Program webpage, https://www.acf.hhs.gov/opre/research/project/evaluation-portfolio-for-the-health-profession-opportunity-grants-hpog (accessed March 1, 2019).

8. To access these reports, see https://www.acf.hhs.gov/opre/research/project/health-profession-opportunity-grants-hpog-impact-studies and https://www.acf.hhs.gov/opre/research/project/pathways-for-advancing-careers-and-education (accessed March 1, 2019).

9. To access the brief, see https://www.acf.hhs.gov/opre/resource/the-hpog-university-partnership-research-grants (accessed March 1, 2019).

10. The HPOG 1.0 and 2.0 management information systems are designed to automatically mask any personally identifiable information for federal staff and other users not authorized to view it.

11. See Plain Language Action and Information Network website, https://www.plainlanguage.gov/howto/guidelines/FederalPLGuidelines/FederalPLGuidelines.pdf (accessed January 17, 2018).

12. For more information, see Career Pathways: http://career-pathways.org (accessed March 1, 2019).

13. Confirmatory outcomes are the main indicators of the extent to which the program is making progress toward its goals. See Harvill, Moulton, and Peck (2015).

14. 29 U.S. Code § 3224(b)(4)(I)

15. To access the full report, see https://www.cep.gov/cep-final-report.html (accessed June 12, 2019).

References

Administration for Children and Families (ACF). 2010. *Funding Opportunity Announcement: Health Profession Opportunity Grants to Serve TANF Recipients and Other Low-Income Individuals.* HHS-2010-ACF-OFA-FX-0126. Washington, DC: Office of Family Assistance, Administration for Children and Families, U.S. Department of Health and Human Services. https://www.reginfo.gov/public/do/DownloadDocument?objectID= 34475901 (accessed February 20, 2019).

———. 2011. *Funding Opportunity Announcement: University Partnership Research Grants for the Health Profession Opportunity Grants (HPOG) Program under the Affordable Care Act (ACA).* HHS-2011-ACF-OPRE-PH-0145. Washington, DC: Office of Family Assistance, Administration for Children and Families, U.S. Department of Health and Human Services. https://ami.grantsolutions.gov/files/HHS-2011-ACF-OPRE-PH-0145_0 .pdf (accessed February 20, 2019).

———. 2012. ACF Evaluation Policy. Washington, DC: Office of Planning, Research, and Evaluation, Administration for Children and Families, U.S. Department of Health and Human Services. https://www.acf.hhs.gov/opre/ resource/acf-evaluation-policy (accessed February 19, 2019).

———. 2015. *Funding Opportunity Announcement: Health Profession Opportunity Grants to Serve TANF Recipients and Other Low-Income Individuals.* HHS-2015-ACF-OFA-FX-0951. Washington, DC: Office of Family Assistance, Administration for Children and Families, U.S. Department of Health and Human Services. https://ami.grantsolutions .gov/?switch=foa&fon=HHS-2015-ACF-OFA-FX-0951 (accessed February 20, 2019).

———. 2016a. ACF Vision, Mission, & Values. Washington, DC: Office of Planning, Research, and Evaluation, Administration for Children and Families, U.S. Department of Health and Human Services. https://www.acf.hhs .gov/about/acf-vision-mission-values (accessed February 19, 2019).

———. 2016b. *Portfolio of Research in Welfare and Family Self-Sufficiency: Fiscal Year 2016.* OPRE Report No. 2016-93. Washington, DC: Office of Planning, Research, and Evaluation, Administration for Children and Families, U.S. Department of Health and Human Services. https://www.acf.hhs .gov/opre/resource/portfolio-of-research-in-welfare-and-family-self -sufficiency-2016 (accessed February 19, 2019).

———. 2017. "What We Do." Washington, DC: Office of Planning, Research, and Evaluation, Administration for Children and Families, U.S. Department of Health and Human Services. https://www.acf.hhs.gov/opre/about/what -we-do (accessed February 19, 2019).

Bell, Stephen H., Eleanor L. Harvill, Shawn R. Moulton, and Laura Peck. 2017. *Using Within-Site Experimental Evidence to Reduce Cross-Site Attri-butional Bias in Connecting Program Components to Program Impacts.* OPRE Report No. 2017-13. Washington, DC: Office of Planning, Research, and Evaluation, Administration for Children and Families, U.S. Department of Health and Human Services. https://www.acf.hhs.gov/sites/default/files/opre/hpog_impact_camic_paper_finalv4_508.pdf (accessed February 19, 2019).

Bernstein, Hamutal, Lauren Eyster, Jennifer Yahner, Stephanie Owen, and Pamela Loprest. 2016. *Systems Change under the Health Profession Oppor-tunity Grants (HPOG) Program.* OPRE Report No. 2016-50. Washington, DC: Office of Planning, Research, and Evaluation, Administration for Chil-dren and Families, U.S. Department of Health and Human Services. https://www.acf.hhs.gov/sites/default/files/opre/final_systems_change_analysis_report_b508.pdf (accessed February 19, 2019).

Fein, David J. 2012. *Career Pathways as a Framework for Program Design and Evaluation: A Working Paper from the Pathways for Advancing Careers and Education (PACE) Project.* OPRE Report No. 2012-30. Washington, DC: Office of Planning, Research, and Evaluation, Administration for Chil-dren and Families, U.S. Department of Health and Human Services. https://www.acf.hhs.gov/sites/default/files/opre/cp_as_a_framework_final_508b.pdf (accessed February 19, 2019).

Harvill, Eleanor L., Shawn Moulton, and Laura R. Peck. 2015. *Health Profes-sion Opportunity Grants Impact Study: Technical Supplement to the Evalu-ation Design Report: Impact Analysis Plan.* OPRE Report No. 2015-80. Washington, DC: Office of Planning, Research, and Evaluation, Administra-tion for Children and Families, U.S. Department of Health and Human Ser-vices. https://www.acf.hhs.gov/opre/resource/hpog-impact-study-technical -supplement-to-the-evaluation-design-report-impact-analysis   (accessed February 19, 2019).

Macoubrie, Jane, and Courtney Harrison. 2013. *The Value-Added Research Dissemination Framework.* OPRE Report No. 2013-10, Washington, DC: Office of Planning, Research, and Evaluation, Administration for Children and Families, U.S. Department of Health and Human Services. https://www.acf.hhs.gov/opre/resource/the-value-added-dissemination-framework (accessed February 19, 2019).

Office of Planning, Research and Evaluation (OPRE). n.d. "Evaluation Portfo-lio for the Health Profession Opportunity Grants (HPOG) Program." Wash-ington, DC: Office of Planning, Research and Evaluation, Administration for Children and Families, U.S. Department of Health and Human Services. https://www.acf.hhs.gov/opre/research/project/evaluation-portfolio-for

-the-health-profession-opportunity-grants-hpog (accessed March 1, 2019).

————. 2017. "University Partnership Research Grants for the HPOG Program, 2011–2016." Washington, DC: Office of Planning, Research and Evaluation, Administration for Children and Families, U.S. Department of Health and Human Services. https://www.acf.hhs.gov/opre/research/project/evaluation-portfolio-for-the-health-profession-opportunity-grants-hpog (accessed March 1, 2019).

Peck, Laura R., Alan Werner, Alyssa Rulf Fountain, Jennifer Lewis Buell, Stephen H. Bell, Eleanor Harvill, Hiren Nisar, David Judkins, and Gretchen Locke. 2014. *Health Profession Opportunity Grants Impact Study Design Report*. OPRE Report No. 2014-62. Washington, DC: Office of Planning, Research, and Evaluation, Administration for Children and Families, U.S. Department of Health and Human Services. https://www.acf.hhs.gov/opre/resource/health-profession-opportunity-grants-hpog-impact-study-design-report (accessed February 19, 2019).

4
Descriptive Implementation and Outcome Findings for Health Profession Opportunity Grants 1.0

Findings from the National Implementation Evaluation

Alan Werner
Abt Associates

Pamela Loprest
Urban Institute

Robin Koralek
Abt Associates

Grantees of the Health Profession Opportunity Grants (HPOG) program design and implement programs to provide eligible participants with education, occupational training, and employment and support services to help them train for and find jobs in a variety of health care professions. Chapter 3 describes in detail the multifaceted HPOG program research agenda developed and managed by the Office of Planning, Research, and Evaluation of the Administration for Children and Families (ACF) of the U.S. Department of Health and Human Services. The National Implementation Evaluation (NIE) was a core part of the Office of Planning, Research, and Evaluation research strategy. It focused on the 27 nontribal grantees receiving five-year grants in 2010 in a first round of HPOG awards (HPOG 1.0)[1] and was organized around three major research questions:

1) How are health professions training programs being implemented across the grantee sites?

2)   What changes to the service delivery system are associated with program implementation?

3)   What individual-level outcomes occur?

The NIE addressed the research questions in three related studies, respectively: the Descriptive Implementation Study, the Systems Study, and the Outcome Study. This chapter summarizes the findings of the Descriptive Implementation and Outcome Studies.[2] Combined, these two studies present a comprehensive picture of HPOG 1.0 design, implementation, and outcomes at the national level, as well as for variations at the local program level and for important participant subgroups. The NIE studies did not estimate impacts.[3] Major findings from these studies include the following:

- Twenty-seven nontribal grantees implemented 49 distinct local HPOG programs, each offering participants access to a range of health care training and financial, academic, and personal support services.

- Over the five-year grant period, HPOG 1.0 nontribal grantees served more than 36,000 individuals and engaged most of them in health care occupational training (88 percent by 18 months after enrollment). Most participants were women, a majority of whom were unmarried with children; more than two-thirds were from racial or ethnic minorities. At the time of enrollment, about 30 percent were in school and 41 percent were working.[4]

- By 36 months after enrollment, 78 percent of participants who began training had completed at least one health care course of training, spending an average of 3.5 months in training.

- At 15 months after HPOG enrollment, 73 percent were employed, with 53 percent employed in health care jobs. On average, those employed worked full-time, and those employed in health care jobs had higher hourly wages and better employment benefits than those who had jobs in other sectors.

- Employment and earnings increased through 12 quarters after participants' exit from HPOG, with steeper increases in earlier quarters. Both participants who completed training and those who did not complete it experienced these increases, but employment rates and earnings were higher for those who completed training (77 percent and $6,433 in the twelfth quarter after completing training, compared to 68 percent and $5,263 for those who did not complete training).

After describing the NIE study design and data collection strategy, this chapter summarizes the major study findings about the design, implementation, and results of HPOG 1.0 in the following order: eligibility criteria and participant characteristics, program content and participant experiences, educational outcomes, employment and earnings outcomes, program and policy implications, and further research. (Unless otherwise noted, HPOG refers to HPOG 1.0.)

STUDY DESIGN, DATA SOURCES, AND ANALYSIS APPROACH

The NIE study was designed to produce a comprehensive description of HPOG implementation and key participant experiences and outcomes aggregated at the national level, as well as accounting for variation at the local program level.

Data Sources

The NIE used a variety of data sources and collection strategies. Principal data sources for its Descriptive Implementation Study were surveys of HPOG grantee representatives, local program management and staff, HPOG partners and stakeholders, and health care employers. These surveys were fielded between November 2013 and April 2014, when HPOG was in its fourth year of implementation. The NIE also used data collected for the HPOG Impact Study through site visits made to programs implemented by 20 of the 27 nontribal grantees.[5]

The NIE Outcome Study used information from the HPOG Performance Reporting System, a participant-tracking and management system in which grantees reported data on participant characteristics, engagement in activities and services, and training and employment outcomes. The study used quarterly wage data from the National Directory of New Hires, a federal administrative database of employer reports to the Unemployment Insurance program. The study also used data from a 15-month follow-up survey of HPOG participants included in the HPOG Impact Study and the Pathways for Advancing Careers and Education (PACE) Study and a sample of HPOG participants from programs not included in either the HPOG Impact Study or PACE.[6]

UNIT OF ANALYSIS

The primary unit of analysis for most of the Descriptive Implementation Study is the local HPOG program, defined as "a unique set of services, training courses, and personnel" (Werner et al. 2016). The program is the major analytic unit because it is where policy and practice interface directly with participants; it is where all HPOG participants are offered the same range of services and training activities regardless of physical location. HPOG grantees may have funded and supervised one or more programs. For some program design decisions, the unit of analysis is the HPOG grantee, since grantee organizations were responsible for funding and overseeing programs. The Descriptive Implementation Study findings are based largely on measures developed from closed-ended survey questions.

The primary unit of analysis of the Outcome Study is the HPOG participant. In reporting participant characteristics, the study includes all those with records in the Performance Reporting System from September 30, 2010, through the end of the HPOG grant period, September 30, 2015. In reporting HPOG participant experiences and outcomes, the study uses the sample of participants with at least 18 months of experience since enrollment in HPOG. This includes 20,384 participants who enrolled prior to April 1, 2014. The only exception to this is for educational outcomes, where we use a sample of participants with 36 months of experience since enrollment. This includes 8,748 participants who enrolled prior to October 1, 2012. The rationale for focusing on this sample is to report training completion outcomes after a longer period after enrollment. Findings on employment and earnings rely on 12 quarters of postenrollment data from the National Directory of New Hires. Results on the characteristics of jobs held by participants are based on a sample of 4,636 participants responding to the follow-up participant survey that was fielded 15 months after enrollment.

ELIGIBILITY CRITERIA AND PARTICIPANT CHARACTERISTICS

The composition of the HPOG participant pool was largely the result of grantee decisions about eligibility requirements and processes. Those decisions were based on grantee judgments about who among the target population could most benefit from and was likely to succeed in training and subsequent employment in the health care industry. This section summarizes grantee choices of eligibility criteria and the demographic and socioeconomic characteristics of HPOG participants.

HPOG Eligibility

The Funding Opportunity Announcement for HPOG specified that grantees were to serve recipients of TANF and other low-income individuals, but it left grantees to define low-income. In addition to exercising discretion over income eligibility limits, grantees also developed a range of eligibility criteria based on applicants' educational attainment and basic skills ability, criminal background or drug use status, and relevant personal characteristics. In developing eligibility criteria and intake processes for their programs, grantees sought to balance the goal of serving individuals who already had many of the skills needed to succeed in training and jobs in health care with the goal of serving individuals who might need significant investments in basic academic skills and work-related knowledge and behavior.

Income eligibility

All HPOG programs considered TANF recipients to be income eligible.[7] In determining income eligibility for those applicants not receiving TANF cash benefits, programs applied one or more measures of income to a variety of standards. These included some percentage of the federal poverty level (FPL) for a specific household size and income eligibility for one or more other assistance programs. For the programs that used some percentage of the FPL to determine income eligibility, the median program eligibility threshold was 200 percent of FPL, and the eligibility threshold ranged from 150 to 250 percent of FPL.

Educational attainment and basic skills requirements

In setting entry requirements for educational attainment and basic skills, programs had to balance the two goals of 1) helping relatively low-skilled applicants improve in the academic skills they needed to enroll in occupational training and 2) meeting HPOG's performance benchmarks for course completions within the five-year term of the grants. Performance benchmarks for each grantee included targets for the number of participants enrolling in HPOG, the percentage of participants completing training courses, and the percentage of participants entering employment.

On educational attainment, programs were almost evenly split on requiring a high school diploma or its equivalent (49 percent required it, 51 percent did not). In addition, most programs (about 80 percent) set minimal eligibility skill levels for math and reading, with a majority of those programs setting skill levels at the eighth grade or above. Because academic skills requirements could vary somewhat by specific training courses, these eligibility screens helped ensure that the pool of participants interested in a particular track would be prepared for that training or would be provided pretraining activities designed to improve skill levels.

Criminal background and other checks

Largely due to state-level restrictions against employing those with a criminal record or users of illegal drugs in many health care jobs, programs screened applicants for past felonies and misdemeanors and for current drug use. Although most HPOG programs used these checks, programs did not necessarily reject all applicants who failed them. Some programs tried to suggest appropriate training courses and career ladders to applicants who had criminal records. Other HPOG programs helped applicants who had criminal records expunge them or apply for certificates of relief, which would allow those applicants to pursue a wider range of health care training courses.

Personal and behavioral screening

Almost all HPOG programs also assessed applicants' relevant personal and psychosocial qualities. In their application processes, about half of the HPOG programs evaluated applicants' career interests, job readiness, and motivation. In addition to screening for low-income status, basic skills, and criminal background, most programs used personal interviewing or formal assessment tools to gauge motivation and suitability for health care training and employment. Using these measures, programs made judgments about applicants' suitability for health care training and employment.

Participant Characteristics

HPOG grantees' decisions about eligibility criteria influenced the types of individuals participating in the HPOG programs. Table 4.1 summarizes demographic characteristics for all HPOG participants at program entry who enrolled in the program and consented to participate in research studies.

The majority of participants (88 percent) were female. Equal proportions of participants were white non-Hispanic (37 percent) and black non-Hispanic (37 percent).[8] Participants were generally young, with close to half in their twenties and another 8 percent younger than 20. Eighty-four (84) percent were single (63 percent had never married and the remainder were divorced, widowed, or separated).

Almost two-thirds of participants had dependent children. The majority of participants cared for dependent children. Fewer than 4 percent fell into any of the following groups (not shown in the figure): veterans, people with a disability, foster children, people experiencing homelessness, people with limited English skills, and people with criminal backgrounds.

HPOG served individuals with diverse educational backgrounds, ranging from those who did not complete high school to those with multiple years of college. At program entry, most HPOG participants had no postsecondary education. Six percent had less than a twelfth grade education, 13 percent had a high school equivalency certificate or GED, and 37 percent had a high school diploma. However, more than one-third (38 percent) had some years of college or technical school, and 7 percent had four or more years of college. Most HPOG programs assessed participants at eligibility determination or enroll-

Table 4.1 Demographic and Socioeconomic Characteristics of HPOG Participants at Enrollment

Characteristic	Number of participants	Percentage of participants
Gender		
Male	3,434	12
Female	26,492	88
Race/ethnicity		
White non-Hispanic	10,993	37
Black non-Hispanic	10,857	37
Hispanic/Latino, any race	5,776	20
Asian or Hawaiian, Pacific Islander	973	3
Native American or Alaska Native	206	1
Two or more races, non-Hispanic	778	3
Age		
< 20	2,494	8
20–29	13,578	46
30–39	7,036	24
40–49	4,119	14
50+	2,615	9
Marital status		
Married	4,690	16
Never married	18,082	63
Divorced, widowed, or separated	5,991	21
Dependent children		
Yes	17,823	62
No	10,854	38
Highest educational attainment		
Less than 12th grade	1,736	6
High school equivalency or GED	3,677	13
High school graduate	10,721	37
1–3 years of college/technical school	10,990	38
4 years or more of college	2,050	7
Literacy at 8th grade or higher		
Yes	21,051	85
No	3,657	15
Numeracy at 8th grade or higher		
Yes	17,640	74
No	6,304	26

Table 4.1 (continued)

Characteristic	Number of participants	Percentage of participants
Currently in school		
Yes	8,512	30
No	19,570	70
Currently employed		
Yes	12,175	41
No	17,532	59

NOTE: Sample is all 29,942 HPOG participants who enrolled in HPOG, consented to participate in research, and were in the HPOG Performance Reporting System as of September 30, 2015. Percentages are of nonmissing responses at enrollment.

Missing: Literacy and numeracy are missing in 17 and 20 percent of responses, respectively, which include those participants for whom these skills were not tested at enrollment. For all other characteristics, missing responses range from 0 to 7 percent.

SOURCE: HPOG Performance Reporting System, 2015.

ment for their levels of literacy and numeracy.[9] Of participants who completed these assessments, 15 percent had less than eighth grade literacy skills, and 26 percent had less than eighth grade numeracy skills.

   Some participants were in school or working when they started HPOG. Almost one-third of participants (30 percent) were in school at the time of program entry. Forty-one percent were working when they enrolled in the program (15 percent worked in a health care occupation and 16 percent for a health care employer).

   HPOG participants had low individual and household incomes, as would be expected given the requirement to serve low-income individuals (see Table 4.2). Almost two-thirds had individual annual incomes of less than $10,000, and almost half were in households with incomes under $10,000. To put these income levels in context, the poverty line in 2014 was $11,670 for a one-person household and $19,790 for a household of three.[10] Fourteen percent of participants were receiving TANF cash assistance at program enrollment, and more than half were receiving SNAP benefits. Almost half were single mothers (44 percent), many of whom were likely eligible or nearly eligible for TANF cash assistance.[11]

Table 4.2 Income and Benefit Receipt of HPOG Participants at Enrollment

Characteristic	Number of participants	Percentage of participants
Individual income ($)		
<10,000	17,980	65
10,000–19,999	6,316	23
20,000–29,999	2,537	9
30,000+	776	3
Missing	2,333	
Household income ($)		
<10,000	12,014	47
10,000–19,999	7,157	28
20,000–29,999	3,857	15
30,000+	2,777	11
Missing	4,137	
Receiving TANF		
Yes	3,973	14
No	24,506	86
Missing	1,463	
Receiving SNAP		
Yes	15,270	53
No	13,597	47
Missing	1,075	

NOTE: SNAP = Supplemental Nutrition Assistance Program. Sample is all 29,942 HPOG participants in the HPOG Performance Reporting System as of September 30, 2015. Percentages are of non-missing responses at enrollment.
Missing: missing responses range from 4 to 14 percent.
SOURCE: HPOG Performance Reporting System, 2015.

HPOG PROGRAM CONTENT AND PARTICIPANT EXPERIENCES

Once enrolled in HPOG, participants had access to a wide range of pretraining and preparatory services; health care training courses; and academic, personal, and financial supports. This section documents the availability of these program offerings and their use by HPOG participants.

Pretraining Services and Activities Offered

To succeed in health care training courses and jobs, many HPOG participants needed additional preparation in one or more areas, including college preparation skills, knowledge of health care career options, soft skills appropriate for the health care workplace, and basic academic skills to participate productively in health care training. Table 4.3 presents findings on the percentage of programs offering specific pretraining activities and the percentage of participants who engaged in those activities.

The most commonly offered and received pretraining activity was soft skills training (85 percent of programs; 44 percent of participants), which focuses on personal and social skills and behavior appropriate

Table 4.3 Pretraining Activities and Remedial Academic Services Offered and Received by 18 Months after Enrollment

Pretraining activity	Percentage of programs	Percentage of participants
Soft skills training (N = 48)	85	44
Introduction to health care careers (N = 48)	54	31
Prerequisite subject courses (N = 48)	31	13
College skills training (N = 49)	29	8
Any pretraining activity (N = 48)	96	64
Adult basic skills (N = 49)	43	5
High school or pre–high school equivalency classes (N = 49)	43	1
ESL classes (N = 49)	18	1

NOTE: ESL = English as a Second Language. For programs: multiple responses were permitted, and therefore results do not sum to 100 percent. N of programs = 48 to 49. N of participants = 20,384. Missing: 0–1 programs. For participants: samples include participants with at least 18 months of experience since enrollment (enrolled by April 1, 2014) and participants with at least 36 months of experience since enrollment (enrolled by October 1, 2012). Participation in multiple activities is included in multiple rows. N = 20,384 for 18-month sample.

SOURCE: HPOG Grantee survey, 2014, Q8.1; HPOG Performance Reporting System, 2014, 2015.

to the workplace. In HPOG, this included emphasis on how to behave around patients and in health care settings. About half of programs (54 percent) offered introduction to health care career workshops, which were attended by about one-third of participants. These workshops explored the range of jobs in health care, potential career pathways, and combinations of academic training and practical experience needed to enter and move along those pathways. Overall, 96 percent of programs offered some pretraining, and almost two-thirds of participants received a pretraining service.

Compared to the pretraining activities described above, HPOG programs were less likely to include formal basic skills education as part of their programs; very few participants enrolled in basic skills training or English as a Second Language classes. For example, fewer than half of the programs offered adult basic skills education directly (43 percent), and only 5 percent of participants received it. Even fewer programs offered high school or pre–high school equivalency classes or English as a Second Language instruction directly, and only 1 percent of participants received them.

Several factors may have contributed to the relative lack of basic skills and other adult education opportunities provided directly by HPOG programs and taken up by participants. For example, programs may have reduced the need for basic skills training by establishing eligibility criteria that specify minimum grade-level requirements in reading and math. Also, some programs reported that adult basic skills training was readily available in their communities, and they did not need to provide the service in-house.[12] Alternatively, 10 programs (31 percent) indicated they integrated basic skills into some health care training courses (not reflected in basic skills counts in the Performance Reporting System) and may not have offered separate basic skills courses.[13]

Health Care Training Offered and Received

HPOG programs provided many health care training activities, which varied in length and intensity, depending on the requirements of the targeted profession. Some training courses for entry-level positions were as short as two weeks, whereas others, such as training for technical or nursing positions, required commitments of as many as four years. Table 4.4 summarizes the breadth of health care training courses

Table 4.4 Occupational Training Offered and Received by 18 Months after Enrollment

Training	Percentage of programs	Percentage of participants who began training
Nursing aides, orderlies, and attendants	90	34
Medical records and health information technicians	80	10
Medical assistants	78	8
Pharmacy technicians	73	4
Licensed practical and vocational nurses	61	10
Registered nurses	59	10
Diagnostic-related technologists and technicians	59	3
Phlebotomists	57	3
Health care support occupations (all others)	55	2
Emergency medical technicians and paramedics	51	2
Health practitioner support technologists and technicians	45	1
Psychiatric and home health aides	43	6
Physical therapist assistants and aides	39	1
Health technologists and technicians	31	<1
Clinical laboratory technologists and technicians	29	1
Occupational therapy assistants and aides	20	<1
Health diagnosing and treating practitioners	18	<1
Community and social service specialists	14	1
Counselors	8	<1
Other	31	<1

NOTE: For programs: multiple responses were permitted, and therefore results do not sum to 100 percent. The types of training courses listed correspond to Standard Occupational Classifications from the Bureau of Labor Statistics.

N = 49 programs. For participants: samples include participants with at least 18 months of postenrollment experience who began health care training programs. Participants who enrolled in more than one type of training are included in multiple rows. Activities are categorized following Standard Occupational Classifications from the Bureau of Labor Statistics. Although classified in the category of Health Care Support Occupations, phlebotomists and pharmacy technicians are recorded separately from that category given their high rates of participation.

N = 16,942 for the 18-month sample. Missing: 0 programs.

SOURCE: HPOG Performance Reporting System, 2015.

provided across HPOG programs, and among participants who began any course, the percentage who enrolled in specific courses.[14]

Most HPOG participants (83 percent) took part in health care training by 18 months after enrolling in HPOG. Among those, most (34 percent) enrolled in training for nursing aides, orderlies, and attendants. Although most enrolled in training for entry-level positions, including a variety of courses for aides and assistants, 20 percent enrolled in longer-term training for a higher-level position, such as registered nurse (RN; 10 percent) or licensed practical nurse/licensed vocational nurse (LPN/LVN; 10 percent).

As part of their training offerings, many HPOG programs included work-based learning opportunities as a way of teaching and reinforcing clinical skills. Most commonly, this came in the form of a clinical section that was part of a course (92 percent of programs offered at least one such course).[15] Some programs also implemented work-based learning outside formal coursework, the most common of which was work experience assignments or transitional jobs, with 7 percent of HPOG participants engaged by 18 months after enrollment (see Table 4.5). By that same time, 2 percent of participants had engaged in on-the-job training, and less than 1 percent had participated in a job-shadowing activity. Because programs were prohibited from using HPOG funds to subsidize wages or pay stipends to participants, paid work experience and on-the-job training had to be funded by other sources.

HPOG Support Services Offered and Received

Comprehensive support services are an important part of the HPOG program and a key feature of the career pathways framework on which HPOG is modeled. This subsection presents findings about the support services local HPOG programs offered and participants received, including case management, academic and career supports, training-related financial assistance, personal and family supports, and services related to employment and job retention.

Case management, academic, and career supports

Almost all HPOG programs (98 percent) employed case managers, who performed a variety of duties intended to support program retention and completion. In most programs, case managers helped par-

Table 4.5 Participation in Work-Based Learning by 18 Months after Enrollment

Opportunity	Percentage of participants
Work experience or transitional job	7
On-the-job training	2
Job shadowing	<1

NOTE: Samples include participants with at least 18 months of postenrollment experience (enrolled by April 1, 2014) and participants with at least 36 months of postenrollment experience (enrolled by October 1, 2012). Participants receiving multiple types of services are included in multiple rows.
N = 20,384 individuals for the 18-month sample.
SOURCE: HPOG Performance Reporting System, 2015.

ticipants by providing academic and career counseling, connections to needed support services, personal and financial advice and guidance, and help finding employment.[16] HPOG program staff were in contact with participants through a variety of modes, including email and other electronic communication and meetings (individually, in groups, and by telephone). On average, staff were in contact with participants two to three times a month in person in an individual setting.[17] Case management was the most commonly provided support, received by 89 percent of participants within 18 months after enrollment (see Table 4.6).

In addition to case management, the most commonly available support services focused on academic success and career choice. Nearly all programs provided these services in multiple ways, including personal advising and counseling, individual and group tutoring, and career workshops. About two-thirds of participants received academic and career counseling (67 percent), and 18 percent were tutored within 18 months of enrollment. Peer support and/or mentoring were available services in 73 percent of programs and were received by 39 percent of participants. Importantly, 94 percent of participants received some academic or training support within 18 months of enrolling in HPOG.

Training-related financial and resource assistance

A major aspect of HPOG programs' support addressed unmet financial needs that could be a barrier for their target population to enroll in and complete occupational training. All programs offered some form of financial assistance for training-related costs. Importantly, 47 programs

Table 4.6 Support Services Offered and Received by 18 Months after Enrollment

Service	Percentage of programs	Percentage of participants
Case management	98	89
Academic and career counseling	92	67
Tutoring	78	18
Peer support/mentoring activities	73	39
Any academic or training support	–	94

NOTE: For programs: multiple responses were permitted, and therefore results do not sum to 100 percent.

N = 49 programs. Missing: 0 programs. For participants: sample includes participants with at least 18 months of postenrollment experience. N = 20,384 individuals for the 18-month sample.

SOURCE: HPOG Grantee survey, 2014, Q8.15, Q9.8; HPOG Performance Reporting System, 2015.

(96 percent) covered all or part of participants' tuition costs, with about half of all programs (24 programs, 49 percent) covering *all* tuition costs.[18] In addition to providing direct tuition assistance, many programs also relied on other sources of financial assistance for participants. The two most common sources of financial support not funded by HPOG were Pell Grants (40 programs, 82 percent) and Workforce Investment Act Individual Training Accounts (28 programs, 58 percent).[19]

In addition to providing resources to cover tuition, all programs covered the cost of books, licensing and certification fees, and exam preparation fees (see Table 4.7). All but one program (98 percent) covered the cost of uniforms, supplies, and tools.[20] Almost half of all programs (22 programs, 46 percent) offered financial support for computers or other equipment. Of the programs that offered assistance for academic-related expenses, about a third (32 percent or more, depending on the specific expense) did so for all participants without request. Programs most commonly offered—without request—assistance for the cost of books (25 programs, 51 percent).[21]

Personal and family supports

HPOG programs also offered services to participants to address personal and family material needs that might have otherwise interfered with stable training participation and completion. Although most pro-

Table 4.7 Academic Resource Assistance Offered and Received by 18 Months after Enrollment

Service	Percentage of programs	Percentage of participants
Books	100	57
Work/training uniforms, supplies, tools	98	53
Exam/exam prep fees (for licensing/certification)	100	36
Licensing and certification fees	100	33
Computer/technology	46	19
Any training or work-related resource assistance	100	72

NOTE: For programs: multiple responses were permitted, and therefore results do not sum to 100 percent.

N = 49 programs. For participants: samples include participants with at least 18 months of postenrollment experience (enrolled by April 1, 2014) and participants with at least 36 months of postenrollment experience (enrolled by October 1, 2012). Participants receiving multiple types of services are included in multiple rows.

N = 20,384 individuals for the 18-month sample. Missing: 0 programs.

SOURCE: HPOG Grantee survey, 2014, Q9.17; HPOG Performance Reporting System, 2015.

grams offered such services directly—most notably transportation and child care assistance—many referred participants in need to available community resources (see Table 4.8).

More than half of participants (53 percent) received personal and family support services within 18 months of enrollment. Transportation assistance was by far the most commonly received by participants (47 percent). Fewer participants received other personal and family support services from programs, including, for example, child care (8 percent) and help with medical care (8 percent), including assistance accessing health care screenings or physicals required by employers.[22]

Employment assistance and job retention services

To help participants obtain employment related to their training, all HPOG programs provided multiple employment assistance services, including advising on careers and job choices, job search assistance, job readiness workshops, and job retention services (see Table 4.9). Participants most commonly received career counseling and job choices advising from a job coach or career navigator (74 percent). Other employment services included job search and placement assistance (52

Table 4.8 Personal and Family Services and Supports Offered and Received by 18 Months after Enrollment

Service/support	Percentage of programs offering service	Percentage of programs providing service			Percentage of participants receiving service
		Directly only	By referral only	Both directly and by referral	
Transportation assistance	98	79	6	15	47
Child care assistance	92	53	27	20	8
Medical care	73	8	86	6	8
Short-term/temporary housing	73	14	78	8	1
Food assistance (other than SNAP)	73	19	69	11	4
Legal assistance	69	3	97	0	1
Addiction or substance abuse services	67	3	94	3	<1
Family preservation services	57	4	89	7	1
Family engagement services	51	8	88	4	1
Driver's license assistance	49	42	50	8	1
Other housing assistance	49	21	79	0	3
Any personal and family services and supports	—	—	—	—	53

NOTE: For programs: the percentages of programs providing services by service delivery strategy (i.e., directly and/or by referral) are the percentages of all programs providing each specific support service and not the percentages of all programs in the study. N = 49. Missing: 0 programs. For participants: sample includes participants with at least 18 months of postenrollment experience. Participants receiving multiple types of services are included in multiple rows.
N = 20,384 individuals for the 18-month sample.
SOURCE: HPOG Performance Reporting System, 2015; HPOG Grantee survey, 2014, Q9.11.

Table 4.9 Employment Assistance Services Offered and Received by 18 Months after Enrollment

Service	Percentage of programs	Percentage of participants
Advising on career and job choices (N = 49)	100	74
Individual job search assistance (N = 49)	100	52
Job search skills/job-readiness workshops (N = 48)	98	25
Job retention services (N = 49)	94	12

NOTE: For programs: multiple responses were permitted, and therefore results do not sum to 100 percent.
N = 48 to 49. Missing: 0–1 programs. For participants: sample includes participants with at least 18 months of postenrollment experience. Participants receiving multiple types of services are included in multiple rows.
N = 20,384 for the 18-month sample.
SOURCE: HPOG Grantee survey, 2014, Q9.21; HPOG Performance Reporting System, 2015.

percent), job readiness workshops (25 percent), and job retention services (12 percent).

EDUCATIONAL OUTCOMES

This section presents findings about HPOG participants' educational outcomes, including health care training completion, credentials obtained, and self-assessment of educational progress. In order to allow a longer period of time for training completion, this section relies on the sample of participants who had at least 36 months postenrollment.

Health Care Training Completion

Of participants who engaged in health care training, 78 percent completed at least one course within 36 months of enrollment (see Figure 4.1). An additional 19 percent dropped out, and only 3 percent were still in a training course.[23]

Completion rates of health care training courses varied by the occupation for which participants were training. The highest completion rates were for psychiatric and home health aides (88 percent of those

Figure 4.1 Completion Status by Health Care Occupation Types among HPOG Participants Who Began Training

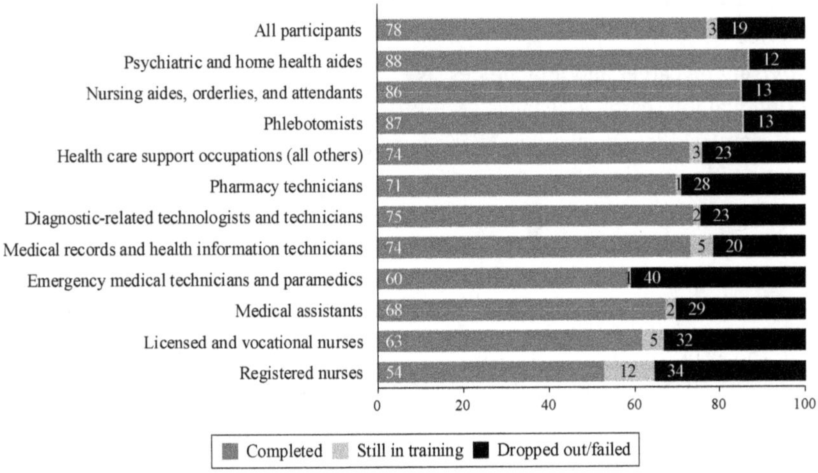

NOTE: The Bureau of Labor Statistics classifies phlebotomists and pharmacy technicians as health care support occupations, but here they are recorded separately from the rest of the category, given their high rates of participation.
Sample includes participants with at least 36 months of postenrollment experience (enrolled by October 1, 2012) who began health care training programs. Participants are represented in each type of training in which they enrolled. Each bar shows percentages of those who enrolled in the corresponding training program. Percentages may not add up to 100 percent because of rounding. Percentages are of participants with known completion statuses. Less than 1 percent of training programs with end dates are missing completion status. The exhibit shows only health care training programs with more than 100 participants in the 36-month sample. N = 7,653 participants for the 36-month sample.
SOURCE: HPOG Performance Reporting System, 2015.

who enrolled completed); phlebotomists (87 percent completed); and nursing aides, orderlies, and attendants (86 percent completed).

The percentages of those who completed courses in 36 months were much lower for LPNs/LVNs (63 percent) and RNs (54 percent). These lower completion rates reflect both higher dropout rates (32 percent for LPNs/LVNs and 34 percent for RNs compared with 19 percent overall) and higher rates of participants still in training (5 percent for LPNs/LVNs and 12 percent for RNs compared with 3 percent overall), given the longer time needed to complete these nursing training courses.

The majority of HPOG participants who completed health care training were in relatively short-term training courses (i.e., six months or less).[24] Figure 4.2 shows the distribution of time spent in health care training. Most participants were in training for a relatively short period, with 72 percent of participants completing training in six months or less and 46 percent in two months or less. Participants who completed a training course within 36 months after enrolling had an average training length of 5.3 months and a median length of 3.0 months.

The length of time participants spent in a particular training course varied significantly by training occupation (see Table 4.10). Participants typically completed more quickly training for occupations that led to entry-level positions for lower-wage jobs. For example, participants spent an average of 1.8 months training for jobs as psychiatric and

Figure 4.2 Time Spent in Health Care Training by HPOG Participants Who Had Completed a Health Care Training Course

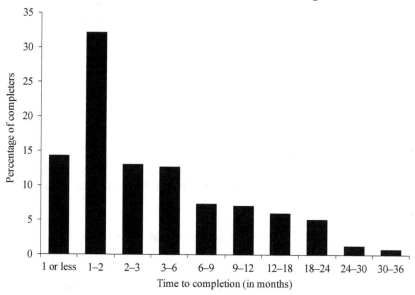

NOTE: Sample includes participants with at least 36 months of postenrollment experience (enrolled by October 1, 2012) who began and completed health care training programs. Participants who enrolled in more than one type of training course are included in the means for each corresponding column. N = 5,974.
SOURCE: HPOG Performance Reporting System, 2015.

Table 4.10 Time to Complete HPOG Health Care Occupational Training

Occupation	Time to complete in months (mean)
Psychiatric and home health aides (N = 529)	1.8
Nursing aides, orderlies, and attendants (N = 3,559)	2.1
Phlebotomists (N = 351)	3.8
Pharmacy technicians (N = 183)	4.2
Emergency medical technicians and paramedics (N = 105)	5.3
Diagnostic-related technologists and technicians (N = 253)	5.6
Health care support occupations (all others) (N = 145)	5.9
Medical records and health information technicians (N = 788)	6.0
Medical assistants (N = 496)	8.9
Licensed and vocational nurses (N = 709)	12.6
Registered nurses (N = 455)	15.2

NOTE: Samples include participants with at least 36 months of postenrollment experience (enrolled by October 1, 2012) who began and completed health care training programs. Participants who enrolled in more than one type of training course are included in the means for each corresponding row.
N = 5,974.
SOURCE: HPOG Performance Reporting System, 2015.

home health aides; 2.1 months for jobs as nursing aides, orderlies, and attendants; and 3.8 months for jobs as phlebotomists—all occupations with relatively high training completion rates.

Other training courses took longer to complete. Participants took more than 15 months to complete training for jobs as RNs, and those in LPN/LVN training reported spending almost 13 months on average to complete.[25]

Participation in and Completion of Multiple Health Care Training Courses

The career pathway framework posits that after completing occupational training students may advance by taking additional training courses, sometimes immediately and sometimes after a period of employment. Most programs gave participants the flexibility to enroll in additional training after completing a first course.[26] Twenty-one percent of HPOG participants who had completed one course within the

36 months after enrollment enrolled in another. The completion rate for those additional courses was 71 percent.

The most common training courses followed by additional trainings were shorter term, such as courses for nursing aides, orderlies, and attendants (a category that includes certified nursing assistant [CNA] training); medical records and health information technicians; and phlebotomists. For example, among the participants who completed CNA training and began a second course, relatively few engaged in higher-level training in nursing, with 8 percent beginning LPN/LVN training and 6 percent beginning RN training. Most of the participants who completed a nursing assistant training enrolled in another relatively short-term training also in the nursing assistant occupational category, which could be training to gain additional certifications beyond a CNA, such as to administer intravenous medication.

Receipt of Certifications, Licenses, or Degrees

A primary goal of HPOG is for participants to receive credentials recognized by health care employers. They might include employer-recognized third-party occupational certifications or licenses, as well as postsecondary degrees. About 44 percent of participants who completed at least one health care training course within 36 months of enrollment received a regulatory license or third-party certification. The percentage of participants obtaining a license or certification varied by the training course occupation. Variation across occupations reflects that not all occupations require or confer third-party certifications; for some occupations, requirements for certifications vary by locality.

About 9 percent of participants received an associate's, bachelor's, or master's degree within 36 months of enrollment. The majority of degrees earned (87 percent) were associate's degrees. Two occupational training courses accounted for most of the degrees received: RNs and LPNs/LVNs made up almost two-thirds (63 percent) of the degrees received.

Participant Self-Assessment of Educational Progress

HPOG programs had the goal of training participants for stable, well-paying jobs in career pathways in health care. HPOG participants were asked in a baseline survey at enrollment about their educational aspirations and then responded to a similar survey question 15 months after enrollment. Table 4.11 presents results on the changes in goals after participation in HPOG.[27]

At 15 months after program enrollment, most HPOG participants expected to attain a postsecondary degree, with the largest number aiming for a bachelor's degree or higher. Compared with their educa-

Table 4.11 Goals for Educational Attainment

Goal	Percentage at enrollment	Percentage at 15 months after program entry
No additional school	2	n/a
Grades 1–12 (no HS diploma/GED)	n/a	<1
High school diploma	11	5
GED or alternative credential	5	2
Alternative nonacademic credential, including industry-recognized credential, certification of completing vocational training, etc.	15	n/a
Some college credit but less than 1 year	n/a	4
One or more years of college credit but no degree	n/a	4
Associate's degree	22	20
Bachelor's degree or higher	46	59
Refused/don't know	0	5

NOTE: Question at program entry in a baseline information form entered by program staff is "What is the highest level of education the participant eventually expects to complete? (choose one category)." Question in 15-month follow-up survey of HPOG participants reads: "What is the highest level of regular academic education that you eventually expect to complete?" Response categories varied between the two surveys, so some responses are not applicable to each sample (indicated by n/a).

For survey at enrollment, N = 4,282 participants at HPOG grantee programs participating in the HPOG Impact or PACE studies (excludes four programs). Missing for this survey item = 103.

For 15-month follow-up survey of HPOG participants, sample is 4,646 participants across all HPOG programs who enrolled in HPOG between September 1, 2013, and September 30, 2014, and responded to the 15-month follow-up survey of HPOG participants. Missing for this survey item = 0.

SOURCE: Baseline survey at enrollment; 15-month follow-up participant survey of HPOG participants; 15-month follow-up survey of PACE participants.

tional aspirations at enrollment, the percentage of participants with any degree aspirations increased overall (from 68 percent at enrollment to 79 percent).

The 15-month follow-up survey also asked for participants' self-assessment of their educational progress: "Would you say you strongly agree, somewhat agree, somewhat disagree, or strongly disagree with the following statement: I am making progress toward my long-range educational goals?" In response, 87 percent of HPOG participants answered either "strongly agree" or "somewhat agree." Only 5 percent answered "strongly disagree."

EMPLOYMENT AND EARNINGS OUTCOMES

One of HPOG's primary goals is to increase participants' employment in the health care industry. This section presents findings on the quarterly employment and earnings outcomes of HPOG participants, using data from the National Directory of New Hires. Findings are based on as many as three years (12 quarters) of data after enrollment and two years (8 quarters) prior to enrollment. In addition, this section reports findings about the quality of jobs held by HPOG participants at 15 months following enrollment, based on responses to the 15-month follow-up survey of HPOG participants.[28]

Quarterly Employment and Earnings

The percentage of employed HPOG participants in the 18-month sample increased steadily in the quarters after HPOG enrollment, from 52 percent employed in the quarter of enrollment to 75 percent employed three years after enrollment (see Figure 4.3).[29] By the second quarter after enrollment, the percentage employed surpassed any of the eight preenrollment quarters examined. Employment levels continued to rise until the tenth quarter (2.5 years) after enrollment and then remained stable over the study period.[30]

Participant earnings also increased steadily after enrollment (see Figure 4.4). Average earnings of employed participants rose from $3,145 in the quarter of enrollment to $6,208 in the twelfth quarter after

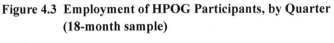

Figure 4.3 Employment of HPOG Participants, by Quarter (18-month sample)

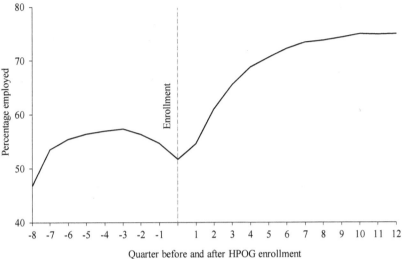

NOTE: Sample includes participants with at least 18 months of postenrollment experience (enrolled by April 1, 2014). N ranges from 18,591 participants eight quarters prior to enrollment, to 19,765 the quarter of enrollment, to 16,502 in the final quarters after enrollment.
SOURCE: National Directory of New Hires.

enrollment.[31] By the fourth quarter after enrollment, average earnings were higher than average earnings in any preenrollment quarter.

Employment and Earnings after Training Completion

In addition to employment and earnings increases for all participants, results show that employment and earnings were higher in the quarters after enrollment for participants who completed a training course than for those who dropped out or failed to complete a training course. Participants are considered to have dropped out if they did not successfully complete at least one training course, indicating that they didn't complete, failed, or never enrolled in a training course.

Figure 4.5 shows employment in the 8 quarters before HPOG enrollment (left panel) and in the 12 quarters after training completion (right

**Figure 4.4 Earnings of Employed HPOG Participants, by Quarter
(18-month sample)**

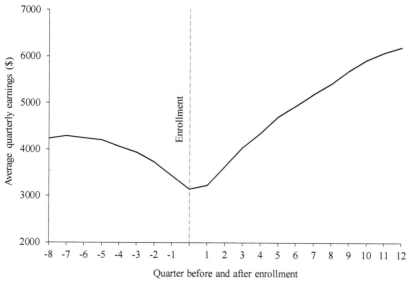

NOTE: Sample includes participants with at least 18 months of postenrollment
experience (enrolled by April 1, 2014) who were employed in a given quarter.
N ranges from 8,074 participants to 14,808 per quarter.
SOURCE: National Directory of New Hires.

panel). For comparison, the figure also presents employment for those
who dropped out or failed to complete a training course.[32] Both groups
of participants saw employment increases after training completion or
dropout relative to employment prior to enrollment, which was similar
for both groups. The highest percentage employed in any quarter prior
to enrollment was 57 percent for those who eventually completed a
training course and 56 percent for those who dropped out or failed to
complete a training course. The percentages employed in the quarter of
completion and dropout were 69 percent and 59 percent, respectively.

In subsequent quarters, participants who completed a training
course had higher employment rates compared to participants who
dropped out of or failed to complete a training course. For example, in
the twelfth quarter after completing training or dropping out, employment for those who completed training was 77 percent compared to 68

Figure 4.5   Employment of HPOG Participants in the Quarters before Enrollment and after Training Completion or Dropout (18-month sample)

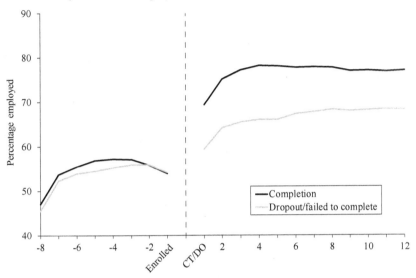

Quarter before enrollment and after training completion or dropout

NOTE: CT/DO = quarter completed training/quarter dropped out of training. Sample includes participants with at least 18 months of postenrollment experience (enrolled by April 1, 2014) who had completed training or failed to complete training and were employed in a given quarter. N ranges from 11,983 participants to 9,928 per quarter for those who completed training and 5,810 participants to 4,871 per quarter for those who dropped out or failed to complete.
SOURCE: National Directory of New Hires.

percent for those who did not. However, there may be other differences across these two groups that could influence outcomes for training completion and employment. This finding, therefore, cannot be interpreted as causal evidence that training completion alone was the reason for training completers' higher rate of employment.[33]

Average quarterly earnings for those employed increased steadily after training completion. Figure 4.6 shows quarterly earnings of employed HPOG participants who completed training for the 8 quarters before enrollment and the 12 quarters after completing training. Quarterly earnings continued to grow steadily for both groups from the

Figure 4.6 Earnings of Employed HPOG Participants in the Quarters before Enrollment and after Training Completion or Dropout (18-month sample)

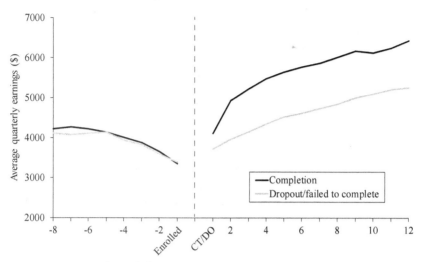

Quarter before enrollment and after training completion or dropout

NOTE: CT/DO = quarter completed training/quarter dropped out of training. Sample includes participants with at least 18 months of postenrollment experience (enrolled by April 1, 2014) who had completed training or failed to complete training and were employed in a given quarter. N ranges from 9,283 participants to 5,310 per quarter for those who completed training and 3,957 participants to 2,518 per quarter for those who dropped out or failed to complete.
SOURCE: National Directory of New Hires.

quarter of completion or dropping out through the twelfth quarter, with those who completed training maintaining higher earnings on average. From the quarter of enrollment to the twelfth quarter after training completion, average earnings for those who completed training had increased by almost 50 percent, from $3,359 to $6,433 per quarter. For comparison, earnings for those who dropped out or failed to complete training also increased steadily, but were substantially lower. From the quarter of enrollment to the twelfth quarter after dropping out, average earnings for this group increased by about 35 percent from $3,401 per quarter to $5,263.

Employment and Earnings by Occupational Training

HPOG participants engaged in many different health care occupational training courses. Participants had different employment and earnings outcomes, depending on the training course completed. Figure 4.7 shows average participant employment in the 8 quarters prior to enrollment and the 12 quarters after training completion for the five most common training courses among the HPOG grantees.

Participants who completed training to become an RN had the highest average employment of the five most common health care trainings. At 12 quarters after completion, 92 percent of RN training completers

Figure 4.7 Employment of HPOG Participants in the Quarters before Enrollment and after Training Completion for the Five Most Common HPOG Health Care Trainings (18-month sample)

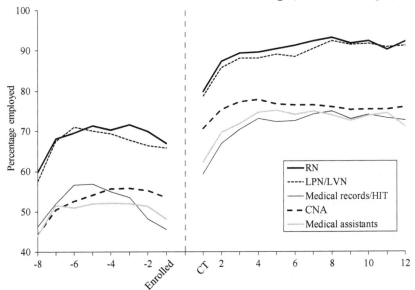

Quarter before enrollment and after training completion or dropout

NOTE: CT = quarter completed training. HIT = health information technician. Sample includes participants with at least 18 months of postenrollment experience (enrolled by April 1, 2014) who had completed training and were employed in a given quarter. N ranges from 6,123 participants to 255 per quarter for those who completed a particular health care training and were employed in the given quarter.
SOURCE: National Directory of New Hires.

were employed. The next highest rate of employment was for those who completed LPN/LVN training, with 91 percent employment in the twelfth quarter after completion. Of those completing CNA training, medical records and health information technician (HIT) training, and medical assistant training, 76 percent, 73 percent, and 71 percent, respectively, were employed. Participants who completed trainings with longer average durations tended to have higher levels of employment.

Compared to preenrollment rates of employment, all participants who completed training courses saw increases in employment. For example, 56 percent of those who completed CNA training were employed in the fourth quarter prior to enrollment; in the twelfth quarter after completion, 76 percent were employed. For each of the most common occupations, rates of employment were relatively flat from the fourth to tenth quarter after completion.[34]

Average quarterly earnings increased after training completion for all of the five most common occupational trainings, but they varied, depending on which training was completed (see Figure 4.8). Participants who completed an RN training course had substantially higher average quarterly earnings than the other four occupations. Those who completed an RN course earned on average $13,247 in the twelfth quarter after training completion—more than twice the average earnings of those who completed CNA training ($5,448 in the twelfth quarter after training completion). Participants who completed an LPN/LVN training course also earned on average substantially more than those who completed any of the three lower-level training courses. In the twelfth quarter after completion, LPN/LVN completers earned $9,361 on average, medical records/HIT completers earned $6,700, and medical assistant completers earned $6,237.

Earnings increased steadily for each of the five most common training courses from the quarter of training completion to the twelfth quarter after training completion. However, for the first four quarters after completing medical records/HIT or medical assistant training, participants' average earnings were lower than preenrollment earnings.

Characteristics of Jobs

The National Directory of New Hires data used above to report on quarterly employment and earnings do not include information about

Figure 4.8 Quarterly Earnings of HPOG Participants before Enrollment and after Training Completion for the Five Most Common HPOG Health Care Trainings (18-month sample)

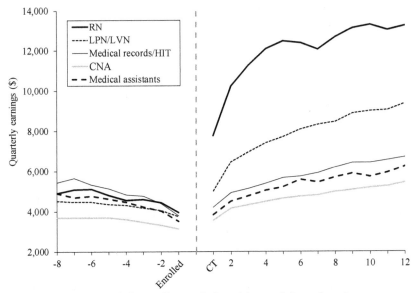

Quarter before enrollment and after training completion or dropout

NOTE: CT = quarter completed training. HIT = health information technician. Sample includes participants with at least 18 months of postenrollment experience (enrolled by April 1, 2014) who had completed training and were employed in a given quarter. N ranges from 4,727 participants to 235 per quarter for those who completed a particular health care training and were employed in the given quarter.
SOURCE: National Directory of New Hires.

the characteristics of jobs, including whether the job was in the health care sector, hourly wage, hours of employment, and availability of health insurance coverage. To fill this gap, the study collected data on employment and job characteristics for a sample of participants who responded to a follow-up survey initiated 15 months after enrollment. This section provides findings on job characteristics for those employed based on these data.[35] Table 4.12 shows employment status 15 months after enrollment and at any time during the 15-month period.

Almost three-quarters of survey respondents (73 percent) reported being employed at 15 months after enrollment. The survey data allow

Table 4.12 Employment of HPOG Participants, 15 Months after Enrollment

Status	At 15th month		Any time in 15 months	
	Number	Percentage	Number	Percentage
Employed	3,369	73	4,060	88
Employed in health care[a]	2,429	53	2,771	60

[a] In a health care occupation or with a health care employer.
NOTE: Sample is 4,646 participants across all HPOG grantees who enrolled in HPOG between September 1, 2013, and September 30, 2014, and responded to the 15-month follow-up survey of HPOG participants.
Missing responses for each survey item range from 6 to 11.
SOURCE: 15-month follow-up survey of HPOG participants; 15-month follow-up survey of PACE participants.

us to determine whether these jobs are in the health care sector; that is, either in a health care occupation or with a health care employer. Of all survey respondents, 53 percent were employed in health care (more than two-thirds of those employed). Note that at 15 months after enrollment some participants had finished training and were no longer in the HPOG program, whereas others were still in training or receiving services. When considering work at any time over the course of enrollment in HPOG through 15 months, 88 percent of participants were employed; 60 percent of participants were employed in health care.

Another goal of HPOG was for participants to secure high-quality jobs as measured by average hourly wage, full-time hours, and availability of employer-based health insurance (see Table 4.13). Participants employed at 15 months after enrollment reported an average hourly wage of $12.99. Those employed in health care jobs reported earning almost $2 more an hour than those employed in non–health care jobs ($13.49 compared to $11.71).

The average hours worked per week for those employed was 34, just below the 35-hour threshold for what is typically considered full-time work. Average hours worked per week was only slightly higher for health care jobs (35 hours) than for non–health care jobs (32 hours). Of participants with health care jobs, 63 percent worked full time (35+ hours per week), whereas 51 percent of those in non–health care jobs worked full time.

Finally, a large majority of survey respondents' jobs offered health insurance. For all employed survey respondents, 72 percent held jobs

Table 4.13 Job Characteristics of Employed HPOG Participants, 15 Months after Enrollment

Characteristic	All jobs (N = 3,369)	Health care jobs[a] (N = 2,429)	Non–health care jobs (N = 940)
Average hourly wage[b] ($)	12.99	13.49	11.71
Average hours per week	34	35	32
Full-time (35+ hours/week) (%)	59	63	51
Job offers health insurance, all jobs (%)	72	77	58
Job offers health insurance, full-time jobs (%)	83	85	76

[a] In a health care occupation or with a health care employer.

[b] Average hourly wage is among those reporting wages.

NOTE: Sample is 4,646 participants across all HPOG grantees who enrolled in HPOG between September 1, 2013, and September 30, 2014, and responded to the 15-month follow-up survey of HPOG participants. Sample for whether job offers health insurance is 4,402 (does not include participants enrolled at HPOG programs participating in PACE). The number of participants missing/refused response ranges from 21 to 125.

SOURCE: 15-month follow-up survey of HPOG participants; 15-month follow-up survey of PACE participants.

that offered health insurance. This rate was much higher for those in health care jobs (77 percent) than in non–health care jobs (59 percent). Of those employed full time, 83 percent held jobs that offered health insurance, and again the rate was higher for those in health care jobs (85 percent) than in non–health care jobs (76 percent).

SELF-ASSESSMENT OF CAREER PROGRESS

The HPOG program ties educational goals to career goals. The 15-month follow-up survey of HPOG participants asked two questions related directly to participants' self-assessment of career progress: "Would you say you [agree] with the following statements? 'I am making progress toward my long-range employment goals' and 'I see myself on a career path.'" Similar to educational progress reported earlier, large majorities either strongly or somewhat agreed with each statement (see Table 4.14).

Table 4.14 Self-Assessment of Career Progress

| | Response to statement: | | | |
| | "I am making progress toward my long-term employment goals." | | "I see myself on a career pathway." | |
Level of agreement	Number	Percentage	Number	Percentage
Strongly agree	2,840	61	3,223	69
Somewhat agree	1,274	27	975	21
Somewhat disagree	292	6	244	5
Strongly disagree	217	5	182	4
Don't know	2	1	2	<1
Total	4,646	100	4,646	100

NOTE: Sample is 4,646 participants across all HPOG programs who enrolled in HPOG between September 1, 2013, and September 30, 2014, and responded to the 15-month follow-up survey of HPOG participants.
Missing for this survey item = 0.
SOURCE: 15-month follow-up survey of HPOG participants; 15-month follow-up survey of PACE participants.

CONCLUDING OBSERVATIONS

The following discussion draws on the findings to provide insights on HPOG for program operators and developers.

- **The policy strategy behind HPOG was successful in one of its major goals—recruiting and training low-income individuals for employment in the health care professions.**

Over the five-year grant period, the 27 nontribal HPOG 1.0 grantees were successful in enrolling more than 36,000 participants in HPOG (well above HPOG's initial estimate based on grant applications of about 30,000 participants) and engaging most of them in health care occupational training. Of those who consented to participate in research (29,942 participants), 88 percent engaged in training within 18 months after enrollment. Of those who enrolled in training, 78 percent completed at least one training, and another 5 percent were still in training, by three years after enrollment.

Three years after enrolling in HPOG, overall participant employment increased from 52 percent to 75 percent. Over the first 15 months after enrollment, 60 percent of participants surveyed reported having held a job in health care; 53 percent reported being currently employed in health care at 15 months after enrollment.

- **Programs like HPOG that are trying to help individuals move along a career pathway need to address how to support longer-term training and encourage and create incentives for completers of short-term training to return for further training for higher-level jobs.**

Most HPOG participants engaged in short-term training for low-wage entry-level jobs, such as CNA and other medical aides positions. The career pathways framework envisions that those who train for entry-level jobs in a given profession might move to higher-paying positions through a combination of work experience and further training. Findings from the NIE suggest that within the three-year window covered by the evaluation, movement up a career pathway through education and training did not occur for most HPOG participants. ACF is supporting follow-up studies that track HPOG participant outcomes and impacts over 36 and 72 months after random assignment to continue to assess whether HPOG participants move forward on a career pathway over time.[36]

The results from the NIE suggest that training programs should continue to support participants in longer-term training for better-paying occupations, but they also should consider strategies to increase the likelihood of additional career-growth training for participants who train for entry-level jobs. One possible strategy is for training institutions to increase outreach and recruitment for training of incumbent entry-level health care workers. Only a handful of HPOG 1.0 programs had agreements with employers to train incumbent workers. Increasing support for incumbent workers through incentives to return to training by developing more partnerships with health care employers could provide a stronger basis for more workers to train for higher-paying jobs along their career pathways.

- **Relatively few applicants with low educational attainment and basic skills enrolled in HPOG.**

A review of the education-related characteristics of HPOG participants (see Table 4.1) reveals that most applicants had relatively high educational attainment and relatively good academic skills compared to the TANF population overall. Only 6 percent of HPOG applicants did not have a high school diploma or equivalency, and 45 percent had one or more years of postsecondary education; 85 percent and 74 percent tested at eighth grade or above for literacy and numeracy, respectively. By comparison, about 40 percent of TANF recipients have less than 12 years of schooling, and only about 8 percent have any educational experience beyond high school (Office of Family Assistance 2015).

Two strategies for program design and implementation could make it possible for training programs to lower eligibility standards while increasing participation in health care training among academically underprepared applicants. One strategy is to increase the degree to which programs integrate adult basic education with health care training. This approach—one prominent model of which is I-BEST—has shown promising results in nonexperimental studies and is currently being tested in an experiment as part of the PACE Study (Jenkins, Zeidenberg, and Kienzi 2009). A second strategy is to develop program structures that create a close connection or pipeline between basic skills instruction and occupational training.

PROSPECTS FOR FURTHER RESEARCH

Though the NIE found that grantees overall implemented HPOG as specified in the authorizing legislation, two important research questions remained:

1) **Did HPOG lead to better outcomes than participants would have achieved in its absence?** This question concerns the impacts of HPOG on participants' and their families' lives and is an important measure of its success relative to existing services and other policy initiatives.

2) **Did HPOG represent a solid first step along a career pathway; that is, will HPOG participants continue to build careers and obtain higher-wage jobs through further work experience and education?** Given the relatively short duration of the HPOG grants, as well as the short observation window available to the NIE to measure outcomes, it was not pos-

sible to address this question adequately. More follow-up time is needed to measure subsequent training and career growth.

To begin to address these questions, ACF funded three subsequent projects. Answering the first question is a core research goal of three studies: 1) the HPOG Impact Study, which uses an experimental design to estimate the effects of HPOG based on a survey initiated at 15 months after random assignment;[37] 2) the Career Pathways Intermediate Outcomes Study, which analyzes results of a follow-up survey fielded at 36 months after random assignment of individuals in the HPOG Impact Study sample and in PACE; and 3) the Career Pathways Long-Term Outcomes Study, which analyzes results from a similar survey at 72 months after random assignment. These longer-term views of HPOG participants' further work and educational experiences and outcomes will help address the second remaining research question.[38]

Further, ACF used findings from the NIE to refine the HPOG program design when issuing the Funding Opportunity Announcement (FOA) for a second round of HPOG grants (HPOG 2.0). For HPOG 2.0, ACF required HPOG 2.0 grantees more explicitly and strictly to do the following:

- **Engage employers**, such as by designing HPOG programs with employers, having job developers or employer specialists on staff, partnering with sector organizations, and providing opportunities for work-based learning, including internships and registered apprenticeships.

- **Align programs with labor market demand**, including thorough analysis of traditional labor market data, real-time labor market trends, occupational wage data, and local training capacity.

- **Link HPOG education and training along clearly defined career pathways**, with priority going to occupations that are expected to be full time, have regular hours, offer benefits, and/ or have strong potential for advancement.

- **Incorporate evidence-based education and training components and practices**, such as specific strategies that promote advancement along career pathways, innovative approaches to basic skills education, and articulation of training along pathways, especially from noncredit to credit-bearing trainings.

- **Involve local TANF agencies in program design and implementation**, such as ongoing partnerships to ensure referrals from the TANF program and willingness to allow its recipients to count HPOG activities toward meeting TANF work participation requirements, if possible, or to combine HPOG activities with countable work activities.

- **Ensure HPOG training results in employer- or industry-recognized credentials**, such as a professional license, third-party certification, or postsecondary educational certificate or degree (as well as a registered apprenticeship certificate).

ACF also funded a national evaluation of the HPOG 2.0 grantees that includes a descriptive evaluation (comprising an implementation study, an outcome study, and a systems study) and an impact evaluation.[39]

Notes

1. In 2010, ACF awarded the first round of five-year HPOG grants (HPOG 1.0) to 32 organizations in 23 states, including five tribal organizations, with approximately $67 million disbursed each year through fiscal year 2015. It awarded a second round of five-year grants in 2015 to 32 organizations across 21 states (HPOG 2.0).
2. In 2016, Abt Associates and its partner, the Urban Institute, published two reports that summarized the findings of the three related studies based on the experience of HPOG through September 2014 (the first four years of the five-year grant period): *Descriptive Implementation and Outcome Study Report* (Werner et al. 2016) and *Systems Change under the Health Profession Opportunity Grants (HPOG) Program* (Bernstein et al. 2016). In 2018, Abt Associates and the Urban Institute published the NIE *Final Report* (Werner et al. 2018), primarily updating findings on HPOG participant experiences through the five-year period of HPOG operations and participant outcomes for up to three years following program entry. The findings reported in this chapter are drawn from the first and third reports.
3. The HPOG Impact Study is estimating HPOG 1.0 impacts (see Chapter 3 for a description of the HPOG Impact Study).
4. Of the 36,000 participants, about 30,000 consented to be in the research study and are represented all or in part in the statistics included in this chapter.
5. See Chapter 3 for description of the HPOG Impact Study.
6. See Chapter 3 for description of the HPOG Impact Study. The PACE Study, also funded by ACF, is a multisite implementation and experimental evaluation of career pathways occupational education programs. For more on PACE see https://www.acf.hhs.gov/opre/research/project/pathways-for-advancing-careers-and-education (accessed March 1, 2019).

7. There is no federal income eligibility standard for TANF. Instead, each state sets its own income eligibility requirement. See http://anfdata.urban.org/databooks/welfare%20Rules%20Databook%202013.pdf (accessed August 13, 2019).
8. Reported characteristics are of all participants through September 30, 2015.
9. Approximately 17 percent of participants are missing information on literacy assessment, and 20 percent are missing information on numeracy assessment. These participants may not have been administered an assessment for literacy or numeracy.
10. FPL guidelines for 2014 can be found at http://aspe.hhs.gov/poverty/14poverty.cfm (accessed March 1, 2019).
11. Single mothers include those who were never married, divorced, widowed, or separated.
12. HPOG Impact Study site visits, 2014.
13. HPOG Grantee survey, 2014, Q8.6.
14. *Training course* here is defined as all the education and training activity needed to prepare for the specific occupation, including multiple classes required.
15. HPOG Grantee survey, 2014, Q8.13.
16. See Werner et al. (2016, p. 63).
17. HPOG Management and Staff survey, 2014, Q20-S.
18. HPOG Grantee survey, 2014, Q9.14.
19. HPOG Grantee survey, 2014, Q9.15.
20. HPOG Grantee survey, 2014, Q9.17.
21. HPOG Grantee survey, 2014, Q9.18.
22. HPOG funds cannot be used for medical care unless it is an integral but subordinate part of a social service for which grant funds may be used.
23. In the Performance Rating System (PRS), participants are considered still in training if they do not have a completion or dropout date entered. Therefore, some participants included in the "still in training" estimate at 36 months after enrollment may be the result of data entry errors in which a completion or dropout date was not recorded by the grantee.
24. The *length* of an HPOG health care training course is defined as the number of months between the first and the last days of training, as indicated in a participant's administrative record. This may include breaks in training and other time away from training and so represents only an approximation of actual training course length.
25. Note that some participants had partially completed these longer-term courses before enrolling in HPOG.
26. Some HPOG programs chose to restrict participants to one training course to maximize the number of people benefitting from the program.
27. Note that the exhibit describes only change over time. Readers should not conclude that such changes are necessarily due to participation in HPOG. Also note that 7 percent of the research sample had four or more years of college at program entry.
28. This section uses the sample of participants with 18 months of postenrollment experience. This allows us to take advantage of this larger sample.

29. *Employment* is defined as having greater than $58 of earnings in a quarter, the equivalent of one day of work at minimum wage.

30. Note that past literature has shown that training participants commonly experience a dip in earnings right before entering the training program, referred to as an "Ashenfelter's dip" (Ashenfelter and Card 1985). The effect of any dip is mitigated somewhat here by examining earnings eight quarters before entry. However, future experimental results will show whether HPOG training caused earnings to increase for those participants offered training.

31. Earnings in the exhibit combine earnings across multiple jobs. Any positive amount of earnings in the quarter is included. Earnings in a quarter were top-coded at $30,000 to limit skewing of averages by potential data error outliers.

32. This includes individuals who started training and dropped out or failed to complete, as well as individuals who enrolled in an HPOG program but never started a health care training.

33. For example, the reasons individuals drop out of training also may affect their success in finding a job.

34. Sample sizes are smaller in the last quarters after completion, especially for longer trainings. This means estimates are measured with less precision.

35. The 15-month follow-up survey of HPOG participants was conducted for all participants who were randomly assigned as part of the HPOG Impact Evaluation and for a subset of participants in grantees that did not participate in the Impact Evaluation. This subset was roughly those who enrolled in HPOG during the same time period in which random assignment had taken place so that survey responses would generally reflect the same time period for all surveyed. It also surveyed individuals who had less than 18 months of follow-up time during the HPOG program. Thus, the survey sample included here overlaps with, but is not the same as, the 18-month sample.

36. The Career Pathways Intermediate Outcomes and Career Pathways Long-Term Outcomes Studies will rigorously evaluate the intermediate and longer-term impacts of career pathways program models on participants' educational progress and employment and earnings. For more information, see https://www.acf.hhs.gov/opre/research/project/career-pathways-intermediate-outcomes-cpio-study and https://www.acf.hhs.gov/opre/research/project/career-pathways-long-term-outcomes-study (accessed March 1, 2019).

37. The *Health Profession Opportunity Grants (HPOG 1.0) Impact Study Interim Report* was released in 2018.

38. The Career Pathways Intermediate Outcomes report on 36-month impacts for HPOG is scheduled for 2019; the Career Pathways Long-Term Outcomes report on 72-month impacts is scheduled for 2021.

39. For more information see: https://www.acf.hhs.gov/opre/research/project/national-evaluation-of-the-2nd-generation-of-health-profession-opportunity-grants-hpog-20-national-evaluation (accessed March 1, 2019).

References

Ashenfelter, Orley, and David Card. 1985. "Using the Longitudinal Structure of Earnings to Estimate the Effect of Training Programs." *Review of Economics and Statistics* 67(4): 648–660.

Bernstein, Hamutal, Lauren Eyster, Jennifer Yahner, Stephanie Owen, and Pamela Loprest. 2016. *Systems Change under the Health Profession Opportunity Grants (HPOG) Program.* OPRE Report No. 2016-50. Washington, DC: Office of Planning, Research, and Evaluation, Administration for Children and Families, U.S. Department of Health and Human Services.

Jenkins, Davis, Matthew Zeidenberg, and Gregory Kienzi. 2009. *Building Bridges to Postsecondary Training for Low-Skill Adults: Outcomes of Washington State's I-BEST Program.* CCR Brief No. 42. New York: Community College Research Center, Teachers College, Columbia University. https://eric.ed.gov/?id=ED505705 (accessed March 14, 2019).

Office of Family Assistance, Administration for Children and Families, U.S. Department of Health and Human Services. 2015. *Characteristics and Financial Circumstances of TANF Recipients, Fiscal Year 2015, Table 20.* https://www.acf.hhs.gov/ofa/resource/characteristics-and-financial-circum stances-of-tanf-recipients-fiscal-year-2015 (accessed June 14, 2017).

Werner, Alan, Robin Koralek, Pamela Loprest, Radha Roy, Deena Schwartz, Ann Collins, and Allison Stolte. 2016. *Descriptive Implementation and Outcome Study Report: National Implementation Evaluation of the Health Profession Opportunity Grants (HPOG) to Serve TANF Recipients and Other Low-Income Individuals.* OPRE Report No. 2016-30. Washington, DC: Office of Planning, Research, and Evaluation, Administration for Children and Families, U.S. Department of Health and Human Services.

Werner, Alan, Pamela Loprest, Deena Schwartz, Robin Koralek, and Nathan Sick. 2018. *Final Report: National Implementation Evaluation of the First Round of Health Profession Opportunity Grants (HPOG 1.0).* OPRE Report No. 2018-09. Washington, DC: Office of Planning, Research, and Evaluation, Administration for Children and Families, U.S. Department of Health and Human Services.

5
Findings from the Tribal Health Profession Opportunity Grants Process and Outcomes Evaluation

Michael Meit
Carol Hafford
Catharine Fromknecht
Noelle Miesfeld
Emily Phillips
NORC at the University of Chicago

Shortages in the health care workforce in the United States have created high demand for well-trained health professionals in under-served communities (National Center for Health Workforce Analysis n.d.). These shortages have been particularly critical in American Indian/Alaska Native (AI/AN)[1] communities, who struggle to retain quality medical providers.[2] At Indian Health Service facilities (IHS) the average physician turnover rate is 48 percent compared to 6.8 percent on average across the United States (American Medical Group Association 2014). To address tribal community workforce shortages while providing employment opportunity for low-income AI/AN individuals, the Health Profession Opportunity Grants (HPOG) program included five tribal grantees out of a total of 32 national grantees to provide education and training opportunities for Temporary Assistance for Needy Families (TANF) recipients and other low-income individuals. In 2010, Administration for Children and Families (ACF) awarded the five Tribal HPOG 1.0 demonstration projects to tribal organizations and tribal colleges: Blackfeet Community College (BCC) in Browning, Montana; Cankdeska Cikana Community College (CCCC) in Fort Totten, North Dakota; College of Menominee Nation (CMN) in Green Bay, Wisconsin; Cook Inlet Tribal Council, Inc. (CITC) in Anchorage, Alaska; and Turtle Mountain Community College (TMCC) in Belcourt, North Dakota. The intent of these demonstration projects was to provide eligible individuals with the opportunity to obtain education and training for occupations in the health care field that pay well and are expected to either experience labor shortages or be in high demand (Administration for Children and Families 2010).

This chapter begins with an overview of some unique aspects of implementing grant programs with AI/AN communities, including a brief history of evaluation with tribal communities and a summary of key components for designing and conducting a culturally responsive evaluation. Next, we share key research questions of the Tribal HPOG evaluation and the methods for data collection and analysis. Following that we provide an overview of the five Tribal HPOG grantees, along with a description of the unique program models and structures that the grantees used to implement their programs. Lastly, we describe the main outcomes across the five grant programs, including the total number of participants who enrolled in the programs, completed health care trainings, and obtained employment, as well as program challenges and stakeholder satisfaction.

EVALUATION IN TRIBAL COMMUNITIES

Research review policies to oversee research and program evaluation in AI/AN communities are important in that they protect tribes and tribal members from harmful research, ensure maximum benefits are gained from the research, and establish tribes' authority as sovereign nations to control research conducted on their lands (Sahota 2009). Research and evaluation studies must be designed in collaboration with the tribal entities that are implementing the program, while at the same time presenting the results objectively. Policies and institutional structures for research review are significant both in light of and as a result of the historical trauma and history of AI/AN communities. Government policies over the past centuries have resulted in removal of AI/ANs from their homelands, prohibition of cultural practices, and removal of children from homes (Pacheco et al. 2013; Struthers and Lowe 2003). Additionally, there is mistrust of the scientific community, given unethical research practices that have been implemented in AI/AN communities (Burnette et al. 2011; Cochran et al. 2008; Pacheco et al. 2013). Further, researchers should be aware that they are sometimes described as "drive-by," "mosquito," or "helicopter" researchers (Johnston-Goodstar 2012, p. 110), referring to those who come into the community only to conduct research and leave or to conduct research that does not benefit the community (Cochran et al. 2008).

Given the history and context of research in AI/AN communities, researchers should be careful to implement research methods to address concerns of the study participants, such as using a community-based participatory research (CBPR) approach (Caldwell et al. 2005), which treats communities as "equal partners at all stages of a research project" and is a "philosophy about how research should be conducted so that community needs are prioritized" (Sahota 2010, p. 1). While the CBPR principles remain the same, they can be implemented using varying strategies across research projects, depending on the needs of the community members and researchers and the overall resources of the research project itself (Sahota 2010). One common component of the CBPR approach is the use of an advisory group to oversee research projects in AI/AN communities. Advisory groups comprised of community members can ensure that the perspective of the community is represented and that the research is relevant to its members (Johnston-Goodstar 2012; Quigley 2006).

In addition to working with an advisory group, other common processes for research design and review in AI/AN communities include review by a federally registered institutional review board, the enforcement of research-specific codes within tribal laws, or review by a tribal ethics review panel. In the absence of an established research review committee that was formed specifically for reviewing research on a regular basis, tribes can form research review consortiums, collaborate with an existing community committee that wants to be involved in research review, and/or rely on their tribal governance (e.g., tribal council) to review and approve research study participation and protocols as the need arises (Sahota 2009). The AI/AN community should be in control of their own review process because they are sovereign nations (Bowman 2006). To ensure that these processes are adhered to, nontribal researchers must recognize that each tribe is unique and should work with the collaborating tribe to determine the appropriate processes, protocols, and reviewers that are relevant to their study (Harding et al. 2011).

Similar approaches for research, including the use of a CBPR approach, are recommended when conducting research among urban AI/AN populations. However, there are unique considerations when working with AI/AN populations living in urban settings versus on reservation lands (Yuan, Bartgis, and Demers 2014). For example, urban AI/ANs do not typically live in localized urban neighborhoods, creating challenges when defining community and garnering community support, and multitribal urban AI/AN communities often have diverse perspectives. Additionally, there is often no single entity that represents the community, as there is no sovereign government elected by the community that can form partnerships on behalf of its members. Researchers should be proactive in addressing the concerns of AI/AN populations regarding research and should consider the differences between populations living in urban settings or reservation lands when conducting research with urban AI/AN's (Yuan, Bartgis, and Demers 2014). Key principles in conducting work with AI/AN communities include acknowledgment of historical experience with research, recognition of tribal sovereignty, understanding of the tribal community and its leaders, and planning for extended time lines to provide time for obtaining tribal approval for conducting research (LaVeaux and Christopher 2009).

Guided by these principles, the Tribal HPOG evaluation team worked to design and conduct an evaluation that was collaborative in nature, respectful of tribal cultures, and responsive to community history and norms.

DESIGNING AND CONDUCTING A CULTURALLY RESPONSIVE EVALUATION

The first step in designing an evaluation that is culturally responsive to tribal ways of life is for researchers to establish trust and demonstrate respect for tribal research partners, cultural beliefs, tribal institutions, and tribal sovereignty (Harding et al. 2011; Oetzel et al. 2015; NCAI Policy Research Center and MSU Center for Native Health Partnerships 2012). The tribal evaluation team encouraged engagement and consensus building with stakeholders in a number of ways. Importantly, the evaluation team built relationships with the Tribal HPOG grantees using dedicated small teams to work exclusively with each of the grantees in order to build and maintain trusted relationships. Each team was led by a senior researcher, who worked with their designated grantees for the duration of the evaluation. The teams engaged with the grantees through in-person meetings, regular telephone calls, and joint conference presentations.

Throughout the five-year evaluation, the Tribal HPOG evaluation team sought input from partners, advisors, and, most importantly, the Tribal HPOG grantees. The team included tribal partners at the National Indian Health Board and Red Star Innovations, a tribally owned small business. In addition to the core evaluation team, project activities were guided by a technical work group comprising tribal researchers and experts in AI/AN higher education, public health, and health care workforce development research. Tribal grantees and the evaluation team collaboratively designed evaluation components. The tribal grantees reviewed drafts of the evaluation plan and participated in evaluation webinars, and the evaluation team sought permissions from tribal councils and/or tribal institutional review boards as required by tribal grantees.

The evaluation team also sought regular input from tribal partner organizations and the project technical working group; both provided guidance on incorporating culturally appropriate methods in the evaluation. The evaluation team engaged with the working group through annual meetings to review findings to date and discuss any needed revisions to the evaluation research questions and approaches. In addition, the working group members and tribal partners provided feedback on the evaluation plan and reviewed the data collection instruments for cultural appropriateness.

To ensure that the evaluation was conducted in an ethical manner and adhered to human subjects and community protections, the evaluation team consulted with and obtained approvals from tribal council and/or tribal institutional review board, as well as approval from NORC's institutional review board. To underscore mutual obligations, the evaluation team and each tribal grantee entered into a memorandum of understanding that specified the objectives of the evaluation, respective roles and responsibilities relative to the evaluation, the scope of information requested during data collection, how the information would be used, and the terms of data privacy.

The evaluation included annual site visits to each of the five tribal grantees, which served as an important component to understanding barriers to and facilitators of implementing and evaluating the program in tribal communities. The site visits included interviews with grantee staff, grantee partners, and program participants; informal tours of educational institutions and employment partners; and observations of the geographic location, physical terrain, and local infrastructure. The trips were two to five days in duration, depending on the program model type and whether the grantee had implementation partners in multiple cities. In addition to collecting qualitative data, these site visits served as an opportunity to continue building a relationship between the evaluation team and the grantee. While communication via email and phone occurred throughout the year, the time spent in person during the site visit was invaluable.

The evaluation team shared evaluation design protocols and outcome reports with the grantees throughout the evaluation. In year 1, the grantees provided feedback on the evaluation plan to ensure that the research questions were meaningful and data were collected in a culturally respectful manner. Grantees also reviewed evaluation products to ensure information about their program was accurately conveyed and that the interpretation of the findings reflected tribal culture and local context. These products included site visit reports summarizing findings from the annual site visits and site-specific practice briefs developed in year 4. Grantees also reviewed the Tribal HPOG Program Evaluation final report (Meit et al. 2016).

Finally, the evaluation team provided technical assistance throughout the course of the evaluation to build grantees' capacity to participate in the Tribal HPOG evaluation activities. This included conducting needs assessment calls with grantees, offering technical assistance during in-person site visits, and responding to grantee requests over the course of the grant period. The evaluation team reviewed grantee performance data related to participant enrollment, health care training completions, and participant employment prior to the in-person site visits in preparation for data quality discussions. The purpose of the data quality discussions was to ensure that program outcomes were accurately reported into the HPOG Performance Reporting System (PRS), the federal management information system for the HPOG program. The evaluation team worked with the PRS team to provide technical assistance to the grantees as necessary.

KEY RESEARCH QUESTIONS AND METHODS

The evaluation studied the structures, processes, and outcomes of the Tribal HPOG 1.0 grantees and addressed three key evaluation questions. Table 5.1 presents these evaluation questions, as well as the related subquestions in distinct focus areas that were developed after a review of the literature on workforce development and AI/AN higher education.

The evaluation team used both qualitative and quantitative methods to address the study's research questions. During annual site visits to the Tribal HPOG programs, the evaluation team collected a majority of the qualitative data. Data collection protocols consisted of focus groups with students currently enrolled in the program and interviews with grantee and partner administrative staff (e.g., program directors, managers), program implementation staff (e.g., instructors, service providers), and local employers. Prior to site visits, all members of the tribal evaluation team participated in a comprehensive full-day training to ensure culturally sensitive and consistent administration of data collection protocols. Following the annual site visits, the team conducted telephone interviews with students who successfully completed their training program as well as students who did not complete their program. Additional qualitative methods included review of grantee documents, grant applications, semiannual reports, training program curricula, and outreach and recruitment materials. The team conducted content analysis using NVivo software to identify common themes across the tribal grantee programs that corresponded to the key research questions. The team disseminated major outcomes and findings in the annual evaluation reports and practice briefs.

To supplement qualitative information, the evaluation team obtained quantitative data on participant enrollment, training completion and employment, along with demographic information, from the PRS. The

Table 5.1 Tribal HPOG Evaluation Questions and Subquestions

	Evaluation question(s)	Subquestions
Structures	What frameworks and relationships did the Tribal HPOG grantees create to implement training and service delivery?	• What is the program type (i.e., academic instruction, on-the-job-training, apprenticeship, other)? Was the program incorporated within, or as an extension of, an existing program?
		• What is the administrative structure of the program?
		• How are local and/or regional partners and the community engaged?
		• What is the program curriculum (i.e., academic lectures, field practicum training manual)? In what ways was the program designed or modified for tribal populations?
		• What are the qualifications of program implementation staff?
		• Does the training program address skills and competencies demanded by the local health care industry?
		• How did the social, economic, and political context of the community influence program design and implementation?
Processes	How were training and support services delivered?	• What support services are offered with the program and how are they incorporated?
		• Were strategies used to engage participants' families, and if so, why and how?
		• What recruitment strategies were utilized? Were these strategies effective?
		• What orientation strategies were utilized? Were these strategies effective?
		• How are program data collected and used? Are data used for program management decisions, performance monitoring, or program correction?
		• Was the program implemented as intended?
		• Was effective instruction delivered?

Outcomes	What outcomes did participants achieve? Was health care workforce capacity enhanced in tribal communities?	• Did participation in the program result in a professional or industry recognized certificate, degree, or licensure? Why or why not? What factors are associated with receiving a certificate, degree, or licensure?
		• Did program participants enter a job or provide a community service in related occupations?
		• Did participation in the program result in any employability-related outcomes (e.g., increased life skills, self-efficacy, confidence, reduced use of income supports)?
		• Did the program help fill vacancies in the tribal health care workforce? Are participants serving tribal populations?
		• Are key program stakeholders satisfied with the program?

PRS was designed for both performance management and program evaluation. The tribal evaluation team coordinated with the PRS team to obtain data from the PRS for all of the Tribal HPOG grantees.

IMPLEMENTATION OF THE TRIBAL HPOG PROGRAM

This section provides background information on the tribal community, grantee organization, HPOG program, and key elements of implementation and partnerships for each of the five Tribal HPOG 1.0 grantees.

Blackfeet Community College (BCC)

BCC is a community college on the Blackfeet Indian Reservation in Browning, Montana. Chartered in 1974 by the Blackfeet Tribal Business Council, BCC is a fully accredited tribal college. Its mission is to provide the Blackfeet Nation and surrounding community with access to quality educational programs. The college offers an array of educational programs that integrate the Blackfeet culture and language into curricula and prepare students for achievement in higher education and meaningful employment.

The BCC HPOG program, known as the Issksiniip Project, provided scholarships and training opportunities in health care fields to Blackfeet community members; AI/AN students at BCC, the grant's lead entity; and Blackfeet and AI/AN students at its five partner institutions across the state.[3] The target populations for the scholarships were those eligible for TANF, individuals who left high school before graduating, low-income individuals, and single mothers with children. The training opportunities available through the Issksiniip Project included programs in nursing, pharmacy, nutrition, social work, dentistry, medical coding and billing, and other allied health professions.

The Issksiniip Project provided financial assistance and extensive support services using a case management model that included mentoring, tutoring, academic advising, referrals to public assistance and behavioral health programs, and career development, such as job shadowing and career fairs. BCC formed partnerships with several educational institutions across Montana to provide scholarships and training opportunities to eligible students. Project partners were Salish Kootenai College (Pablo), University of Montana Missoula (Missoula), Montana State University Bozeman (Bozeman), Great Falls College–Montana State University (Great Falls), and Montana State University Billings (Billings). At each academic institution, students applied their Issksiniip Project scholarship to a variety of health profession training programs (Meit, Hafford, et al. 2015).

Cankdeska Cikana Community College (CCCC)

CCCC serves the people of the Spirit Lake Nation and the surrounding communities near Fort Totten, North Dakota. Chartered in 1975 by the Spirit Lake Tribal Council, CCCC is a fully accredited tribal college. Its mission is to provide "opportunities that lead to student independence and self-sufficiency through academic achievement and continuation of the Spirit Lake Dakota language and culture." CCCC offers a variety of academic programs, including associate's degree programs and certificates.

The CCCC HPOG program was titled "Next Steps: An Empowerment Model for Native People Entering the Health Professions." It provided scholarships and training opportunities in health care fields to students at CCCC as well as to students at partner institutions across North Dakota. The training opportunities available through Next Steps included programs in nursing, nutrition and wellness, medical coding and billing, and other health professions.

Next Steps provided financial assistance as well as academic and social support services that enabled students to pursue training and promoted completion of training programs. A critical component of the program model was the use of mentors to empower students and help them achieve their goals. CCCC partnered with three other tribal colleges in North Dakota—United Tribes Technical College in Bismarck, Fort Berthold Community College in New Town, and Sitting Bull College in Fort Yates—which, along with CCCC, served as the point of entry for most students in Next Steps. In general, students began their education at one of the four tribal colleges and, after graduating with an associate's degree in a health profession, could continue their training at a four-year university, such as the University of North Dakota in Grand

Forks, for a bachelor's or master's degree. Through CCCC's partnership with the Recruitment/Retention of American Indians into Nursing (RAIN) Program at the University of North Dakota, a dedicated mentor served at each of the four tribal college sites, along with a fifth mentor to offer outreach support to the Next Steps students enrolled in other colleges and universities throughout the state (Meit, TenBroeck, and Miesfeld 2015).

College of Menominee Nation (CMN)

Populations of Menominee Nation, neighboring tribal nations, and surrounding communities in Wisconsin attend CMN. The main campus is located on the Menominee Indian Reservation in Keshena, and a second campus is located in Green Bay. Chartered in 1993, CMN is a tribally controlled and accredited community college. It offers students a range of options to pursue higher learning, including baccalaureate and associate's degree programs, technical diplomas and certificates, and continuing education opportunities.

The CMN HPOG program targeted individuals from the Menominee Reservation, other area reservations, and regional rural and urban communities who are unemployed, underemployed, low-wage workers, displaced workers, or incumbent workers, as well as TANF recipients. The CMN HPOG program offered a nursing career ladder that allowed students to progress from the prenursing level through the registered nurse level. The program served a range of students, from those seeking immediate employment to those who were working toward a more advanced nursing certificate, licensure, or degree.

The CMN HPOG program offered academic and social support services to students. Academic support services included academic counseling, advising, supplemental lab instruction, tutoring, and career placement support. Social support services include case management, as well as financial assistance to help cover transportation, housing, and child care costs. The program was implemented at both the Keshena and Green Bay campuses (Meit, Meyer, et al. 2015). CMN developed partnerships with several state and local agencies, including Bay Area Workforce Development, Green Bay; Fox Valley Workforce Development, Appleton; Workforce Development Area-Workforce Investment

Board; Community Resource Center, Keshena; local health care and long-term care providers; and the Department of Transit Services.

Cook Inlet Tribal Council, Inc. (CITC)

CITC serves Alaskan Native and other American Indians within the Municipality of Anchorage and throughout the Cook Inlet Region. The AI/AN population in Anchorage is not reservation based but includes people from rural Native villages and regions across Alaska who have migrated to the Anchorage metropolitan area. Established in 1983, CITC is a nonprofit tribal social service organization. It administers Tribal TANF within the municipality of Anchorage and serves as a one-stop service center, which provides a range of support services to low-income AI/AN job seekers in one location.

The CITC HPOG program provided health professions training to Alaska Natives and other Native Americans who live in Anchorage and the Cook Inlet region who receive Tribal TANF or who are low-income. The tribal council partnered with the Alaska Vocational Technical Education Center to provide academic instruction to program participants through offering certified nursing assistant, licensed practical nursing, registered nursing, medical billing and coding, and medical office assistant training programs.

CITC led the recruitment and screening of HPOG participants and provided support services, including rental assistance, gas cards or bus passes, child care assistance, food cards, tuition and textbook payments, and equipment for students to complete their required practical experience in a clinical setting. It partnered with the Alaska Vocational Technical Education Center to provide academic training and the South Central Area Health Education Center to deliver the orientation for program participants and expose them to health care professions through job shadowing experiences at local medical facilities (Meit, Gilbert, and Fromknecht 2015).

Turtle Mountain Community College (TMCC)

TMCC is located within the boundaries of the Turtle Mountain Indian Reservation in Belcourt, North Dakota. Founded in 1972, it is a tribally controlled and accredited college. The college primarily serves the educational needs of the Turtle Mountain Band of Chippewa Indians, but enrollment is open to any person who is pursuing higher education. TMCC offers a variety of associate's degrees and certificate of completion programs, as well as four-year degrees in education.

The TMCC HPOG program was called "Project CHOICE: Choosing Health Opportunities for Indian Career Enhancement." The goal was to create educational opportunities for TANF recipients and other low-income individuals through health profession training programs located at TMCC. Project CHOICE offered students a variety of programs: the Clinical/Medical Lab Technician Program, which included a certificate program in phlebotomy; the Pharmacy Technician Program; the CNA Program; the Licensed Vocational Nursing Program; and the Health Information Management Program.

Project CHOICE provided a range of support services to TMCC students to address both academic and social support needs. These services included reimbursement for transportation mileage and child care costs, financial assistance for tuition and other training expenses, tutoring, access to technology, and job placement and employability services. Project CHOICE established local and state partnerships with Job Service North Dakota, North Dakota Department of Commerce, North Dakota Department of Human Services, and the North Dakota State Office of Apprenticeship (Meit, Knudson, et al. 2015).

Incorporating Native Culture into Curricula

All of the Tribal HPOG 1.0 grantees served American Indian and Alaska Native populations. Some of the programs adapted or modified their health care training curricula to be culturally relevant and to align with the specific needs of their student population. The importance of incorporating tribal culture and language is noted in the mission, vision, and values of all of the Tribal HPOG grantees.

Culturally tailored curricula are a central component of the tribal colleges as a whole. Two of the Tribal HPOG 1.0 grantees designed a specific cultural component for the health profession programs. For the Quality Service Provider program, CCCC designed a curriculum that incorporated Native Elder Care, which was developed in collaboration with the National Resource Center on Native American Aging.[4] CMN's nursing program was structured around the five principal clans of the

Menominee People (Bear, Golden Eagle, Wolf, Crane, and Moose), which recognizes each clan as having a duty, that no one duty is more important than the others, and that no one can be successful in isolation. Every course that was integrated into the nursing program was designed to address these teachings. Program administrators and staff explained that the curriculum design instills cultural sensitivity into the practices of the students.

Tribal HPOG grantees that were tribal colleges developed culturally tailored programming to facilitate academic success. For example, BCC formed a society program on campus to aid in student academic success, which incorporates elements of Blackfeet cultural heritage. Both faculty and students were assigned to one of 17 societies whose names represent important figures in Blackfeet culture. Each society was composed of individuals from different departments at the college, which fostered community building campuswide. TMCC's organizational mission was to provide educational and research opportunities in which the cultural and social heritage of the Turtle Mountain Band of Chippewa is present in the curricula. Some of the programs offered at the college incorporated Native teachings into the curricula. In addition, staff at TMCC remained in contact with American Indian Student Services at other universities to create a support network for students who wished to pursue education opportunities off the reservation. Those partner universities included the University of North Dakota's RAIN Program and North Dakota State University's Native Research Center.

Recruitment and Enrollment Strategies

Tribal HPOG 1.0 grantees used many different recruitment strategies to market their programs to potential students. All five grantees developed promotional materials, such as brochures and flyers, at the beginning of the HPOG programs to assist with recruitment efforts. Some grantees also advertised the HPOG program in local newspapers or on local radio, which are important communication venues in tribal communities. Word of mouth was the most effective recruitment tool for reaching potential students, with students, instructors, and community members relaying information to family and friends.

Grantees also reached out directly to students and accepted referrals from instructors. For example, TMCC notified all of the current students about the HPOG program when it began. BCC and its college and university partner sites advertised programs on their websites and through student listservs. Some grantees mailed information directly to their current nursing students. At CCCC and its partner sites, mentors informed students and other eligible individuals about the HPOG program. The RAIN Program at the University of North Dakota also provided information to RAIN students who qualified for the HPOG program.

HPOG grantees also accepted referrals from human service and workforce development organizations, including those that administer TANF and promote job training in their communities. Some HPOG programs were more successful than others in obtaining referrals from these organizations. CITC had success with internal referrals from its TANF caseload, particularly clients who visited the Alaska's People Center, the career development center at CITC, as these individuals were in the process of seeking training or employment. TANF case workers at CITC referred both new walk-ins as well as existing clients to the HPOG program if they expressed an interest in health care. BCC also had success recruiting HPOG students through case managers and career counselors at Blackfeet Manpower, a one-stop center that administers the TANF program in Browning, Montana. Although CMN had set up a referral process to recruit potential students from the TANF program at the local Community Resource Center, several did not pass background checks (for example, because of a felony) and were not eligible for the program.

Other recruitment strategies used by HPOG grantees included attending job and career fairs to reach out to potential students, marketing the program to those already enrolled in home health aide classes, and holding information sessions about the HPOG program, especially to reach potential students who had not considered pursuing higher education. Four out of five grantees (the exception being CCCC) conducted outreach at local high schools, with the goal of building a pipeline for health care training and professions.

In addition to modifying recruitment strategies established in the first year of the grant, and trying new recruitment approaches to determine what worked best, grantees also needed to adapt their recruitment strategies based on the year of the grant. Grantees were encouraged to enroll students who would complete their training programs prior to the end of the grant in September 2015. Therefore, in the later years of the grant period, grantees focused primarily on enrolling students in short-term training programs, such as the certified nursing assistant (CNA) program. In addition, some grantees recruited students who were already enrolled in health care training programs and met the eligibility requirements to enroll in the HPOG program if they were on schedule to graduate prior to the grant ending.

Orientation Strategies

All five Tribal HPOG grantees offered a formal orientation for newly enrolled HPOG students to introduce them to the program and program staff, and to convey program expectations. Four of the five grantees hosted one- to two-day group orientations with HPOG students prior to the start of their training programs. One grantee, CCCC, had students meet one-on-one with their assigned mentors to learn about the HPOG program instead of offering a group orientation. Similar topics were covered at each grantee's orientation, including expectations around attendance, punctuality, grades, and professionalism. At BCC and TMCC, students were required to sign contracts or letters of commitment stating they understood and would meet program expectations. Most grantee orientation processes evolved over the course of the grant period. For the most part, grantees expanded the length of orientation to include additional content. The biggest change to orientation overall was the addition of activities focused on employment and job readiness, such as sessions on soft skills and assistance with résumé development. CITC and BCC also began inviting current or past HPOG students to the orientation to share personal testimonies about the program and answer students' questions.

Support Services

All the grantees provided a variety of support services designed to help students overcome barriers to pursuing their education and to comprehensively address the students' basic living needs. Support services typically fell into one of three categories: academic, social, and employment. Table 5.2 lists all services provided to HPOG participants by Tribal HPOG grantees. Many of the HPOG students said that they

Table 5.2 Support Services Offered by Tribal HPOG Grantee

Support services	Blackfeet Comm. College	Cankdeska Cikana Comm. College	Cook Inlet Tribal Council	College of Menominee Nation	Turtle Mountain Comm. College
Academic services					
Tuition and fees	✓	✓	✓	✓	✓
Books	✓	✓	✓	✓	✓
Tutoring	✓	✓		✓	✓
Academic counseling	✓	✓			✓
Exam/certification fees	✓	✓			✓
Exam review materials	✓		✓		✓
Lodging for exam					✓
Uniforms	✓	✓	✓		✓
Other training supplies	✓	✓	✓		✓
Computers	✓	✓			✓
Social services					
Child care	✓	✓	✓	✓	✓
Transportation	✓	✓	✓	✓	✓
Food	✓	✓	✓		✓
Rent assistance	✓		✓	✓	✓
Utilities assistance	✓			✓	
Internet access	✓			✓	
One-time emergent needs	✓	✓		✓	✓
Financial literacy	✓			✓	✓
Employment services					
Career counseling	✓	✓			
Life skills training	✓	✓			✓
Résumé/cover letter	✓	✓	✓	✓	✓
Job searching	✓	✓	✓		✓
Interview preparation	✓		✓		✓
Financial assistance for moving for employment	✓				✓

SOURCE: Key informant interviews and participant focus groups during annual site visits.

could not have completed their degree program without the aid of the support services, specifically the social support services, such as transportation and child care. Tribal colleges are experienced in securing financial assistance for their students in the form of grants and scholarships, but most of those programs only cover academic costs. HPOG was unique in its ability to cover academic and social services, such as child care and transportation. Additionally, Tribal HPOG grantees assisted program graduates with obtaining their certifications by providing gas money for travel to the testing site, lodging if needed, test registration fees, and study materials. Support services also included job readiness and employment assistance, ensuring that graduates had career readiness skills such as résumé writing, job searching, and interview techniques.

Figure 5.1 shows the percentage of Tribal HPOG participants who received each type of support service as identified in the PRS. The most commonly received support services included preenrollment and intake assessments (90 percent), case management (89 percent), training and work-related resources (90 percent), and counseling (84 percent).

Figure 5.1 Participants Receiving HPOG Support Services across Tribal HPOG Grantees (%)

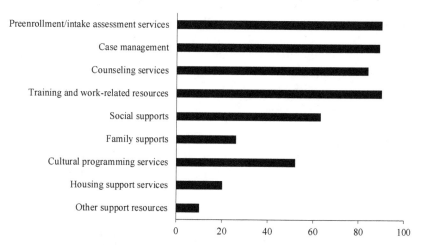

NOTE: N = 2,270. Participants who received more than one type of support service may be represented in more than one category, but only once within each category.
SOURCE: Performance Reporting System, 2015.

Academic Support Services

Academic support services were similar among all grantees. Tribal HPOG grantees provided financial assistance for tuition and fees, textbooks, exam and certification fees, uniforms, and other training supplies. Three of the grantees—BCC, CCCC, and TMCC—provided laptops and tablets for students that did not have them. TMCC HPOG staff believed that tablets would improve students' access to technology and textbook content via e-books. The staff shifted away from traditional textbooks to combat the rising costs. A few instructors expressed concern about this change, indicating that some of their textbooks were not available as e-books. Tribal HPOG grantees also covered the costs of transportation, lodging, and meals for students during clinical training periods and trips to state testing facilities for their health professions certification exams.

Nonfinancial academic supports included mentoring, academic counseling, tutoring, remedial classes, and additional lab hours. Most of these academic services were offered by the colleges and available to all students, regardless of HPOG affiliation; however, one of the secondary implementation sites of BCC made a concerted effort to create a support community specifically for HPOG students. At Great Falls College-Montana State University, tutoring and academic services for HPOG students were housed at the Issksiniip Center, which was established exclusively for BCC HPOG students and provided a quiet, lounge-like atmosphere for students to do homework, have tutoring sessions, and meet with classmates.

Social Support Services

Social support services refers to financial assistance for nonacademic needs of the students. Among all Tribal HPOG grantees, transportation and child care were the most widely used and appreciated nonacademic services. Depending on the grantee, financial assistance covered housing (security deposit and first month's rent), child care (payment to a licensed provider), transportation (gas cards or mileage reimbursement), and food (meal provision or payment). Over the years, some of the grantees modified eligible uses of funding, depending on the needs of their HPOG students and the amount of other funding streams that could be leveraged. All the grantees also used financial assistance to cover unique emergent needs, such as car repairs, temporary housing, and driver's license assistance. Grantees also referred students to social service organizations in the community to access TANF, employment assistance, and mental health services.

In addition, some grantees provided counseling or other one-on-one support services. For example, at BCC, counseling services were offered to students for academic issues and nonacademic issues, such as grief or family relationships. At CCCC, students also received individualized assistance from the mentors, such as arranging child care or transportation to class and checking in with a phone call or text message.

Grantees provided other types of social support services as student needs were identified. For example, the CITC HPOG program offered transitional assistance for up to one year after program completion. However, in the later years of implementation, staff discussed the possibility of reallocating some of these funds by reducing the amount of time graduates could receive assistance. Program staff believed that while this assistance was useful for the program graduates, one year was more time than needed for participants to stabilize themselves. BCC provided support after graduation to students who planned to continue their education at another institution. Additionally, BCC provided transportation funds for support related to moving for employment and financial assistance to purchase supplies such as uniforms, textbooks, or tablets.

Employment-Related Services

While grantees had employment-focused components and services from the beginning of their programs, employment-related support services became a more central component of the Tribal HPOG programs during the final two years of implementation. BCC, CITC, CMN, and TMCC all hired additional staff to focus on employment assistance during the second half of the grant period. The smaller grantees, CMN and TMCC, did not identify the need for employment services until year 3. At the end of the program, all the grantees reported that they should have identified the need for employment-related services at the beginning of the grant period.

168   Meit et al.

Generally, employment services included career counseling, job searching and placement assistance, and job retention services. Figure 5.2 shows the percentage of Tribal HPOG participants enrolled in employment development activities throughout the five-year grant period. The two most common employment development activities among participants were employment assistance (44 percent of participants), such as assistance with searching for jobs, completing applications, and developing résumés, and soft skills/life skills training (37 percent), which includes training to develop skills such as self-confidence and ability to get along with others and work in a team.

Grantees used existing employment assistance services offered by their partners through a process of referral or collaboration. For example, CITC referred students to employment-related services at the Alaska's People Center, also housed at CITC. At CMN there was a class dedicated to showing students how to access the Job Center of Wisconsin website, upload their résumés, and navigate the website to apply for employment upon completion of the program. In Montana, BCC

Figure 5.2 Participants Enrolled in Employment Development Activity across Tribal HPOG Grantees (%)

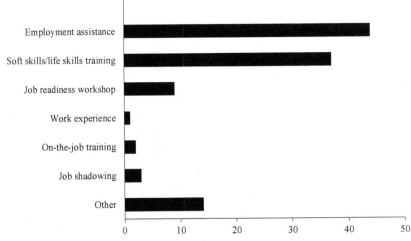

NOTE: N = 2,270. Participants who engaged in more than one type of activity may be represented in more than one category, but only once within each category.
SOURCE: Performance Reporting System, 2015.

partnered with Benefis Health System to provide job shadowing for HPOG students prior to beginning their training programs. Not only did this opportunity help students learn about their fields, it also gave them exposure to a potential employer; some BCC students were employed at Benefis.

Grantees also developed their own programs to enhance their students' job search skills. In year 4, TMCC held an employability boot camp to support students' transition to employment and help build connections with employers outside the local area. The boot camp also taught soft skills (attitude, professionalism, how to present oneself), which were identified by program staff as an area for improvement among the HPOG students. In the final year of the program, BCC developed an initiative to boost employment among their HPOG graduates across all implementation sites. The initiative, which was run by the job developers, was called the "Where are you now?" campaign, and its mission was to reach out to past students to learn what they had accomplished since graduating and to help with finding jobs. At some of the secondary implementation sites for BCC—MSU-Bozeman, for example—HPOG students used existing student support services to gain job readiness training or life skills coaching. The services included a career coach who was available to work with all students at the university but was highly involved in the Native studies program.

Job retention services were offered in the form of transitional funds for individuals establishing themselves in a new job and moving, if necessary. As stated earlier, CITC provided financial assistance for one year following program completion. CCCC implemented a system to provide funding for HPOG graduates who secured employment and were required to move; the funding decreased gradually over time. The financial assistance could be used for transportation and child care costs.

Retention Strategies

The main retention strategies grantees used included extensive screening processes, implementing systems for accountability, and support services. Both CITC and TMCC cited the thorough screening processes they implemented as a key to retention, as it allowed them to identify dedicated, motivated individuals who would be committed to completing the program. Grantees also conducted academic assessments at intake to ensure that prospective students had the required reading, writing, and math skills to be successful in their training programs. Once enrolled in HPOG, grantees implemented systems designed to ensure accountability for HPOG students. Three of the grantees—CCCC, BCC, and TMCC—required students to submit attendance and grade reports to their mentors or retention counselor on a weekly or biweekly basis. This strategy enhanced students' accountability to the program while allowing mentors and HPOG program staff to recognize issues and respond to challenges before they escalated.

Grantees also noted that the support services offered by the HPOG program were key to student retention. Often the provision of a support service was seen as the difference between students staying in school or leaving their training program. Grantees reported that both social support and academic services were important for student retention. Students often shared how important the support services were to their success, for example, as described by a participant: "This whole program is life changing for me. I don't know if I would've come back to school. I always wanted to be a nurse, but financially, being a single mom, there is no way I could have done it without this program. This program just makes me want to go, go, go. . . . I can't believe I am here and done and it is all because of this program supporting me through it all. It has completely changed my life."

Although all grantees noted that these strategies improved student retention, they did have students who were unable to complete their training programs. According to grantees, some students did not complete their programs because of academic challenges with the course material. Personal challenges and family issues were also frequently cited as a contributing factor for students who did not complete their training programs.

Honoring Family

The Tribal HPOG grantees, particularly the tribal colleges, created an environment that welcomed and honored their students' extended families' structure and recognized the importance of familial involvement and support (HeavyRunner and DeCelles 2002). Involving families in the Tribal HPOG 1.0 program varied across grantees. While not a separate component of most of the implementation plans, all the Tribal

HPOG 1.0 grantees organized at least one family event per year and generally encouraged families to support and participate in their family member's HPOG education. For example, secondary implementation sites for BCC hosted family-centered events, such as powwows and Native American Day celebrations. All HPOG students and graduates were invited and encouraged to bring family members to share in the events. Other grantees also invited families to graduation and other recognition ceremonies. During holiday dinners, luncheons, and other events hosted at the college, HPOG staff used the opportunity to inform families about the importance of creating a supportive environment for their family member to pursue an education. Over time, some grantees saw an increase in students who brought their family members to those events, and staff welcomed and encouraged their participation. In addition, HPOG staff, especially the case managers, helped make family accommodations on a daily basis so that students could attend class, such as helping to find babysitters, sending reminders to students about class schedules and tests, and checking on availability of transportation.

The academic clan and society distinctions in the nursing program at CMN and collegewide at BCC, respectively, also emphasized familial and community support. As mentioned previously, CMN's nursing program instilled the cultural teachings of the five principle clans of the Menominee People and BCC incorporated figures of Blackfeet culture into the names of 17 societies composed of students, staff, and instructors. Both of these examples demonstrate how grantees structured academic programs using cultural elements to build a sense of community around a shared identity. According to the BCC staff members, engaging families increases the likelihood that students will receive support at home. Family members of BCC participants were invited to orientation, seminars, and campus visits so they could become familiar with the staff and setting where the students' training occurred. One of BCC's secondary implementation sites, Salish Kootenai College, hosted a family night every year that was arranged by the student senate to which the HPOG students were invited. In addition, the college offered orientation for families to coincide with student orientation, during which families learned about student responsibilities and experiences, such as long study hours and increased stress during exam times. Some students at other colleges expressed the desire for more organized family engagement to help family members cope with the demanding education and work schedule. Many students noted that they were the first in their families to pursue higher education, and family members were "both proud and worried when students [left] home." This sentiment was echoed by a staff member who said that some family members "pull back" as the student becomes more immersed in her education, and this is what a family-focused educational component would address.

An unanticipated benefit was the effect that HPOG seemed to have on the perception of education in the home. During focus groups conducted by the evaluation team and in conversations with Tribal HPOG 1.0 staff, many HPOG students described the interactions that they had with their children, working on homework together and forming an expectation that education should be a priority. Students reported that they took it upon themselves to include their children in their education. Some parents studied with their children to create an environment at home that placed an emphasis on education and support. Students noted that they were able to show their children that it was possible to pursue an education and find employment. Though this was reported by a subset of HPOG participants, the effect on families may have implications for a majority of HPOG students, over half of whom reported having at least one dependent child.

TRIBAL HPOG OUTCOMES

Over the five-year grant period, 2,270 students were enrolled in HPOG among all five Tribal HPOG 1.0 grantees. Final outcome data were calculated from the PRS in September 2015. At intake, the majority of participants were female (87 percent), never married (61 percent), and had one or more dependent children (64 percent). Nearly half of participants (47 percent) were below the age of 30. Approximately two-thirds of participants were AI/AN. Nearly half of participants (44 percent) had one to three years of college or technical school, and 43 percent of participants were high school graduates or equivalent. Many of the participants were low-income. At intake into the HPOG program, 41 percent of participants were in households with annual incomes below $10,000, and another 20 percent of participants were in households with incomes between $10,000 and $19,999. In addition, 16 percent of the Tribal HPOG 1.0 participants were TANF recipients at intake.

Educational Attainment

By the end of the grant period, 1,483 out of the 2,270 enrollees (65.3 percent) had completed one or more health care trainings. There were 433 participants who started a second training program, of which 238 completed the second training. There were 703 participants who exited without completing a training program (31 percent).[5] The remaining 4 percent had neither completed a training program nor exited the program. Figure 5.3 shows the cumulative Tribal HPOG program enrollment, training completion, and exits without completion.

Across the Tribal HPOG 1.0 grantees, the health care training program with the most enrollees was the CNA program; this program also had the highest percentage of completers among training programs

Figure 5.3 HPOG Enrollment, Health Care Training Completion, and Exiting without Completion

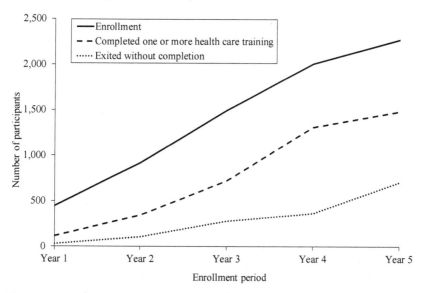

NOTE: N = 2,270
SOURCE: Performance Reporting System, 2015.

(79.6 percent) (Table 5.3). The program with the second-highest completion rate, at 75 percent, fell under the Miscellaneous Community and Social Service Specialist Standard Occupational Classification system, which included programs such as behavioral health aide and diabetes specialist. CNA programs, typically three to eight weeks long, were among the shortest training programs offered by grantees, which may help explain the higher number of completions. The programs with the lowest completion rates were the emergency medical technicians and paramedics (24.8 percent completion rate), pharmacy technician (28 percent completion rate), and the diagnostic-related technician (25 percent completion rate, though there were only four total enrollees in this

Table 5.3 Number of Tribal HPOG 1.0 Participants Who Enrolled in and Completed Each Training Program (Listed by Most to Least Number of Participants Enrolled

Training programs (SOC)	Number enrolled	Number completed	Percent completed
Nursing assistant, aide, orderly, attendant	1,170	931	79.6
Licensed practical and vocational nurses	351	205	58.4
Misc. community and social service specialist	175	131	74.9
Registered nurses	172	101	58.7
Medical records and health information technician	157	95	60.5
Emergency medical technicians and paramedics	129	32	24.8
Misc. health care support occupation	103	49	47.6
Home health aide	37	15	40.5
Pharmacy technician	25	7	28.0
Phlebotomist	24	15	62.5
Medical assistant	8	5	62.5
Diagnostic-related technician	4	1	25.0
All other SOCs[a]	107	56	52.3

[a] Other SOCs include health practitioner support technologists and technicians, clinical laboratory technologists and technicians, physical therapist assistants and aides, miscellaneous health diagnosing and treating practitioners, miscellaneous health technologist and technicians, and counselors.

NOTE: N = 2,270.

SOURCE: Performance Reporting System, 2015.

program). It was reported that the low completion rate for emergency medical technician may be due to difficulties with taking and passing the licensure exams.

Participants expressed how completing their training program and earning a degree impacted their outlook toward the future and their potential to support their families: "[Earning my degree] has given me the feeling that I now have my future secured. It taught me that hard work pays off and there are programs out there to help us Natives in completing our goals and making a better life for our families. It feels good knowing that I can do more for my daughters and family."

Employment Outcomes

Two measures of employment outcomes among Tribal HPOG 1.0 participants were calculated. The first measure was participants' employment status at intake and whether they became employed at any point after intake.[6] At program intake, 65 percent of participants (1,468) were unemployed, 20 percent (458) were employed in a non–health care field, and 15 percent (134) were employed in a health care field. Almost half of the participants who were unemployed at intake became employed at some time after intake, most of them obtaining health care–related employment. Of those who were employed in health care at intake, 39 percent experienced a wage increase at some point after intake.

The second employment outcome measure is average wages and full-time equivalents earned, or annual earnings calculated based on the equivalent of one employed person working full-time (40 hours per week x 52 weeks = 2,080 hours per year), by participants who gained employment after intake (Table 5.4).[7] The average hourly wage among all occupations was $15.47, which is about $32,000 annually for a full-time employee. Average hourly wages ranged from $10.58 ($22,000 annually) for Home Health Aides to $27.58 for Miscellaneous Health Diagnosing and Treating Practitioners ($57,000 annually). Within the nursing professions, CNAs averaged $12.34 an hour ($25,600 annually), LPNs averaged $18.13 an hour ($37,700 annually), and RNs averaged $22.72 an hour ($47,200 annually). All the occupations listed in Table 5.4 had annual full-time equivalent earnings that exceeded the 2015 federal poverty level for a family of three in the contiguous 48 states

Table 5.4 Wages of Tribal HPOG 1.0 Participants

Occupation (SOC)	Number employed	Average hourly wage ($)	Annual full-time equivalent earnings ($)
Nursing assistant, aide, orderly, and attendant	468	12.34	25,657.47
Licensed practical and licensed vocational nurse	107	18.13	37,720.70
Miscellaneous community and social service specialists	77	13.64	28,367.42
Registered nurse	65	22.72	47,266.88
Counselors	53	13.49	28,057.63
Medical records and health information technician	48	14.36	29,875.30
Miscellaneous health care support occupations	36	14.11	29,340.71
Medical assistant	24	15.29	31,801.47
Home health aide	24	10.58	22,003.80
Emergency medical technicians and paramedics	16	12.49	25,977.90
Miscellaneous health diagnosing and treating practitioners	9	27.58	57,361.78
Phlebotomist	6	14.96	31,109.87
Pharmacy technician	6	14.82	30,829.07
Health technologists and technicians, misc.	6	13.63	28,340.00
Health practitioner support technologists and technicians	5	15.02	31,241.60
Clinical laboratory technologists and technicians	4	16.10	33,477.60
Physical therapist assistants and aides	3	16.33	33,973.33
Diagnostic-related technologists and technicians	3	14.33	29,813.33

NOTE: N = 960. Includes Tribal HPOG 1.0 participants who were employed at any time after program intake, including during enrollment, at program exit, or at follow-up. Only includes participants that had an SOC and wage recorded in the PRS. If more than one employment record, the most recent record is reported.
SOURCE: Performance Reporting System, 2015.

and District of Columbia. Excluding the home health aide, wages for the occupations exceeded the federal poverty level for a family of four in the contiguous 48 states and District of Columbia. Alaska has higher federal poverty levels. In Alaska, approximately half of the occupations listed had annual full-time equivalent earnings that exceeded the federal poverty levels for a family of four, and all but one (Home Health Aide) exceeded the federal poverty level for a family of three (Assistant Secretary for Planning and Evaluation 2015).

During qualitative interviews, the grantees reported that students increased their soft skills, such as how to communicate effectively and dress professionally, through job readiness activities and trainings offered by grantees, which made them more employable. Students also reported increases in their soft skills during focus groups. Grantees reported that most students retained their employment, and some students were promoted within their places of employment. Several Tribal HPOG 1.0 graduates advanced to the role of director of nursing at their respective places of employment.

Although many students across the five Tribal HPOG 1.0 grantees completed one or more training programs and became employed, some grantees experienced challenges that prevented them from reaching their employment-related goals. During program planning and implementation, grantees reviewed labor market data to identify workforce needs and aligned their training programs to meet these demands. However, these data focused more broadly on opportunities in the larger region or statewide, rather than at the local level; for some grantees in smaller communities there were limited employment opportunities. This was a particular challenge for the more rural grantees (TMCC, BCC, and CCCC) where there were fewer medical facilities in the local community. Although in some cases employment opportunities existed outside the local community, many students were unwilling or unable to move for employment.

As discussed with grantees and students in the programs, there are several reasons graduates did not want to or were unable to leave their communities to seek employment. The importance of family connectedness is very strong on the reservation, and moving away from home and family members for a job would not always lead to an improved quality of life. For example, many students at BCC reported that they had never left the reservation and home before; they reported experiencing culture shock as well as racial discrimination when they moved to urban areas. The absence of their extended family and support system added to the hardships students faced when attending college and living away from home. Grantee staff also reported that the cost of moving and the additional expenses associated with living off the reservation (e.g., higher rent, child care) were barriers to students moving away from the reservation for employment. For example, housing costs in some areas of

North Dakota increased during the oil boom on the Bakken Formation because the influx of workers seeking lucrative jobs increased housing demand. CCCC, TMCC, and BCC offered financial support for a period of time to lessen the cost burden on graduates willing to move; however, they found that this was not enough of a motivator because challenges were still too great for many to move off the reservation.[8]

Program Satisfaction

Among all five grantees, program staff, instructors, and students reported that they were satisfied with the Tribal HPOG 1.0 Program. Many students mentioned that they would not have been able to complete a program without both the social and financial support of HPOG. They appreciated the support services offered to them, which helped lessen the barriers to completing their programs. According to one participant, "It helps a lot. I wouldn't have made it through college without it. Everyone was so caring, my teachers and such, they all still keep in contact with me." Students said that the program helped them become more self-sufficient and better able to take care of their families. One student reported, "This program . . . gave me an opportunity to have the job skills to never be dependent on public assistance again. It does so much for me personally and financially so that I can take care of my son and myself [as a single mom]." Another student said the program "increased my self-esteem [and] gives me a sense of accomplishment."

Program staff also reported a high level of satisfaction with the program. For instance, staff at BCC commented on how the program has been beneficial for students of all ages: "The way the students trust in Issksiniip to turn their lives around, not just younger, but the older generation are going back to school because of Issksiniip, because some barriers are removed. Issksiniip has [also] helped the older generation."

Staff at TMCC commented on how the Tribal HPOG program has had a positive impact on not just the students but their families as well: "Taking people off welfare means not just a lot to that person but also to their kids. It sets an example and motivates them to be like their parent."

Local employers near TMCC described the program as mutually advantageous because students were provided experience at clinical sites and then they were able to fill open positions when they graduated. Local employers near CCCC were pleased with the performance of HPOG graduates. One employer stated, "[I would] definitely want to hire other Next Steps graduates in the future."

Building Native Health Care Workforce Capacity

All five grantees reported that they had been successful in training AI/AN students to enter health professions and to address workforce needs locally. They spoke about the importance of having skilled AI/AN health care providers serving AI/AN people, especially in the direct care professions. A local employer near CCCC remarked on the benefit of training and hiring Native Americans: "They are more sensitive to social issues and the clients that they serve, and the historical perspective of how we arrived here."

Providing culturally sensitive care according to Native beliefs and traditions has many benefits for patients, including greater adherence to medical advice, increases in health care–seeking behavior, and more successful patient education (Lehman, Fenza, and Hollinger-Smith 2004). It is also beneficial for AI/AN individuals to receive services provided by people of their cultural background. For example, a study by the Seattle Indian Health Board found that AI/AN elders saw many benefits to having an AI/AN provider, such as feeling more at ease during the visit and a better ability of the provider to understand the patient (Urban Indian Health Institute 2004).

At the start of the program, each grantee identified health care workforce needs in their communities, in various regions, and throughout the state in order to offer training programs with the most potential for employment. Over the course of the grant period, grantees identified additional needs of local employers and opportunities to train more students in the areas of most need. By assessing local workforce needs, three grantees adapted to changing circumstances and added new programs during the grant period. CCCC recognized the large need for medical coders in North Dakota, so they started the Medical Coding program. Staff reported that many times medical coders can work remotely, thus eliminating their need to move away from home to find employment. BCC added two new programs, Medical Billing and Coding and Phlebotomy, to meet the needs of the local workforce. The Medical Billing and Coding students completed practicums at the local IHS hospital and reported that they had found job opportunities even before completing their programs. In the middle of the grant period, CITC changed their Medical Billing and Coding program to a Medical Office Assistant program. This change occurred for two reasons: 1) CITC discovered that most Anchorage-area health facilities were outsourcing medical billing and coding to contract entities in the lower 48 states, thereby limiting employment opportunity, and 2) CITC recognized that a more general office assistant program would provide skills that could be useful in a variety of office settings. Staff report that most of the Medical Office Assistant students have found local employment in health-related office settings.

Employers from each grantee area reported being pleased with the Tribal HPOG 1.0 graduates that they hire. Several grantees maintained relationships with employers in their community who had hired HPOG graduates. For example, CITC has a relationship with the Alaska Native Medical Center, which is committed to hiring all of the CNAs that are trained through the CITC HPOG program. Several CITC Medical Office Assistant graduates are also working in the human resources department at Alaska Native Medical Center. CCCC built a network of employers to link students with employment across the state. One employer reported using this network to find CNAs to work across their several health care campuses. CCCC has used the network to send information about the Tribal HPOG program to 18,000 employers across the state.

CONCLUSION

All five Tribal HPOG 1.0 grantees established programs that led to health care training completion and employment. They built on existing resources to enhance administrative structures and offer additional academic programs to facilitate training and create opportunities for employment in the health care professions. Partnerships were key to implementation of HPOG programs in grantees' communities, particularly for grantees that partnered with multiple secondary implementation sites or training partners. Partnering with additional academic institutions allowed grantees to expand their geographic reach and the types of academic training programs offered to HPOG students. Grantees also formed partnerships with employers in their communities and regions.

These relationships helped facilitate employment for HPOG graduates as employers became aware of the HPOG program and training that students received.

Over time, grantees adapted program offerings to meet student demand and local health care workforce needs. Other grantees modified academic programs to better align with employment opportunities in the community.

Grantees implemented structures to administer two of the primary Tribal HPOG program components: academic programs and support services. While faculty provided academic instruction, staff such as case managers or support service specialists assessed student needs and delivered services as appropriate. When possible, grantees leveraged resources available from other programs to help support participants. Program staff and students reported that the comprehensive academic and social support services were vital to student success in their academic training programs.

Over the grant period, grantees implemented streamlined processes for recruitment and screening of participants. Word of mouth was reported as the most effective method for recruitment, although grantees employed a variety of strategies. Screening processes not only allowed grantees to confirm prospective participants' eligibility but also enabled them to identify dedicated students who met academic readiness requirements. In addition, grantees developed formal orientation processes to inform students about the services provided through HPOG and program expectations regarding attendance, grades, and job readiness skills. The program processes established over the course of the grant period appeared to enable smooth implementation of Tribal HPOG programs.

By establishing processes for the assessment and distribution of support services to students, grantees addressed students' needs throughout the duration of their training programs. All grantees had designated staff to assess student need and coordinate support services, although the staff members responsible for this function varied across grantees.

Educational attainment and employment were the key participant outcomes assessed. Over the five years of the Tribal HPOG 1.0 Program, a total of 2,270 students were enrolled across the five Tribal HPOG grantees. With the support of the Tribal HPOG program, 63.5

percent of students completed one or more health care training programs between September 2010 and September 2015.

After completing a health care training program, graduates often sought employment, although some elected to continue their training. Because grantees could only support students who could complete their training programs before the end of the grant period, HPOG students who enrolled in the earlier part of the grant period had greater opportunities to continue training toward more advanced degrees, such as CNA to LPN to RN.

Among participants who completed and exited the program where employment status was known, 69 percent were employed at exit (85 percent of those participants were employed in health care), and 31 percent were unemployed. All grantees trained AI/AN students to enter health professions. Qualitative data collected from students and employers show that many students were able to gain employment locally, building the Native health care workforce capacity in their communities.

Stakeholders, including program staff, instructors, and students, reported satisfaction with the Tribal HPOG 1.0 Program. Many students noted that they would not have been able to complete a program without both the financial and social support services offered. In describing their satisfaction with the program, many stakeholders commented on the broader influence of Tribal HPOG, noting that graduates serve as role models within their families and communities.

Notes

1. The words *American Indian/Alaska Native* (AI/AN), *Native American,* and *Tribal* are used interchangeably throughout the chapter.
2. Testimony of the National Indian Health Board Oversight Hearing on Indian Country Priorities for the 114th Congress, Senate Committee on Indian Affairs, January 28, 2015. National Indian Health Board. https://www.indian.senate.gov/sites/default/files/upload/files/1.28.15%20SCIA%20Witness%20Testimony%20%20Stacy%20Bohlen%20-%20NIHB.pdf (accessed January 28, 2019).
3. In the Blackfeet language, *Issksiniip* means "a way of knowing" or "the concept of gaining knowledge."
4. Qualified service providers are individuals or agencies that have agreed to provide services to clients who receive services funded by the North Dakota Depart-

ment of Human Services. For additional information see https://www.nd.gov/dhs/services/adultsaging/providers.html (accessed March 15, 2019).

5. Program exit is defined by each grantee, but generally indicates the participant is no longer receiving HPOG services.

6. "After intake" includes while enrolled in the program, at program exit, and at follow-up. If a participant is marked as "employed" at any of these times, they are included as having gained employment after intake. If a participant is employed at intake, and is also marked as employed at any of the times mentioned above, they are included as employed.

7. Average wages/full-time equivalents are calculated for participants who are employed after intake (which includes while enrolled in the program, at program exit, at follow-up) and who have an SOC and wage recorded in the PRS. If multiple wages/SOCs are recorded, signifying wage increases or different types of employment at different times, the most recent employment record that has both a wage and SOC is used.

8. Assistance for costs associated with moving for employment differed from the transitional assistance that grantees provided. Moving assistance provided support to students who were physically moving off the reservation to pursue work elsewhere, usually in a city. Moving assistance included rental deposit, moving costs, gas cards, and child care assistance to help participants while they were settling in a new location away from family and friends.

References

Administration for Children and Families. 2010. *Funding Opportunity Announcement: Health Profession Opportunity Grants to Serve TANF Recipients and Other Low-Income Individuals*. HHS-2010-ACF-OFA-FX-0126. Washington, DC: Office of Family Assistance, Administration for Children and Families, U.S. Department of Health and Human Services.

American Medical Group Association (AMGA). 2014. "Physician Turnover Remains High as More Physicians Retire." *ScienceDaily*, August 21. www.sciencedaily.com/releases/2014/08/140821115632.htm (accessed January 28, 2018).

Assistant Secretary for Planning and Evaluation. 2015. "2015 Poverty Guidelines." Washington, DC: U.S. Department of Health and Human Services. http://aspe.hhs.gov/2015-poverty-guidelines (accessed February 21, 2019).

Bowman, Nicole. 2006. "Tribal Sovereignty and Self-Determination through Evaluation." Paper presented at the National Congress of American Indians Mid-Year Session, Sault Ste. Marie, MI.

Burnette, Catherine E., Sara Sanders, Howard K. Butcher, and Emily Matt Salois. 2011. "Illuminating the Lived Experiences of Research with Indigenous Communities." *Journal of Ethnic and Cultural Diversity in Social Work* 20(4): 275–296.

Caldwell, Joyce Y., Jamie D. Davis, Barbara Du Bois, Holly Echo-Hawk, Jill Shephard Erickson, R. Turner Goins, Calvin Hill, Walter Hillabrant, Sharon R. Johnson, Elizabeth Kendall, Kelly Keemer, Spero M. Manson, Catherine A. Marshall, Paulette Running Wolf, Rolando L. Santiago, Robert Schacht, and Joseph B. Stone. 2005. "Culturally Competent Research with American Indians and Alaska Natives: Findings and Recommendations of the First Symposium of the Work Group on American Indian Research and Program Evaluation Methodology. *American Indian and Alaska Native Mental Health Research: The Journal of the National Center* 12(1): 1–21.

Cochran, Patricia A., Catherine A. Marshall, Carmen Garcia-Downing, Elizabeth Kendall, Doris Cook, Laurie McCubbin, and Reva Mariah S. Gover. 2008. "Indigenous Ways of Knowing: Implications for Participatory Research and Community." *American Journal of Public Health* 98(1): 22–27.

Harding, Anna, Barbara Harper, Dave Stone, Catherine O'Neill, Patricia Berger, Stuart Harris, and Jamie Donatuto. 2011. "Conducting Research with Tribal Communities: Sovereignty, Ethics and Data-Sharing Issues." *Environmental Health Perspectives* 120(1): 6–10.

HeavyRunner, Iris, and Richard DeCelles. 2002. "Family Education Model: Meeting the Student Retention Challenge." *Journal of American Indian Education* 41(2): 29–37.

Johnston-Goodstar, Katie. 2012. "Decolonizing Evaluation: The Necessity of Evaluation Advisory Groups in Indigenous Evaluation." *New Directions for Evaluation* 2012(136): 109–117.

LaVeaux, Deborah, and Suzanne Christopher. 2009. "Contextualizing CBPR: Key Principles of CBPR Meet the Indigenous Research Context." *Pimatisiwin* 7(1): 1.

Lehman, Dawn, Paula Fenza, and Linda Hollinger-Smith. 2004. "Diversity & Cultural Competency in Health Care Settings." A Mather LifeWays Orange Paper. Evanston, IL: Mather LifeWays.

Meit, Michael, Tess Gilbert, and Catherine Fromknecht. 2015. "Cook Inlet Tribal Council Tribal Health Profession Opportunity Grants (HPOG) Program—Overview and Preliminary Outcomes." OPRE 2015-08. Washington, DC: Office of Planning, Research and Evaluation, Administration for Children and Families, U.S. Department of Health and Human Services. http://www.acf.hhs.gov/sites/default/files/opre/year_4_practice_brief_citc _2_19_15_508_1.pdf (accessed February 20, 2019).

Meit, Michael, Carol Hafford, Catherine Fromknecht, Alana Knudson, Tess Gilbert, and Noelle Miesfeld. 2016. *Tribal Health Profession Opportu-*

nity Grants (HPOG) Program Evaluation: Final Report. OPRE Report No. 2016-38. Washington, DC: Administration for Children and Families, U.S. Department of Health and Human Services. http://www.acf.hhs.gov/programs/opre/resource/tribal-health-profession-opportunity-grants-hpog-program-evaluation-final-report (accessed June 19, 2019).

Meit, Michael, Carol Hafford, Tess Gilbert, and Noelle Miesfeld. 2015. "Blackfeet Community College Tribal Health Profession Opportunity Grants (HPOG) Program—Overview and Preliminary Outcomes." OPRE 2015-31. Washington, DC: Office of Planning, Research and Evaluation, Administration for Children and Families, U.S. Department of Health and Human Services. http://www.acf.hhs.gov/sites/default/files/opre/year_4_practice_brief_bcc_2_19_15_508_0.pdf (accessed February 20, 2019).

Meit, Michael, Alana Knudson, Catherine Fromknecht, and Noelle Miesfeld. 2015. "Turtle Mountain Community College Tribal Health Profession Opportunity Grants (HPOG) Program Overview and Preliminary Outcomes." OPRE 2015-07. Washington, DC: Office of Planning, Research and Evaluation, Administration for Children and Families, U.S. Department of Health and Human Services. http://www.acf.hhs.gov/sites/default/files/opre/year_4_practice_brief_tmcc_1_08_15_formatted.pdf (accessed February 20, 2019).

Meit, Michael, Katherine Meyer, Catherine Fromknecht, and Tanisha Carino. 2015. "College of Menominee Nation Tribal Health Profession Opportunity Grants (HPOG) Program—Overview and Preliminary Outcomes." OPRE 2015-90. Washington, DC: Office of Planning, Research and Evaluation, Administration for Children and Families, U.S. Department of Health and Human Services. https://www.acf.hhs.gov/sites/default/files/opre/year_4_practice_brief_cmn_9_16_15_508.pdf (accessed February 20, 2019).

Meit, Michael, Shannon TenBroeck, and Noelle Miesfeld. 2015. "Cankdeska Cikana Community College Tribal Health Profession Opportunity Grants (HPOG) Program—Overview and Preliminary Outcomes." OPRE 2015-91. Washington, DC: Office of Planning, Research and Evaluation, Administration for Children and Families, U.S. Department of Health and Human Services. http://www.acf.hhs.gov/sites/default/files/opre/year_4_practice_brief_cccc_9_21_15_b508pdf.pdf (accessed February 20, 2019).

National Center for Health Workforce Analysis. n.d. Washington, DC: Health Resources and Services Administration, U.S. Department of Health and Human Services. https://bhw.hrsa.gov/national-center-health-workforce-analysis (accessed February 21, 2019).

NCAI Policy Research Center and MSU Center for Native Health Partnerships. 2012. *"Walk Softly and Listen Carefully": Building Research Relationships with Tribal Communities.* Washington, DC, and Bozeman, MT: Authors.

Oetzel, John G., Malia Villegas, Heather Zenone, Emily R. White Hat, Nina Wallerstein, and Bonnie Duran. 2015. "Enhancing Stewardship of Community-Engaged Researchthrough Governance." *American Journal of Public Health* 105(6): 1161–1167.

Pacheco, Christina M., Sean M. Daley, Travis Brown, Melissa Filippi, K. Allen Greiner, and Christine M. Daley. 2013. "Moving Forward: Breaking the Cycle of Mistrust between American Indians and Researchers." *American Journal of Public Health* 103(12): 2152–2159.

Quigley, Dianne. 2006. "Perspective: A Review of Improved Ethical Practices in Environmental and Public Health Research: Case Examples from Native Communities." *Health Education and Behavior* 33(2): 130–147.

Sahota, Puneet Chawla. 2009. "Research Regulation in American Indian/ Alaska Native Communities: Policy and Practice Considerations." Washington, DC: NCAI Policy Research Center

———. 2010. "Community-Based Participatory Research in American Indian and Alaska Native Communities." Washington DC: NCAI Policy Research Center.

Struthers, Roxanne, and John Lowe. 2003. "Nursing in the Native American Culture and Historical Trauma." *Issues in Mental Health Nursing* 24(3): 257–272.

Urban Indian Health Institute. 2004. "Urban American Indian/Alaskan Native Long-Term Care Needs Assessment." Seattle, WA: Seattle Indian Health Board.

Yuan, Nicole P., Jami Bartgis, and Dierdre Demers. 2014. "Promoting Ethical Research with American Indian and Alaska Native People Living in Urban Areas. *American Journal of Public Health* 104(11): 2085–2091.

6
Culturally Effective Organizations

Revisiting the Role of Employers in Workforce Development

Janet Boguslaw
Brandeis University

Jessica Santos
Brandeis University

Trinidad Tellez
New Hampshire Department of Health and Human Services

The nation's policy agenda for employment and training increasingly includes efforts to create health career pathways for low-income and skilled individuals—from new entry through advancement—by engaging employers as key partners in workforce development through sector-based partnerships (National Skills Coalition 2018). This chapter presents findings from the Health Care Employer Research Initiative, a four-year partnership between the New Hampshire Office of Minority Health and Refugee Affairs (OMHRA) and the Institute on Assets and Social Policy (IASP) at the Heller School for Social Policy and Management, Brandeis University.[1]

The goal of this research initiative was to examine how New Hampshire health care employers and other key stakeholders might improve the hiring, retention, and advancement opportunities for racial, ethnic, and linguistic minority populations in the state who were new or incumbent health care employees. The project revealed and demonstrated an ongoing need for greater and different collaborations between the workforce development system and health care employers, and a need for building new institutional practices within health care organizations to improve equity in hiring and advancement. We suggest that employer engagement is critical to developing career pathways that advance health professionals of color. Workforce development programs will move forward with greater success when tied to the related agendas of improving health care performance and reducing area health disparities.

This chapter presents two main areas of findings. First, we categorize key barriers to workforce diversity and inclusion in health care identified through in-depth fieldwork. We find that while New Hampshire had a growing health equity initiative in place, related employment and advancement opportunities in health care were not addressing career advancement for diverse populations, despite an understanding of the benefits of patient-provider concordance. In fact, dominant narratives of meritocracy, resistance to institutional change, and embedded organizational norms excluded low-income workers of color from advancing and achieving family financial security through health care work. The research revealed a consistent narrative that it is up to individuals to become educated and advance, with little insight into how the institutional structures, networks, and organizational cultures of the workplace may influence hiring, retention, and advancement outcomes. These findings provided the partners an opportunity to explore and build conversations and knowledge about new types of institutional practices.

This study went beyond identifying barriers, however, by working with employers and key stakeholders to investigate, think through, and design new approaches to advance workforce development and diversity. Findings demonstrate an ongoing need for greater and different collaborations between the workforce development system and health care employers, as well as new institutional practices within health care organizations to improve equity in workforce development, hiring, and advancement. The research suggests that this career advancement work is likely to move forward with greater success when tied to the related agendas of improving health care performance and reducing area health disparities.

Thus, the second area of findings describes a new framework and theory that emerged to explain the intersection between institutional practices in health care organizations and the advancement of diverse populations in health careers. The framework of "culturally effective organizations" is explained here to inform a new understanding of the problem and to identify levers for change. OMHRA and IASP's framework for culturally effective organizations outlines a new form of coordination and commitment, both within the health care organizations and between employers and external stakeholders (Doupé et al. 2016). Culturally effective organizations are structured to create and sustain a diverse workforce that is representative of the community served. The team's research elaborated and publicized a wide range of benefits to organizations that seek to become culturally effective, including higher quality of care, safety, patient satisfaction, the reduction of regional health disparities, increased revenue or cost savings, and ultimately the economic security, stability, and economic well-being of those who have traditionally been left out of quality health care jobs.

The chapter concludes with a discussion of the ripple effects that continue in New Hampshire today as a result of this work, and it offers considerations for workforce development and/or health equity initiatives interested in partnering to restructure opportunities and policies for systemic and long-term change.

BACKGROUND

The federal investment in the national Health Profession Opportunity Grants (HPOG) program was premised on two important areas of research. First, data indicate that there are good opportunities to educate and train low-income and Temporary Assistance for Needy Families recipients in the health care field for positions that pay well and are expected to either experience labor shortages or be in high demand. HPOG grantees are encouraged to adopt a career pathways framework in structuring and delivering occupational training and other program services. The goal is to "secure positions that have opportunity for advancement and sustainability, ultimately leading these individuals on a pathway to financial self-sufficiency" (Office of Family Assistance 2017).

Second, data indicate that persistent disparities in health outcomes for patients among diverse communities could be reduced by increasing the concordance of health providers and the potential patient community. The Affordable Care Act (ACA) recognized that racial and ethnic minorities are underrepresented in the U.S. health care workforce, which is a problem because, as the Health Resources and Services

Administration found, minority patients tend to receive "better inter-personal care from practitioners of their own race or ethnicity, particularly in primary care and mental health settings" (Cronk and Weiner 2015). Through this research, the partnership had the opportunity to identify pathways that bring low-income populations out of poverty while contributing to a reduction in area health disparities. As the findings presented here suggest, developing strategies to accomplish these broad national goals requires a multidimensional and multistakeholder approach: one that expands beyond the current workforce development rhetoric focused on simply producing a skilled labor force to meet labor market demands.

National data reveal significant underrepresentation among historically disadvantaged workers of color in the health care workforce. Although non-Hispanic blacks make up 12.2 percent of the population, they account for 6.3 percent of active physicians, 5.8 percent of registered nurses (RNs), and 4.2 percent of physician assistants. Hispanics make up 16.3 percent of the population, yet they account for 5.5 percent of physicians, 3.9 percent of RNs, and 4.7 percent of physician assistants. In contrast, non-Hispanic whites and Asians make up 68.4 percent of the population, 86.5 percent of physicians, 83.2 percent of RNs, and 90.8 percent of physician assistants (Cronk and Weiner 2015).

These interrelated points, including underrepresentation, the need for career opportunities that lead to financial self-sufficiency, and the need for greater provider-patient concordance, highlight a growing imperative to develop strategies to improve career advancement opportunities for health care employees of color.

In the context of the changing health care landscape created by the Affordable Care Act, in 2010 OMHRA partnered with a few key champions and organized a statewide effort to raise awareness of health disparities. Together they facilitated the development of the New Hampshire Health and Equity Partnership, a multistakeholder network of organizations and individuals committed to health equity and equity across social determinants of health domains. Guided by recommendations detailed in the *Plan to Address Health Disparities and Promote Health Equity in New Hampshire* (State Plan Advisory Work Group 2011), this group of more than 60 members aimed to diversify the health care workforce to better reflect the populations served and to encourage employers to dedicate resources to recruitment, training, and retention of racial, ethnic, and linguistic minorities for staff and leadership positions (State Plan Advisory Work Group 2011). A key strategy to achieve this goal was to apply for and be selected as the recipient of one of 32 Health Profession Opportunity Grants (HPOG) from the Administration for Children and Families. HPOG provides funds to prepare minority and low-income individuals for entry into high-demand health care occupations and offers advancement opportunities for incumbent workers, providing a unique opportunity to advance this work in New Hampshire.

In designing and implementing its HPOG project, OMHRA faced two challenges. First, low-income health professionals of color struggled to secure full-time, quality jobs and/or achieve career advancement. Second, health care employers were unconvinced that workforce diversity should be a priority in New Hampshire, a predominately rural and white but rapidly diversifying state. The HPOG project, the New Hampshire Health Profession Opportunity Project (HPOP), supported 1,051 low-income individuals to pursue health occupation training, of which 845 completed training in health careers, and 782 attained employment, with 692 employed in health care. In addition, HPOP expressed an intentional focus on workforce diversity in its proposal and successfully engaged 28 percent of participants from racial, ethnic, and language minority populations, exceeding the target of 25 percent (Office of Minority Health and Refugee Affairs 2016).

These job placement and advancement objectives were achieved through a multilevel workforce development model. In addition to working with individuals and families by providing case management and support services and facilitating training, OMHRA dedicated additional HPOP funds to capacity-building initiatives with key workforce partners, employer-based training initiatives, and regional business advisory councils. Still, the primary focus was on job training and matching the labor supply with positions in demand.

IASP partnered with OMHRA to examine specific questions related to what, if anything, was required beyond human capital investments in individuals and job matching, to ensure the hiring, retention, and advancement of those enrolled in education and training. IASP's research was designed to investigate the links between participant-level barriers and systemic, sectorwide barriers to successful workforce development and advancement in health care for racial, ethnic, and linguistic minorities.

Diversity and Disparities in New Hampshire

In 2010, when this project started, many politicians, business leaders, and residents believed that issues related to diversity did not apply in New Hampshire. However, demographic trends illustrated that this was not the case. The state's minority population grew from 4.7 percent in 2000 to 7.7 percent in 2010 and accounted for 50 percent of the state's population growth from 2000 to 2010 (Johnson 2012). Moreover, diversity in New Hampshire is spatially concentrated; in metropolitan areas in the southern part of the state, people of color represent a significant percent of the population: 18 percent in Manchester and 21 percent in Nashua in 2010, about 20 miles south. Furthermore, diversity was increasing across every age demographic, but especially among its youngest residents. New Hampshire's Latinx youth population grew 52.7 percent from 2000 to 2008, fourth in the nation for greatest percentage change (Moeller 2010).

Over 20 years of refugee resettlement also contributed to New Hampshire's changing demographics, including the arrival of Vietnamese, Bosnians, Mesketian Turks, Liberians, Iraqis, Bhutanese, and others. Refugee families are primarily resettled in the cities of Nashua, Manchester, Concord, and Laconia. Adult refugees bring a wide range of professional and educational backgrounds, and many are highly motivated to further their education. The HPOP program covered each of these newcomer communities in addition to Native-born people of color.

New Hampshire's poorest residents are disproportionately racial and ethnic minorities. In the years leading up to HPOP, nearly one-quarter (24.4 percent) of the state's African American population lived below the federal poverty line, as did 16.6 percent of the Latinx population, and 18.2 percent of the Native American population. Additionally, 19.7 percent of all other diverse populations were considered poor, compared with only 7.4 percent of New Hampshire's white residents. Rising wealth and income inequality, changes in the structures of work that have increased inequality within and between firms, and the rise of temporary work and contingent employment all contribute to these inequities (Blank 2009; Kalleberg 2013; McKernan et al. 2017).

At the time this study was conducted, the state was still reeling from the effects of the recession. In New Hampshire, the unemployment rate for racial minorities from 2007 to 2011 was 9.1 percent and for Hispanics/Latinos was 12.6 percent. For whites, it was 6.1 percent (6.3 percent for the state as a whole). These trends were reflective of national economic and sector-specific inequalities. One in five adults working in full-time jobs earned an hourly wage that placed them below the federal poverty line for a family of four, and people of color composed 47 percent of this population of working poor, despite being only 30 percent of the total U.S. labor force (Osterman and Shulman 2011). The recession also slowed staff turnover of older, more experienced health care workers who postponed retirement. This limited opportunities for new positions to be filled by younger workers and delayed employer interest in the upskilling of incumbent workers.[2]

Career advancement over the life course and larger social mobility patterns are typically explained as the result of a combination of factors, including an individual's level of education and skill and whether the labor market in any particular region and sector has a demand for individuals with those skills (Holzer 2004; MDRC 2013; National Conference of State Legislatures 2015). Our study expands this individualistic perspective by explaining the institutional and relational factors, as well as social patterns of privilege, tied to race and class that affect workforce development and diversity efforts. To ground this broader perspective in local evidence, we gathered data describing actual workforce demographic and advancement barriers faced by diverse low-wage health care professionals in New Hampshire and explored strategies to overcome them.

RESEARCH DESIGN AND METHODOLOGY

The partnership goals and research strategies were shaped by a shared definition of the problem. Long-term success, which includes the economic self-sufficiency of participants of color, requires the participation of health care employers in three new ways: 1) to develop more effective employer commitments to this goal through new policies and practices, 2) to be partners in the development of skill and placement components of workforce training, and 3) to be more fully engaged in long-term partnerships with the communities they serve.

Data were collected through in-depth qualitative interviews, literature reviews, local data analysis, and the engagement of employers and other stakeholders in the development of findings. IASP and OMHRA's collaborative study was designed around the following three central questions:

1) How can New Hampshire health care employers create a more diverse workforce and foster greater recruitment, retention, and advancement for racial, ethnic, and linguistic minorities in the state?

2) How can the workforce development field better prepare and support both workers and employers in the health care sector to improve minority hiring, retention, and advancement along career pathways in the state?

3) What opportunity structures or bridges need to be developed or leveraged to build and sustain a more diverse and upwardly mobile minority health care workforce in New Hampshire?

In this research, the use of the term *diversity* is limited to racial, ethnic, and linguistic diversity. Data collection and ongoing engagement were structured around three core areas:

1) **Regionally based research.** IASP surveyed and interviewed over 100 New Hampshire health care employers, industry association leaders, job developers, incumbent health care workers across a range of positions, and community leaders to document challenges, strategies, and best practices for developing a diverse health care workforce and related career mobility pipeline. We included hospitals, long-term care facilities, home health care agencies, community health centers, mental health centers, and dental care service providers from across HPOP's four geographic areas. All the research took place in southern New Hampshire, which was the operational target area for the HPOG grant. All interviews were recorded, transcribed, and coded for relevant themes.

2) **Employer engagement and feedback.** IASP engaged directly with employers throughout the study. In addition to conducting

employer interviews, IASP presented materials and engaged industry employers at two statewide annual meetings: the home health care association and the long-term care association. At these meetings, employers actively engaged in discussion about the issues. OMHRA organized regional Business Advisory Council meetings several times each year, and IASP presented and engaged participant employers around its ongoing work regularly, building employer knowledge and learning from these interactions. Finally, the partnership created a research advisory group that included two employer representatives who provided feedback and insights as the project developed. The research team vetted findings from interviews with employers and industry leaders throughout the project to document reactions, key questions, and areas of incongruence between the literature and the local context.

3) **Engagement with the workforce development community.** IASP built on OMHRA's existing partnerships with the community college system, the statewide apprenticeship program, the Temporary Assistance for Needy Families program, and state and local workforce development directors. The research team engaged these six experts in vetting initial findings and identifying actionable steps to align workforce diversity efforts with existing programs and the needs of employers.

Throughout the project, IASP reviewed and synthesized literature, triangulating key findings related to workforce diversity and inclusion in New Hampshire with findings from the wider field. This helped ground our work in the health sector and was instrumental in making a case for culturally effective organizations, as described below.

OMHRA and IASP also formed an advisory committee comprising leaders from local foundations, employer associations, employers, state government, and the community college system. These partners provided feedback on draft reports, helped align findings with local policy priorities, and were instrumental in identifying additional resources that allowed IASP researchers to expand on key findings from the Employer Research Initiative (ERI), as the project came to be referred to over time. Two subsequent studies funded by the New Hampshire Endowment for Health extended elements of this project: *Beyond Supply and*

Demand, which focused on the role of networks in career advancement and racial equity, and a case study of a community health center that was actively working to become a more culturally effective health care organization (Santos 2015; Santos et al. 2016).

The overall goal of this study was to inform, improve HPOP, and support longer-term statewide efforts for workforce diversity in health professions. The four-year initiative produced a range of reports, briefs, research, and a case study, all designed to actively engage health care employers and industry associations, the workforce development system and its providers, and the wider community of stakeholders interested in issues of health disparities, health access, and employment equity (Boguslaw et al. 2016). Indeed, this work helped energize and coalesce interested stakeholders in the state, expanding, solidifying, and continuing the work as this is written, more than two years after the formal end of the project.

THE UNIVERSITY PARTNERSHIP PROCESS

This partnership process and model of engagement provided opportunities for employers, educators, workforce development leaders, and community organizations to share their experiences with workforce diversity and to learn from experts in the field of workforce diversity. This work occurred through the quarterly Business Advisory Council meetings, which were facilitated by IASP and HPOP staff; HPOP leadership meetings that included representatives from state agencies; and through participation in the New Hampshire Health and Equity Partnership Workforce Diversity Work Group, which brought together interested partners and stakeholders. IASP also had the opportunity to present to two statewide industry association member meetings in home health care and long-term care.

One of the unique aspects of this partnership was that a staff member from OMHRA, who had several years of experience with the agency, was able to become a half-time staff member with the Brandeis team while continuing to work half-time at OMHRA (with a different scope of responsibilities). This individual provided a bridge between the two organizations and was able to offer important context and access to

New Hampshire–based resources. Her work with IASP was separate from her position at OMHRA, so the actual partnership process was between IASP and other OMHRA staff, as well as its director. Additionally, OMHRA's director had a history of working with universities in community-academic research partnerships, and had knowledge about what a participatory community partnership required, including a process for making a partnership participatory, equitable, mutually respectful, and engaged. These factors facilitated a close partnership designed to engage and unite the unique perspectives of both researchers and practitioners. It enabled IASP to achieve a high level of embeddedness in the New Hampshire workforce and health equity communities, producing higher quality and more relevant findings.

OMHRA contracted with Lutheran Social Services (now Ascentria Care Alliance) to implement the case management and training portion of the HPOP, with OMHRA playing a very engaged supervisory role and serving to introduce innovative elements to the program design and delivery. IASP's partnership was with OMHRA, and thus IASP participated in program review meetings, but its work was implemented in partnership primarily with OMHRA and not the direct service provider. This partnership structure appropriately kept the research focus on the broader contextual and systemic factors that affect the success of health professionals of color, and it helped separate IASP's role from a more traditional evaluation partner focused on participant outcomes. University-conducted research brings a sense of validation and reliability about the findings. Being from "out of state" meant that IASP was not perceived as one of the state's stakeholders who might have conflicts due to confidentiality, prioritization of findings, or self-interest.

FINDINGS

New Hampshire Workforce Demographics: Missing or Missing Out?

We began by investigating where people of color were working in health care in the regions of HPOP focus in New Hampshire. In 2004, a landmark national report, *Missing Persons: Minorities in the Health Professions* (Sullivan 2004), drew attention to the fact that African

Americans, Hispanics, American Indians, and certain segments of the Asian/Pacific Islander population were missing from the U.S. health care workforce. We investigated this notion in New Hampshire and discovered that these populations were in fact not missing from the health care workforce. Instead, they were overrepresented in the lowest wage positions and in workplace settings with few opportunities for advancement.

In 2008, the aggregate Equal Employment Opportunity Commission report for New Hampshire hospitals reported 29,251 total employees, with only 1,167 minority workers (4.0 percent). Ambulatory care was even less representative of the population, with 7,276 employees statewide and only 231 minorities (3.1 percent). Two of Manchester's largest hospitals employed a workforce that significantly underrepresents the city's increasingly diverse population: 6.2 percent (119 minorities out of 1,895 total employees) at one hospital and 2.6 percent (88 minorities out of 3,381) at the other.[3]

While overall representation in the workforce illustrates part of the picture, a closer look at the distribution of workers in more granular occupational categories by race and ethnicity reveals significant opportunity gaps. In 2008, there were 7 minority executive/senior level officials or managers in New Hampshire's entire hospital system and 23 minority first/mid-level officials and managers. The majority of diverse hospital workers were concentrated in low-level professional, technician, office/clerical, and service worker positions, indicating that New Hampshire's minority health care workers were missing from the more coveted higher quality jobs.

In addition to sector-based and occupational segregation, IASP's research demonstrated that the type of employer (and the quality of work offered through that workplace) contributes to inequities in career entry and advancement opportunities. For example, LNAs (licensed nursing assistants) in nursing homes and residential care settings report a different work experience and compensation package than LNAs in hospitals, despite holding the same occupational title. Hospitals provide higher wages, more stability, and better benefits, and they are most likely to have opportunities for advancement when compared to community health centers, long-term care facilities, and in-home care providers. For many health professionals, hospitals represent the ultimate workplace for good jobs—those with full-time work, benefits, and opportunities for advancement. Figures 6.1 and 6.2 show that across the state, as well as in the primary HPOP service area of Hillsborough County, health professionals of color are overrepresented in the nursing and residential care workforce (13 percent) and underrepresented in the hospital workforce (6.5 percent) compared to their participation in the labor force (9.5 percent) (Santos 2014). Average monthly wages in 2012 in ambulatory care were $5,288, in hospitals $4,395, and in nursing/residential care $2,436. These wage data indicate how the type of workplace, in addition to the type of occupation, affects the economic security and well-being of the workforce.

These data demonstrate the presence of racial and ethnic inequalities between and within occupations and workplaces in New Hampshire (Boguslaw et al. 2013, 2015, 2016; Doupé et al. 2016; Santos 2014; Santos and Boguslaw 2015; Santos, Boguslaw, and Venner 2014). Through conversations with employers and workforce development leaders, IASP and OMHRA realized that this more detailed approach to understanding workforce "diversity" challenged current assumptions. Contrary to the national narratives focused on the idea that minorities were "missing persons" in the health care workforce, this study found that health professionals of color were not missing in the sector as a whole. Rather, they were "missing out" on opportunities to advance out of low-wage positions and jobs at workplaces with fewer benefits into higher-quality, higher-level jobs. Employers in New Hampshire, especially long-term care and in-home health care providers that employed a large percentage of low-wage workers of color, were responsive to these findings. As a result, this project was able to shift the conversation away from a focus on recruitment and hiring and toward a more accurate, needed focus on retention and advancement.

Barriers to Opportunity

Entry-level workers seeking jobs and advancement in health care face barriers from multiple sources, including an individual's insufficient education and training for specific positions, knowledge about opportunities, experience, and different levels of interest in particular forms of health care work (Holzer 2015). Our research corroborates existing work that suggests that in addition to individual barriers, health

Figure 6.1 Minority Health Care Workforce, New Hampshire

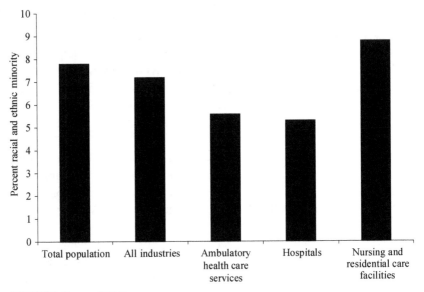

SOURCE: Santos (2014).

care workers of color seeking to advance face a range of structural barriers that are institutional, relational, and organizational in nature. These
fall into three key areas. The first is discrimination embedded in institutional structures. Here we found an absence of formal organizational
commitment to and understanding of the value of workforce diversity across professional positions, variations in leadership to address
issues, and, as a result, unequal opportunity. The second area of findings revealed the way that informal labor networks function to restrict
access to new opportunities for entry and advancement for health care
professionals of color, limiting inclusion and equity. The third is how
employers understand and make decisions that impact diversity in the
context of their perceived bottom line. Together, these structural issues
contribute to a new way of thinking about policies and practices that
improve the entry, retention, and advancement of diverse populations
in health care positions.

Figure 6.2 Minority Health Care Workforce, New Hampshire and Hillsborough County

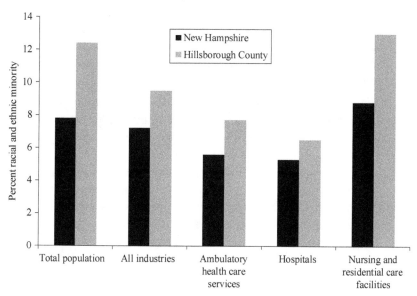

SOURCE: Santos (2014).

Finding 1: Institutional Structures and Embedded Discrimination

New Hampshire health care employers and employees hold a wide range of opinions about the advancement challenges faced by diverse populations in health care. These perspectives reflect a sector and population in transition. Some employers manage their changing patient and workforce population with intention, while others produce negative impacts due to lack of attention to, or understanding of, structural barriers to job entry, retention, inclusion, and advancement. Overall, our research revealed at that time an unwelcoming climate in professional health care institutions for people of color in New Hampshire, with some exceptions. Positive examples of change came from key employers leading intentional efforts to embrace, manage, and promote diversity and equity within their own organizations.

Several employers aware of the demographic changes under way led their health care organizations to embrace concentrated efforts to diversify their workforce and through this diversity provide quality care to the community or region. One health care employer explained:

> *We changed [our practices around hiring? Recruiting?] purpose-fully because . . . you're part of the community so you want . . . to look like what the community looks like. So, it was actually taken on as a strategic initiative of the board of directors and the executive leadership . . .*

In this instance, the organization's patient population was more diverse than other area health care providers', thus they were more sensitized to the issues of patient-provider concordance to meet the goals of outreach and adherence to treatment and follow-up procedures.

On the other hand, respondents recognized that not all employers were sufficiently prepared to recruit and manage a diverse workforce, and that with demographic change, stereotypes and discrimination also become a key factor in hiring and advancement. Discrimination, avoidance hiring, and a wide variation in management approaches all contribute to unequal outcomes in career advancement. Examples include situations in which the scheduling manager gives less desirable shifts to people of color, the hiring manager will not hire people of color, or the director says that the organization needs to prioritize the comfort of their patients. From these examples we understand they are referring to implicit bias and that both staffs and patients act in ways that reflect their discomfort with difference. The source of these problems stems from decision making and discretion at different levels within the organization, but solutions need to be comprehensive in order to rise above implicit bias and discomfort. Some examples below illustrate this point.

Employer perceptions were frequently raised and discussed at length, with one health care employer reflecting,

> *Everybody has opinions. People who are here, just because their culture is different, they think they're illegal or something.*

Another explained,

> *I think that there's enough New Hampshire employers that have insufficient experience at managing a diverse workforce that they may imagine the worst. You may have to address fears that people have about, oh, they're [i.e., people of color] all lazy, or, oh, none of them know how to tell time and they're not going to show up on time. Or, "I can't have them all sittin' in the lunch room speaking*

*Spanish and leaving everybody else out." Or, whatever unfortu-
nate negative stereotypes people may bring to the table as well.*

Employees also reported the concern that despite their qualifications they may face discrimination in hiring. One health care employee
of color said,

*Sometimes I wonder . . . [there are] times where I put my name on
something . . . like an online application, and then should I lie? Do
I put "Chavez" on there—then I'm not going to get a call back?
And I think about that a lot, which is awful . . .*

While another health care employee of color was told by friends to
apply only online:

If they see you, they won't hire you.

At the same time, some people in the field consider diverse language
and cultural backgrounds to be an asset. One HPOP job developer said,

*I told them to put on their résumé that they speak more than one
language. Employers have said, "I am hiring you because you
speak Spanish."*

These findings indicate that there are many mixed messages in New
Hampshire about how diversity is or is not valued in the health care
workforce, and that the degree to which health professionals of color
feel welcome depends largely on the leadership and organizational culture of each workplace.

Health care employees, both white and nonwhite, described a pattern of observed or experienced discrimination. One white health care
supervisor described the environment for diverse populations:

*We used to hear it from the hospital all the time, "She doesn't like
me because I'm Spanish, she doesn't like me because I'm Islamic."
It was terrible . . . I had a Jewish employee that was asking for
High Holy days off and the other supervisor was having a fit. I was
like, "For God's sake, she's going to work Christmas and Thanks-
giving, what do you care? Just switch it!"*

Another health care employee of color reflected on the example of
a supervisor, also a person of color, who had left the job:

*I don't know if this is the reason she left, but the next boss is not
black, isn't minority. It's just really different. She is treated differently [i.e., better] by our highest boss. And I'm not the only one
who is seeing it—they are not minority, but they are witnessing it.*

Managers who arrange schedules for health professionals have significant influence on schedules, hours worked, and opportunities for advancement. One health care employee of color describes here how her ability to work was restricted by a manager's discretion.

> *My schedule was, like, stable. I had clients. . . . I was there eight months. . . . I was used to working overnights with them and I said I don't want to work overnight shifts. Can you guys give me morning hours? . . . When the month got there they sent me the overnight schedule. . . . Then I called them, I'm like, didn't you see my letter . . . ? They took away all my hours and I didn't have any hours for a month. When I went in there, they had hours, but she didn't give it to me. I know, I was sitting right next to her and I could see the hours she had available, but she was just like . . . she wouldn't give them. I'm like, "Wow."*

This individual continued to explain that she was sure it was discrimination, that night shifts were perceived as okay for a person of color, and that neither the schedulers nor the clients would schedule a person of color for daytime work.

When asked about the work environment in health care for employees with diverse backgrounds, one white health care employee said,

> *Yeah, I think it's harder for them. . . . In New Hampshire, there is still, in my opinion, this underlying expectation of, you know, this population is lazy, and this population doesn't show up. That population, no they're not going to last.*

These perceptions and experiences stem from institutional structures that enable staff to assert unequal workplace benefits and work conditions, which have a direct impact on the financial instability of families of color. What emerged from interviews with many employers was that leadership in this area is critical, but even with strong leadership, equity efforts may not necessarily be supported at all levels of the organization. For example, in long-term care, one director shared how patients (typically elderly white residents) were often uncomfortable with providers who speak a primary language other than English and have accents. This puts the employer in a position where they must navigate a delicate balance between pleasing their paying customers while also defending their choice to hire a skilled employee. Although not yet the norm, another director describes how to explicitly encourage patients to remain open to a range of providers:

*And I'll say to a patient, "Today you're having difficulty because
this is new. Once you've heard this person speak for a while, you'll
begin to become accustomed to the rhythm of the language, you
will, and you'll love her or you'll love him," and they do . . .*

In cases like these, organizational leaders must be acutely aware of
the different manifestations of discrimination in their workplace and
intervene. In other cases, interpersonal dynamics in the workplace may
lead to ambiguity. Another employer provided an example of not being
sure if discrimination was taking place with the following account:

*One of our nursing assistants . . . was a preceptor to two women,
both from African countries. So, some accent, the color differences, and she felt that when she told them what to do, they should
do it. They felt, well, we've had education, we've had experiences
in other environments, let's be collaborative. You know, you say
we should do it this way can we talk about . . . we've done it this
way in other places, maybe, you know, why is it different here?
And her feeling was, no, I tell you what to do, and you do it. And
we didn't know whether or not that had a racial bias or a cultural
bias. What we said is that, "this is not the way we converse with
people. You're a preceptor, here is your role, there's human dignity
involved here," so we want to be open to the conversation.*

In discussions with employers about how to improve the hiring,
retention, and advancement of diverse populations in the health care
setting, it was clear that an intentional process needs to be put in place
by leadership, and that some misconceptions about the value or importance of diversity for the health care setting could be addressed more
directly.

Related to the first issue, intentionality and leadership, one health
care employer suggested one challenge for the field is that

*there has to be kind of a way to talk about what people bring in
addition to their language skills that may be beneficial for your
organization, because there is a lot.*

And, a white health care employee reflected,

*Hispanic culture keeps their elderly with them at home. It has a
huge impact on the whole family. So they may need to go home
at lunch to look after them . . . if we're going to embrace their
language and culture to help us deal with these people coming
through, then we have to deal with that, have to accept it. We can't*

> *just say, we want your language and your cultural knowledge, but forget your real life.*

And another white health care employee suggested,

> *I think maybe they could have some sort of guidelines. People in a hospital, you might tend to pick someone who's white. . . . I think they might not accept as many other applications because they're, you know, the ratio of people who are white to people who are not white is very high. . . . Cause, they might not be doing it consciously. They might just be, in the back of their mind, and they're not even realizing who they're picking, I guess . . .*

Indicated through these and other interviews, the research team concluded that without institutional attention to the issues of diversity, its contribution is not valued, thus it is not introduced as part of job descriptions in hiring or as qualities or skills that might drive retention and advancement in addition to skills and other more traditional criteria.

The research team also found that employer and workforce leaders lacked an understanding of how diversity and equity affect community economic stability and mobility, institutional performance, quality of care, and the reduction of health disparities. The project team met with a group of employers to discuss initial findings and next steps after the completion of sector interviews to gauge leadership responses. One of the strong messages that came out of this meeting and several others that followed was health care employer beliefs that the absence of diverse populations across job categories had no negative effect on their bottom line or on population-level health disparities. Further, without evidence of these ties, employers believed that hiring based strictly on skill, education, and experience constituted a functional opportunity structure and should continue, perpetuating a diversity-blind approach to workforce development and advancement. Issues of diversity in the workplace were confined to a discussion of cultural competency training, which was covered as part of human resources orientation or training for new employees and was believed to be sufficient.

Finding 2: The Role of Informal Networks in Career Advancement

> *I've seen the staff treated by patients, certainly . . . you know, racist terms and things said, but no, I think [our organization is] very open and very diverse, and the hiring process is very fair.*

This study found that in addition to the explicit forms of discrimination described above, the structure of informal internal labor markets perpetuates a more subtle form of network-based racial inequality at work. Some individuals and groups of people enter the labor market with strong networks that can link them to opportunity, while others must work to intentionally establish, build, and maintain these networks to produce the same level of opportunity. While the role of social capital and personal networks in job attainment is well documented, how it exacerbates the exclusion of diverse populations' career advancement is understudied (Granovetter 1977; Lin 2000). The white respondent below recognized the privilege that her networks provided at different stages of her career path.

> My first position at the [location] would normally have never have happened for a new grad except for that I knew someone . . . my supervisor there at the time when I got hired . . . and the school nursing jobs that I took, again would have never been given to a new grad, but I knew the school nursing supervisor.

Network advantages are not only reserved for white health professionals. Several respondents of color expressed pride in the fact that their high-quality work was recognized by their employer and that they were encouraged to make referrals from within their ethnic community.

> No, I think they prefer us because I think they found when they will hire one or two people at first . . . then they look for [more from the same ethnic background]. . . . [From ___'s] husband's experience they were happy to hire me and . . . my other sister.

It is widely recognized that networks are the most common way to get a job (Hensvik and Skans 2016). However, what is less understood is how these processes become institutionalized and racialized, affecting career advancement and career paths (Bayer, Ross, and Topa 2008). Employers frequently use their existing employees' networks to recruit new hires or to take recommendations for employees who should advance, with the argument that increased networks create a larger pool from which to choose the most skilled candidate. Thus, the workforce recognizes the role of networks while also reinforcing the idea that occupational status reflects both skill and merit. However, networks do more than broaden the pool from which employers hire. The following quotes illustrate how networks help people advance in their careers—for example, by guaranteeing that the candidate is considered based on who she knows, and by gaining access to a competitive high-quality hospital job with benefits.

> *My mother worked at ___ Hospital... so she said "Well if you don't want to work there anymore, why don't you try working at ___? I love working [there]." And I went, "Okay, who do I call?" And she gave me a number and I called up and I said "My mom said I should call you." And she said "Who's your mom?" and I said "[name]" and she said "Oh well come on down." I went down and it was almost like a formality. Here, fill out these papers.*

> *I used to play [___ sport], and last year my friend, I told her I wanted to get back into health care because I wanted to go to school and she told me that they were hiring at [name of Hospital]. It's really about who you know and I got really lucky. . . . It's really hard to get into a hospital, especially a hospital like that with so many great benefits. I got really lucky.*

Are these employees "lucky," or are they tapping into broader social stratification patterns to get ahead? How do these patterns relate to workforce diversity and equity? In New Hampshire, as we have demonstrated, hiring managers and others in positions of power are predominantly white. Our research with incumbent health professionals revealed that networks in the health care sector in southern New Hampshire are relatively small and insular, and health professionals in New Hampshire stay connected to the same people (their teachers, supervisors, coworkers) over time, even when changing jobs. This means that relationships and reputations hold valuable currency that influences career advancement decision making as noted in the literature (Alvó-Armengol and Jackson 2004; Cappellari and Tatsiramos 2015). As the following quote from a nursing professor demonstrates, these close relationships mean that to recommend someone, managers or professors don't even need to pick up the phone to call someone—they can just make referrals or recommendations throughout the course of their daily life.

> *Or the fact they [nurse friends] work there [at an employer where the student wants to work] and they say to them "I just told so and so to come over and apply. You're going to love her." It's not even like we're calling. We're talking to the people and you're seeing them all the time.*

These close-knit networks can be either beneficial or exclusionary, depending on relationships and power dynamics in school, work, and communities. While some supervisors and organizations encourage career advancement, others do not. The following quote illustrates how one health professional felt blocked from advancing in her job because of a lack of encouragement and support from her supervisor.

> *So, I reported to this person . . . [she] was not supportive in [my] continuing after she went to get her master's and was supported [by the same organization]. She wouldn't . . . didn't want me to succeed. It was challenging.*

Employment and training programs can also foster a welcoming or exclusionary environment. One student of color explained how she felt excluded in her LNA program because of the lack of instructors of color, as well as the "resistance" she believed her classmates and teachers expressed to diversity. This experience affected her ability to develop positive networks during her training program and also affected her academic performance and aspirations for what she believed she could achieve in her career.

> *The people [at school] there were definitely welcoming, but I kind of felt excluded. Even if I sat on the front row I still kind of felt excluded. I wish that there was a diverse crowd. I didn't really talk to anybody in my class. I'm a very welcoming person, but I just feel like people are very resistant towards diversity. . . . I definitely felt excluded and I know if I was in a more diverse crowd, I would have done better in LNA school. Not just recruiting, but even the teachers . . . it kind of would have given me more hope like, "Oh, if they did it then I can do it too." That is the only thing that I would probably change about my whole education experience.*

A more extreme theme of network-based exclusion came from a set of white health professionals who expressed concern about the growing diversity in New Hampshire, perceived affirmative action, and the implications of these trends on job competition. The following health professional expressed her feeling that

> *we need to help our own people,*

meaning that she would be much more likely to extend or share opportunities with other white health professionals over people of color.

> *I've heard they have an advantage because they have to hire so
> many [people of color] and that's okay, but I feel that we need to
> help our own people and I think we're at a point where we're just
> helping so many that we're in a mess. I mean, we really are.*

These findings show that health professionals in southern New Hampshire leverage resources through informal networks that we often believe are provided through internal labor markets and formal institutional procedures. In addition, relational factors operate differently for people of color compared to whites due to exclusionary environments and the hoarding of opportunities by people in power. If networks played no role in career advancement, we would have a more meritocratic system in which the level of education, human capital, and value to the broad mission of the organization of each individual might contribute in a larger way to their career success. Instead, we observe a system in which individuals are embedded in networks, and those networks are embedded in a society that produces racial inequality because of institutional and systemic structures.

Finding 3: Diversity and the Bottom Line

The majority of New Hampshire employers, at the level of director or unit manager, expressed significant skepticism about the importance or need for hiring a diverse workforce in order to improve community wealth, patient outcomes, or business performance. Two issues were raised.

First, there was general agreement that it was not the business of the health care organization to address wealth inequalities in the community that might be ameliorated through greater attention and prioritization of hiring and intentional advancement. Meritocracy and an assumption of individual responsibility was the normative frame. The most common managerial response when faced with discussions about the value of recruiting and retaining an increasingly diverse workforce was to state that they provide staff cultural competence training. In doing so, employers revealed what we theorize to be either a lack of understanding that workforce diversity is about bringing in new diverse workers, and has little to do with staff training on issues related to culture, or a reflexive resistance to engaging with a new topic that touches upon issues of race (Emerson 2017; Kowal, Franklin, and Paradies 2013).

Individual and organization-level cultural competence is widely accepted as an essential component of health care delivery. The National Quality Forum (2012) defines cultural competency as the "ongoing capacity of health care systems, organizations, and professionals to provide for diverse patient populations high-quality care that is safe, patient and family centered, evidence based, and equitable." Culturally competent care is shown to improve patient satisfaction and service utilization patterns, and increase adherence to treatment plans, particularly when health care professionals and patients share similar backgrounds—known as "patient-provider concordance" by race, ethnicity, and language (Cooper and Powe 2004), a dimension of workforce diversity. However, cultural competency training, in the provider organizations reached through this research, was not broadly embedded throughout institutions. In cases where training is offered, it typically occurs as part of the initial orientation process. A few organizations reported offering an annual or biannual refresher. Employers who provide any training at all strongly believe it to be sufficient (Powell 2016; Villarruel 2004).

Second, while cultural competency has been espoused as a strategy to enhance customer satisfaction, facilitate internal communication within the workforce, and improve organizational performance, employers did not understand the connection between a diverse workforce and their bottom line performance (Weech-Maldonado et al. 2012). Thus, we were asked on numerous occasions to "prove it," or no investments or shifts of practice would be made.

In summary, the research findings indicate that health care employers are largely unaware of the benefits of a diverse workforce for building community wealth, improving business performance, and reducing health disparities. Bias or discrimination occurs through the absence of formal institutional practices to improve opportunities for hiring diverse workers, and through informal networks that restrict opportunity structures for entry and advancement. The findings suggest that there are important roles for both employers and key stakeholders to play in moving the opportunity structure to function in a more inclusive and equitable fashion, with important benefits for the community and the health care system.

A FRAMEWORK FOR OPPORTUNITY: CULTURALLY
EFFECTIVE HEALTH CARE ORGANIZATIONS

These research findings led the partnership and its advisors to dedicate significant time to creating a framework that would address, in a comprehensive way, many of the challenges to employment inclusion and advancement among southern New Hampshire's diverse populations.

The research team conducted a systematic review of standards, best practices, and recommendations from national standard-setting organizations seeking to improve quality of care and reduce health disparities via organizational cultural competence. While as a project we maintained our primary focus on the hiring, retention, and advancement of diverse populations in health care positions, it appeared that in order to raise awareness of diversity as a priority, health care employers had to become engaged through a range of strategies. This led to the development of a new framework for "culturally effective organizations" that illustrates the intersections of workforce development, diversity, and inclusion in the workplace; organizational performance; and the reduction of health disparities. In this section we discuss this model and how each component of the framework advances health care job opportunities, institutional health care performance, and community health equity.

Culturally effective organizations enable, cultivate, and support the delivery of high-quality health care for all groups of people. The result is improved quality of care, enhanced patient safety and satisfaction, better health outcomes, a stable and skilled workforce with higher employee retention rates, administrative and management improvements, reduced health disparities, lower risk of liability, and fiscally sound health care organizations. Seven fundamental elements form a framework to guide the development of culturally effective organizations. The elements (see Figure 6.3) include leadership, institutional policies and procedures, data collection and analysis, community engagement, language and communication access, staff cultural competence, and workforce diversity and inclusion. Creating a culturally effective organization requires attention to all aspects of diversity. Although racial, ethnic, and linguistic diversity was the focus of this project, this framework

Figure 6.3 Framework for a Culturally Effective Organization

SOURCE: Gaiser et al. (2015).

led to active discussions about diversity of age, gender and sexuality, physical and mental disabilities, religion, and more. "Inclusion puts the concept and practice of diversity into action by creating an environment of involvement, respect, and connection" (Jordan 2011).

Culturally effective organizations are actively shaped and reshaped through the implementation of each of these seven elements. Reshaping occurs as organizations periodically evaluate progress toward organizational goals, while providing regular staff and management training, education, mentorship, and coaching. Each of the elements outlined below is followed by examples of potential action steps in which health care organizations and their leadership can engage to achieve cultural effectiveness.

1) **Leadership.** Executive leadership and boards of directors formally model the organization's commitment by including consideration of cultural effectiveness in the strategic planning process and overall organizational expectations and practices. Leadership is responsible for guiding the organization to address biases and overcome resistance to change, as well as each of the following tasks:

- Establish concrete goals, objectives, and strategies to meet cultural competency- and diversity-related targets with both executive and midlevel management.

- Gather results of formal assessments of organizational performance toward reaching these goals and report them to the board of directors on an ongoing basis.

- Use assessment findings to inform leadership and management decision making and fine-tune the direction the organization is taking to reach its goals.

- Establish expectations for leaders to communicate with staff and the community at large about the organization's commitment to diversity and cultural effectiveness.

- Recruit a board that reflects the community's racial and ethnic composition to ensure that community needs, cultural views, and expectations will be represented at the leadership level during strategic planning and throughout the plan's implementation.

2) **Institutional policies and procedures.** Health care organizations take a systematic approach to formalizing their commitment to cultural effectiveness by articulating their vision through written policies, procedures, goals, and practices. They

- incorporate the organization's commitment to cultural effectiveness in the mission statement;

- implement policies that promote the collection of race, ethnicity, and language data to measure and support enhanced cultural effectiveness;

- stratify data by race, ethnicity, and language to identify and address disparities as part of all quality improvement efforts; and

- provide cultural competency training, mentoring, and coaching for all levels of staff on a regular basis.

3) **Data collection and analysis.** Data related to cultural effectiveness and workforce diversity informs strategic planning and tailors service delivery to meet community needs. Data are also used to identify treatment variations and differences in patient outcomes and satisfaction across groups, and to monitor the impact of cultural effectiveness-related policies and activities on health equity and outcomes. These data can serve to partially fulfill the core meaningful use objectives set forth in the Health Information Technology for Economic and Clinical Health Act (Title XIII of the American

Recovery and Reinvestment Act of 2009 economic stimulus bill). Data are used to

- assess characteristics of the communities served (e.g., patient demographics) and the resources that already exist in these communities;

- evaluate community health needs, a process that the federal government now requires for 501(c)(3) hospital organizations, at least once every three years; and

- prioritize data collection objectives and allocate time for staff to carefully develop the design and implementation of data collection and analysis plans.

4) **Community engagement.** Organizations are more effective when they engage the community in a two-way process to learn, communicate, and share knowledge. This requires establishing relationships that position the community as an active partner in organizational decision making. This is accomplished when organizations

- engage community leaders to help structure and conduct community health needs assessments;

- communicate health needs assessment findings to community leaders and others to help interpret and validate findings and receive input on implications for service delivery (Health Research and Educational Trust 2013); and

- use community input in organizational decision making and ensure that Patient and Family Advisory Councils reflect the diversity of the community.

5) **Language and communication access.** Effective communication is essential to the provision of quality and culturally competent care. Several federal civil rights laws require communication assistance: Title VI of the Civil Rights Act of 1964, the Americans with Disabilities Act of 1990, and Section 504 of the Rehabilitation Act of 1973. In response, organizations are establishing policies and systems to

- identify and track patients' communication access needs, including preferred language, and to provide appropriate interpretation, translation, and communication assistance services (Gaiser et al. 2015);

- ensure that printed and multimedia materials, as well as signage, are translated into languages commonly found in the communities served and provide patients and family members with timely access to interpreters;

- make information about the availability of no-cost language interpreters and document translation highly visible; and

- establish formal policies to ensure all internal and external interpreters are qualified for their work by setting minimum credential, competency, and/or training requirements.

6) **Staff cultural competence.** Health care organizations implement a range of practices to ensure that patients from all racial and ethnic backgrounds receive optimal patient care. To meet accreditation standards, health care organizations are integrating patient preferences into care delivery and supporting these changes with organizational policies and procedures that enable staff members to fulfill these expectations. The cultural competence of all staff requires continuous learning and professional development and is achieved when organizations

- individualize the delivery of care to meet patients' cultural needs;

- provide culturally appropriate food selections, chaplaincy services, and plans of care, including the integration of traditional practices with Western medicine;

- respect cultural traditions for care delivery, particularly in the areas of end-of-life and patient-provider gender interaction; and

- support staff members as they learn to confront biases about their peers as well as patients and advance their cultural competence.

7) **Workforce diversity and inclusion.** Health care organizations can address underrepresentation by diversifying their workforce and introducing practices to ensure that employees from all backgrounds have the opportunity to contribute meaningfully to the workplace. They can achieve this goal when they

- establish relationships with cultural leaders, venues that serve diverse populations, and media outlets—such as non-English newspapers and churches that serve specific ethnic groups—to assist with recruitment;

- require search firms and recruiters used for management and advanced skill positions to present a field of candidates that reflects the diversity of the community; and

- engage in targeted retention and employee career promotion efforts to build and maintain workforce diversity at all levels.

Structured and intentional organization-level interventions are an important step for those who strive to improve quality, remain competitive, and meet regulatory requirements to ensure the health and strength of entire communities. The seven elements outlined here provide a framework for achieving these goals. Organizations that aspire to become culturally effective find it useful to begin with an organizational assessment to provide a baseline and help identify where to focus improvement efforts. It is also important for organizations to remember that becoming culturally effective is an ongoing process. Once implementation efforts have been initiated, these practices need to be continuously monitored for opportunities for improvement, and to hold executive-level management accountable for their success.

BENEFITS TO BECOMING A CULTURALLY EFFECTIVE HEALTH CARE ORGANIZATION

> *We found that current evidence supports the notion that greater workforce diversity may lead to improved health, primarily through greater access to care for underserved populations and better interactions between patients and health professionals.*
> —U.S. DHHS Health Resources and Services Administration 2006

It is widely acknowledged that the lack of a diverse health care workforce can be a contributing factor to health disparities. According to the 2004 Sullivan Commission for Diversity in the Health Care Workforce, "The fact that the nation's health professions have not kept pace with changing demographics may be an even greater cause of disparities in health access and outcomes than the persistent lack of health insurance for tens of millions of Americans" (Sullivan 2004, p. 1). Research shows that culturally effective organizational practices positively impact quality of care by improving the following for diverse patients:

- *Utilization patterns* increase access to and use of the appropriate health care services at the appropriate time.
- *Patient and family satisfaction* leads to better postvisit or post-discharge patient survey scores.
- *Treatment adherence* generates improved attention to follow-up care and treatment plans.
- *Levels of patient trust* enhance trust in providers. Studies show that this can have a positive impact on treatment adherence and health outcomes.

The American Hospital Association contends that elements of diversity awareness and practice should be integrated with quality measures in the health sector. It states, "Diversity management represents a business requirement that will grow in intensity as the general population, and accordingly the patient population, continues to become more racially and ethnically varied" (Health Research and Educational Trust, Institute for Diversity in Health Management 2011, p. 5).

The health care industry may benefit not only from having greater internal capacity for linguistic resources and cultural competency due to workforce diversity, but also from increased patient satisfaction and improvements in access to care, utilization of services, patient compliance, and health outcomes for minority populations (Cohen, Gabriel, and Terrell 2002). The American Hospital Association notes that workforce diversity, as it contributes to improved patient outcomes, improves the overall performance of the organization, thus putting the hospital at a competitive advantage and benefiting the greater society.

Select employers in New Hampshire understand these benefits and shared their rationale for diversifying the workforce and instituting various forms of organizational change for inclusion. Examples include seeking out and valuing language and cultural skills that match the demographics of the patient population, and working to create a welcoming and inclusive environment for all, with the knowledge that this will improve quality of care. One community health center employer said,

> *So, someone comes here and I ask them in the interview if they're multilingual and they say "yes" . . . they are actually compensated*

*at a different percent; they are given additional pay because of the
skill set they have.*

At the same time, this change process takes time. Leaders can influence the direction of change by setting goals and policies, modeling inclusive behaviors, and working with staff or "lighting the candle" as they learn to adapt to transition. According to one hospital manager,

> *You need the support of leadership to promote training in cultural
> competency and acceptance and support for diversity in the workforce. It was my VP who started lighting the candle for me. . . . I
> also had the support of the hospital CEO and the president and
> other VPs . . .*

SUSTAINING HEALTH AND EMPLOYMENT EQUITY INITIATIVES

This chapter was written two years after the end of the funded partnership initiative, enabling time for perspective and reflection about the impact of this research for advancing the hiring, retention, and promotion of diverse populations in the state. We provide these insights organized by the lessons learned for partnership development and for understanding new relationships between employers and the workforce development system.

Lesson 1: Align Partnership with Existing Priorities for Policy and Practice

Stakeholder interest and engagement in this work is most effective if driven and supported by the coordinated and mutually reinforcing actions of health care employers and employees, community actors, educators and educational institutions, and patients.

IASP's role was to be a facilitator of research and knowledge engagement, standing outside the power structure of local interests. It is possible that due to our neutrality, employers may have been more frank talking to researchers from outside the local area. The partnership and research direction benefited from partners' strong weekly communication and the complement of position, commitment, interest, and knowledge.

One essential component of this work was for the university partner to listen to multiple state actors' insights about the New Hampshire–specific starting point for this work. In collaboration with OMHRA and several other key leaders from health care, community colleges, and philanthropy, an appropriate strategy for state actors was developed, one that they could buy into and advance through each of their own constituency networks. All of this was discussed in the context of Joint Commission requirements and recommendations from other national authorities and experts in the health care field. IASP contributed by doing the crosswalk of national standards to bring existing knowledge and best practices together in a way that would resonate in New Hampshire.

Additionally, it was beneficial to have a "bridge" person—an inside researcher/staff member who could bridge communications and knew all or most state actors, facilitating communication and knowledge sharing, and embedding the work regionally. Some employers and partners were reticent to engage with state government, so the positionality of OMHRA proved challenging at times for local engagement. IASP's role as a nonlocal actor helped facilitate knowledge gathering and reduced some potential barriers to conducting this research.

Lesson 2: Maintain Engagement with Key Champions

The research partners were not always the right messengers or communicators to bring employers into this work, although they were the right partners for identifying the need and conducting the research. This type of sector-based work that ended up focusing on the institutional practices within the workplace requires, for implementation, the right champions or advocates to move it forward. Therefore, OMHRA and IASP learned when to "own" the work or message and when to let go and see that it became embedded as part of the ongoing work of local partners.

Several leaders took on roles that were critical for ensuring the visibility of the work and providing guidance around language and strategies. These included the president of one of the community colleges, the director of a community health center, the director of a local United

Way, the director of the local Area Health Education Center, program officers from two local foundations, the regional officer from the office of apprenticeship training, and two long-term care employers. Without champions, this project would not have achieved the same scale of research or attempted this level of breadth of findings.

Upon reflection, there could have been more time built in to share findings and for stronger relationship building between the partners and OMHRA. At times IASP built the relationship with employers, but OMHRA did not always meet all the employers, simply due to time constraints. This limits OMHRA's ability to continue to actively engage with employer networks. Thus, dedicating resources to build champions during the project is essential, but finding ways to keep those supporters active upon project completion will require additional reflection and new strategies for future partnership projects.

Lesson 3: Create and Provide Clear Guidance for Implementation

While evidence-based research enumerates the benefits of having a diverse workforce, our study revealed that the state's health care providers as a whole did not prioritize this work. They had no clear understanding of the benefits of or guidance for employing and advancing racial, ethnic, and linguistic minorities in the health care professions and were at a loss as to where to start. The culturally effective organization framework responded to this need by providing concrete strategies for implementation. Workforce diversity appears in the framework as one of seven elements, but the overall framework helps employers understand how these elements and strategies overlap and reinforce each other to improve quality and advance equity.

In the future, this type of project would benefit from additional resources to help develop pilot initiatives, with implementation plans at several worksites that put into place structures to support operationalization of the framework. The disciplines of translational science and implementation science remind us that converting theory into practice is challenging even when just dealing with technical change. Here, we are dealing with adaptive change around topics that can cause discomfort for some who are not comfortable acknowledging that there are real disparate impacts of race and ethnicity that require intentional structural efforts for improvement (Fixsen et al. 2005; National Implementation Resource Network 2016).

The research project contributed significantly to the state's knowledge base, according to both OMHRA and the advisory group partners. The drawback, we learned, is that the research produced an overwhelming amount of knowledge but did not sufficiently plan for a final dissemination and application phase to move the work forward. A key priority for future projects is to provide technical assistance to support health care organizations to operationalize the culturally effective framework in inter- and intraorganizational ways. Quality technical assistance could help employers discover and document more fully the benefits of becoming culturally effective organizations. It would also outline what employers can do and how to do it. Thus, the project generated important awareness about the workplace, workforce, and community health issues, but it fell short in learning how to engage employers in this knowledge to effect long-standing institutional and systemic change.

Lesson 4: Invest in Dissemination to Make Results Last

It took four full years for this research to be conducted and analyzed, and for a first round of research briefs to be written, vetted, and presented to key stakeholders. Additional efforts in formalizing dissemination processes certainly would have broad impacts on the sector and its potential or existing workforce. Efforts to engage health care employers in findings, especially those with some level of institutional influence who will listen and act, has still not occurred at any level of scale.

Today, two years after the project has ended, there is an active legacy. Some highlights are noted here:

- The OMHRA website and the New Hampshire Health and Equity Partnership website post materials created, and information on this topic is updated continuously in ways people can understand.

- The Culturally Effective Organizations Work Group and the Workforce Diversity Work Group of the New Hampshire Health and Equity Partnership draw on the knowledge and materials created and work to further disseminate the learning. Both work groups seek to engage employers and create resources to support organizations in implementing the framework.

- The Manchester Community Health Center, a lead partner in the HPOP and ERI work, created a Culturally Effective Organizations online tool kit in partnership with the Southern New Hampshire Area Health Education, OMHRA, and the Culturally Effective Organizations Work Group. This was an outcome of its own efforts to pilot implementation of the framework elements in working to create a Center of Excellence for Culturally Effective Care.

This kind of adaptive organizational change requires internal leadership buy-in, institutional commitment, external champions, time, and energy. Without resources to drive the dissemination of this new knowledge, it is hard to change the culture of the environment. Knowledge "sticks" when organizations are actively engaged in learning and testing, and when those who understand the framework educate others. Only then does it start to take hold. Resourcing research translation and dissemination is a challenge and could be built into future research partnership models from the beginning.

EXPANDING THE ROLE OF EMPLOYERS IN WORKFORCE DEVELOPMENT TO BUILD HEALTH AND EMPLOYMENT EQUITY

This examination of the institutional structures, relational factors, and interorganizational relations that underlie health and employment equity suggests that the traditional focus on development of workforce skills and individual efforts to advance in the labor market will not suffice to effect change. A dedicated effort to build leadership understanding and commitment and institutionalize culturally effective organizational change is imperative to enabling the economic advancement of diverse populations into health career pathways.

The framework for culturally effective organizations developed through the HPOG-university-community partnership in New Hampshire gave employers the ability to understand and accept their role in this larger system. However, more research is required to understand how this organizational change process can be effectively disseminated and implemented, as well as how to measure its direct effect on patients, the workforce, the community, and the health care organization itself. As communities across the United States become increasingly diverse, it is more important than ever to align policy, research, and practice by focusing on the intersections of workforce development, access to quality jobs, upward mobility, organizational performance, and health equity.

Notes

1. The New Hampshire Office of Minority Health and Refugee Affairs (OMHRA) has since changed its name to the New Hampshire Office of Health Equity.
2. Health Care Employer Interviews conducted by IASP researchers as part of the Health Care Employer Research Initiative, 2011–2012.
3. Specific hospital EEO reports, shared with OMHRA by phone and email on July 22, 2011.

References

Alvó-Armengol, Antoni, and Matthew O. Jackson. 2004. "The Effects of Social Networks on Employment and Inequality." *American Economic Review* 94(3): 426–454.

Bayer, Patrick, Stephen L. Ross, and Giorgio Topa. 2008. "Place of Work and Place of Residence: Informal Hiring Networks and Labor Market Outcomes." *Journal of Political Economy* 116(6): 1150–1196.

Blank, Rebecca M. 2009. "Economic Change and the Structure of Opportunity for Less-Skilled Workers." *Focus* 26(2): 14–20. https://www.irp.wisc.edu/publications/focus/pdfs/foc262c.pdf (accessed February 22, 2019).

Boguslaw, Janet, Melanie Doupé Gaiser, Laurie Nsiah-Jefferson, Jessica Santos, and Sandra Venner. 2016. "Good Jobs, Good Health: Diversifying the Workforce through Policy and Practice." Waltham, MA: Institute on Assets and Social Policy, The Heller School for Social Policy and Management, Brandeis University. https://heller.brandeis.edu/iasp/pdfs/jobs/good-jobs-good-health.pdf (accessed February 25, 2019).

Boguslaw, Janet, Melanie Doupé Gaiser, Laurie Nsiah-Jefferson, Jessica Santos, Sandra Venner, and Trinidad Tellez. 2015. "Culturally Effective Healthcare Organizations: A Framework for Success." Waltham, MA: Institute on Assets and Social Policy, The Heller School for Social Policy and Management, Brandeis University. https://heller.brandeis.edu/iasp/pdfs/jobs/culturally-effective.pdf (accessed February 25, 2019).

Boguslaw, Janet, Sandra Venner, Jessica Santos, and Laurie Nsiah-Jefferson. 2013. "Perspectives and Practices of New Hampshire Health Care Employers: Improving Quality, Reducing Costs, and Planning for the Future by Building Culturally Effective Health Care Organizations." Waltham, MA: Institute on Assets and Social Policy, The Heller School for Social Policy and Management, Brandeis University. https://heller.brandeis.edu/iasp/pdfs/jobs/perspectives-practices.pdf (accessed February 25, 2019).

Cappellari, Lorenzo, and Konstantinos Tatsiramos. 2015. "With a Little Help from My Friends? Quality of Social Networks, Job Finding, and Job Match Quality." *European Economic Review* 78(C): 55–75.

Cohen, Jordan J., Barbara A. Gabriel, and Charles Terrell. 2002. "The Case for Diversity in the Health Care Workforce." *Health Affairs* 21(5): 90–102.

Cooper, Lisa A., and Neil R. Powe. 2004. *Disparities in Patient Experiences, Health Care Processes, and Outcomes: The Role of Patient-Provider Racial, Ethnic, and Language Concordance.* Baltimore: Johns Hopkins University.

Cronk, Imran, and Janet Weiner. 2015. "The Affordable Care Act and Minority Health: Part IV (Workforce Diversity): Significant Racial and Ethnic Disparities Persist." Philadelphia: Leonard Davis Institute of Health Economics, University of Pennsylvania. https://ldi.upenn.edu/affordable-care-act-and-minority-health-part-iv-workforce-diversity (accessed February 22, 2019).

Doupé Gaiser, Melanie, Jessica Santos, Tanya Lord, Sandra Venner, Janet Boguslaw, and Laurie Nsiah-Jefferson. 2016. "Patient and Family Advisory Councils: Advancing Culturally Effective Patient-Centered Care." Waltham, MA: Institute on Assets and Social Policy, The Heller School for Social Policy and Management, Brandeis University. https://heller.brandeis.edu/iasp/pdfs/jobs/PFAC.pdf (accessed February 25, 2019).

Emerson, Joelle. 2017. "Don't Give Up on Unconscious Bias Training—Make It Better." *Harvard Business Review*, April 28. https://hbr.org/2017/04/dont-give-up-on-unconscious-bias-training-make-it-better (accessed May 24, 2019).

Fixsen, Dean L., Sandra F. Naoom, Karen A. Blase, Robert M. Friedman, and Frances Wallace. 2005. *Implementation Research: A Synthesis of the Literature.* Tampa: University of South Florida.

Gaiser, Melanie Doupé, Laurie Nsiah Jefferson, Jessica Santos, Sandra Venner, Janet Boguslaw, and Trinidad Tellez. 2015. "Culturally Effective Healthcare Organizations: A Framework for Success." Issue brief. Waltham, MA: Institute on Assets and Social Policy at the Heller School for Social Policy and Management at Brandeis University.

Granovetter, Mark S. 1977. "The Strength of Weak Ties." In *Social Networks: A Developing Paradigm*, Samuel Leinhardt, ed. New York: Academic Press, pp. 347–367.

Health Research and Educational Trust. 2013. *Becoming a Culturally Competent Health Care Organization*. Chicago: Health Research and Educational Trust.

Health Research and Educational Trust and Institute for Diversity in Health Management. 2011. *Building a Culturally Competent Organization: The Quest for Equity in Health Care*. Chicago: Health Research and Educational Trust; Chicago: Institute for Diversity in Health Management. http://www.hret.org/quality/projects/cultural-competency.shtml (accessed February 25, 2019).

Hensvik, Lena, and Oskar Nordström Skans. 2016. "Social Networks, Employee Selection, and Labor Market Outcomes." *Journal of Labor Economics* 34(4): 825–867.

Holzer, Harry J. 2004. "Encouraging Job Advancement among Low-Wage Workers: A New Approach." Policy brief, Welfare Reform & Beyond No. 30. Washington, DC: Brookings Institution. https://www.brookings.edu/wp-content/uploads/2016/06/pb30.pdf (accessed February 22, 2019).

———. 2015. "Job Market Polarization and U.S. Worker Skills: A Tale of Two Middles." Economic Studies at Brookings. Washington, DC: Brookings Institution. https://www.brookings.edu/wp-content/uploads/2016/06/polarization_jobs_policy_holzer.pdf (accessed February 25, 2019).

Johnson, Kenneth M. 2012. "New Hampshire Demographic Trends in the Twenty-First Century." The Carsey Institute at the Scholars' Repository. Paper No. 164. Durham, NH: Carsey Institute, University of New Hampshire. http://scholars.unh.edu/carsey/164 (accessed February 22, 2019).

Jordan, T. Hudson. 2011. "Moving from Diversity to Inclusion." *Profiles in Diversity Journal*, March 22. http://www.diversityjournal.com/1471-moving-from-diversity-to-inclusion / (accessed November 21, 2018).

Kalleberg, Arne L. 2013. *Good Jobs, Bad Jobs: The Rise of Polarized and Precarious Employment Systems in the United States, 1970s to 2000s*. New York: Russell Sage Foundation.

Kowal, Emma, Hayley Franklin, and Yin Paradies. 2013. "Reflexive Antiracism: A Novel Approach to Diversity Training." *Ethnicities* 13(3): 316–337.

Lin, Nan. 2000. "Inequality in Social Capital." *Contemporary Sociology* 29(6): 785–795.

McKernan, Signe-Mary, Caroline Ratcliffe, C. Eugene Steuerle, Caleb Quakenbush, and Emma Kalish. 2017. *Nine Charts about Wealth Inequality in America*. Washington, DC: Urban Institute. http://apps.urban.org/features/wealth-inequality-charts/ (accessed February 22, 2019).

MDRC. 2013. *Promoting Employment Stability and Advancement among Low-Income Adults.* New York: MDRC. https://www.mdrc.org/publication/promoting-employment-stability-and-advancement-among-low-income-adults (accessed February 22, 2019).

Moeller, Marguerite. 2010. "America's Tomorrow: A Profile of Latino Youth." Statistical Brief 2010. Washington, DC: National Council of La Raza. http://publications.unidosus.org/handle/123456789/501 (accessed February 22, 2019).

National Conference of State Legislatures. 2015. *Career Pathway Program: Helping Low-Income People Increase Skills and Access Good Paying Jobs.* Washington, DC: NCSL. http://www.ncsl.org/research/human-services/pathways-for-advancing-careers-and-education.aspx (accessed February 22, 2019).

National Implementation Resource Network. 2016. "Active Implementation Practice and Science." Chapel Hill, NC: National Implementation Resource Network. https://nirn.fpg.unc.edu/sites/nirn.fpg.unc.edu/files/resources/NIRN-Briefs-1-ActiveImplementationPracticeAndScience-10-05-2016.pdf (accessed May 24, 2019).

National Quality Forum. 2008. *Endorsing a Framework and Preferred Practices for Measuring and Reporting Culturally Competent Care Quality.* Washington, DC: National Quality Forum. http://www.qualityforum.org/projects/Healthcare_Disparities_and_Cultural_Competency.aspx.

National Skills Coalition. 2018. *Skills for Good Jobs: Agenda 2018.* Washington, DC: National Skills Coalition. https://www.nationalskillscoalition.org/resources/publications/file/Skills-for-Good-Jobs-Agenda-2018.pdf (accessed February 22, 2019).

Office of Family Assistance. 2017. *What Is HPOG?* Washington, DC: Office of Family Assistance, Administration for Children and Families, U.S. Department of Health and Human Services. https://www.acf.hhs.gov/ofa/programs/hpog/what-is-hpog (accessed February 22, 2019).

Office of Minority Health and Refugee Affairs. 2016. New Hampshire Health Opportunity Project (HPOP) Expanded Analysis. Internal document. Concord, NH: New Hampshire Department of Health and Human Services.

Osterman, Paul, and Beth Shulman. 2011. *Good Jobs America: Making Work Better for Everyone.* New York: Russell Sage Foundation.

Powell, Dorothy L. 2016. "Social Determinants of Health: Cultural Competence Is Not Enough." *Creative Nursing* 22(1): 5–10.

Santos, Jessica. 2014. "Missing Persons? Health Care Workforce Diversity in New Hampshire." Waltham, MA: Institute on Assets and Social Policy, The Heller School for Social Policy and Management, Brandeis University. https://heller.brandeis.edu/iasp/pdfs/jobs/missing-persons.pdf (accessed February 25, 2019).

————. 2015. "Beyond Supply and Demand: Networks of Opportunity and Inequality in Health Careers." PhD diss., The Heller School for Social Policy and Management, Brandeis University.

Santos, Jessica, and Janet Boguslaw. 2015. "The Networked Workforce: Maximizing Potential in Health Careers; A Study of Career Paths and Opportunity in Southern New Hampshire's Healthcare Workforce." Waltham, MA: Institute on Assets and Social Policy, The Heller School for Social Policy and Management, Brandeis University. https://heller.brandeis.edu/iasp/pdfs/jobs/networked-workforce.pdf (accessed February 25, 2019).

Santos, Jessica, Janet Boguslaw, and Sandra Venner. 2014. "Strengthening New Hampshire's Health Care Workforce: Strategies for Employers and Workforce Development Leaders." Waltham, MA: Institute on Assets and Social Policy, The Heller School for Social Policy and Management, Brandeis University. https://heller.brandeis.edu/iasp/pdfs/jobs/NH-health -care-workforce.pdf (accessed February 25, 2019).

Santos, Jessica, Sandra Venner, Janet Boguslaw, Selma Trahija, and Kris McCracken. 2016. "Becoming a Culturally Effective Organization: A Case Study of the Manchester Community Health Center." Waltham, MA: Institute on Assets and Social Policy, The Heller School for Social Policy and Management, Brandeis University. https://heller.brandeis.edu/iasp/pdfs/jobs/MCHC.pdf (accessed February 22, 2019).

State Plan Advisory Work Group. 2011. *Plan to Address Health Disparities and Promote Health Equity in New Hampshire.* Concord, NH: New Hampshire Department of Health and Human Services. https://www.dhhs.nh.gov/omh/documents/disparities.pdf (accessed February 22, 2019).

Sullivan, Louis. 2004. *Missing Persons: Minorities in the Health Professions; A Report of the Sullivan Commission on Diversity in the Healthcare Workforce.* http://health-equity.lib.umd.edu/40/1/Sullivan_Final_Report_000 .pdf (accessed February 22, 2019).

U.S. Department of Health and Human Services. 2006. "The Rationale for Diversity in the Health Professions: A Review of the Evidence." Rockville, MD: Bureau of Health Professions, Health Resources and Services Administration, Bureau of Health Professions.

Villarruel, Antonia M. 2004. "Introduction: Eliminating Health Disparities Among Racial and Ethnic Minorities in the United States." *Annual Review of Nursing Research* 22(1): 1–6. New York: Springer.

Weech-Maldonado Robert, Janice L. Dreachslin, Julie Brown, Rohit Pradhan, Kelly L. Rubin, Cameron Schiller, and Ron D. Hays. 2012. "Cultural Competency Assessment Tool for Hospitals: Evaluating Hospitals' Adherence to the Culturally and Linguistically Appropriate Services Standards." *Health Care Management Review* 37(1): 54–66.

7

Cultural Competency in Workforce Development

Perspectives from a Rural, Native American Project

Loretta Jean Heuer
North Dakota State University

Cynthia Lindquist
Cankdeska Cikana Community College

Marilyn G. Klug
University of North Dakota

Mary Leff
North Dakota State University

There is a critical shortage of American Indian and Alaskan Native health professionals who can provide competent, culturally sensitive health care that draws from traditional and Western wisdom and practices. The shortage of American Indian health professionals poses significant challenges for recruitment of qualified providers, especially on rural reservations. According to the Indian Health Service (IHS), the vacancy rates and total number of vacancies for key professional providers continue to remain high, even when compared to federally funded health centers. For example, in 2015 vacancy rates for physicians were 25 percent; for nurse practitioners, 25 percent; for nurses and dentists, 18 percent; and for pharmacists, 6.6 percent (IHS 2015).

As the demand for American Indian health care professionals increased across the United States, North Dakota also experienced greater workforce needs, especially in rural areas and on tribal reservations. In 2011, of the 15,600 nurses in North Dakota, 95 percent were Caucasian and only 1.4 percent were American Indians, which decreased from 2 percent in 2009 (Moulton 2012). A pressing need existed to establish evidence-based interventions that built sustainable career pathways while increasing the diversity workforce.

Through partnerships and interdisciplinary approaches, several projects and strategies were implemented that educated multi-age American Indians about health care careers (i.e., building the pipeline), and recruited students into health care programs (i.e., filling the pipeline), and placed graduates into health care positions (i.e., proving the pipeline) (NDSU School of Nursing and Cankdeska Cikana Community College 2013, 2014, 2015, 2016). Accordingly, the Sustaining Career Pathways for American Indian Health Professionals in North Dakota: Building Workforce Options with the Next Steps Health Profession Opportunity Grants (HPOG) program was launched to research and evaluate the interventions designed to increase American Indians' health professional capacity. This chapter provides an overview of the North Dakota American Indian demographics, HPOG Next Steps Program, HPOG University Partnership Research Grants, interdisciplinary projects, nursing recruitment/retention projects, and lessons learned.

AMERICAN INDIAN DEMOGRAPHICS AND SOCIAL DETERMINANTS

In 2010, the total population of all races in North Dakota was 672,591. Of that number, 42,996 (6.4 percent) were American Indians of one race alone or in combination with one or more other races. From 2000 to 2010, the American Indian population, one race alone or in combination with one or more other races, increased by 22.1 percent. While 16,628 (45.4 percent) American Indians of one race live off North Dakota reservations, 19,963 (54.6 percent) of one race live on one of the five reservations communities (North Dakota Indian Affairs Commission 2010).

North Dakota American Indian populations have more substandard social determinants than others who live in the state, including a lower health status. Life expectancy (54 years vs. 76 years) and extreme disease burden exists because of historical trauma, insufficient education, disproportionate poverty, discrimination, and cultural differences (IHS

2018). In North Dakota, American Indians have a significantly greater prevalence of diabetes, heart disease, smoking, obesity, and heavy alcohol use than the general population (Holm et al. 2010). These diseases are rooted deeply in economic adversity, poor social conditions, and insufficient education (IHS 2018).

American Indian high school graduation rates continue to be much lower than the overall North Dakota graduation rate of 86.3 percent. When comparing graduation rates over time, the economically nondisadvantaged rate is at 93.4 percent and continues to increase, whereas the economically disadvantaged rate is 70.9 percent, a slight increase. In 2015–2016, the graduation rate in North Dakota was 88.3 percent compared to 65.16 percent for American Indian students (Emerson 2017).

According to the 2010 census, the median American Indian household income was $25,255 compared to $48,670 for North Dakota. Overcrowding is the most common substandard concern on the reservations, with Spirit Lake having slightly larger proportions of overcrowding in both owner- and renter-occupied housing than North Dakota overall (31 percent and 12 percent, respectively). Standing Rock has the largest proportions of both owner- and renter-occupied housing units lacking complete plumbing and kitchen facilities (all less than 4 percent).

Poverty and unemployment continue to be an issue in the five North Dakota reservation communities. There are 13,230 (39.8 percent) American Indians living below poverty level compared to 84,895 (13.0 percent) in North Dakota (U.S. Census Bureau 2015). The percentage of American Indians living below the poverty level include Fort Totten, 65.8 percent; Fort Yates, 38.0 percent; Turtle Mountain, 31.6 percent; and Fort Berthold, 18.5 percent (U.S. Census Bureau 2016). While North Dakota's seasonally adjusted unemployment rate for the whole state (December 2017) was 2.6 percent, unemployment rates in reservation communities were much higher (Bureau of Labor Statistics 2018). In 2010 the percentage of North Dakota Tribes that were unemployed was 57 percent for Spirit Lake (Lindquist 2016), 63 percent for Standing Rock Sioux Tribe, 44 percent for Three Affiliated Tribes of the Fort Berthold Reservation, and 60 percent for Turtle Mountain (U.S. Department of the Interior 2014).

North Dakota American Indians are employed primarily in one of seven sectors, listed here from highest employed to lowest: 1) public administration; 2) arts, entertainment, and recreation; 3) accommodation and food services; 4) construction; 5) retail trade; 6) health care and social assistance; and 7) educational services (North Dakota Census Office 2015).

HPOG NEXT STEPS PROGRAM

To address the severe underrepresentation of American Indians in the health care sector, Cankdeska Cikana Community College (CCCC) partnered with the University of North Dakota Recruitment-Retention of American Indians into Nursing (RAIN) Program to implement an HPOG program titled "Next Steps Program: An Empowerment Model for Natives Entering Health Professions" (University of North Dakota College of Nursing 2011). This statewide program provided opportunities for American Indian citizens to access "educational pathways" that led to careers in various health professions.

The Next Steps program incorporated a comprehensive mentor model developed by the RAIN Program staff. RAIN mentors were strategically placed at CCCC, the primary grant site; each of the three secondary sites—United Tribes Technical College, Nueta Hidatsa Sahnish College on the Mandan, Hidatsa and Arikara Nation, Sitting Bull College on Fort Yates Reservation—and a statewide mentor located at the University of North Dakota RAIN Program. These five mentors provided comprehensive oversight to American Indian students, including intensive mentoring, case management, counseling/advising, and referrals to public assistance and behavioral health programs when needed. The Next Steps Program provided funding for tuition, uniforms, fees and books, transportation, and support services such as child care (Meit, TenBroeck, and Miesfeld 2015). If students graduated from a program requiring licensure to practice, funding was provided for the review course and licensure testing. Additionally, the Next Steps Employment Specialist provided career counseling, job search and placement assistance, and employability and life skills training to assist the graduates in securing employment (Meit, TenBroeck, and Miesfeld 2015). In the provision of these services, CCCC partnered with three other tribal colleges in North Dakota and collaborated with 13 other educational institutions that included two- and four-year colleges and universities, employment and training organizations, and health care agencies across the state.

The overall five-year Next Steps Program outcomes included 269 American Indian students enrolled in health care occupational education and training, with 216 (80 percent) completing one health care training. Among students who completed and exited the Next Steps Program, 191 (71 percent) were employed by their completion of the program (see Table 7.1). The Next Steps Program has made a significant impact on the health delivery system in North Dakota and its ability to serve Indian populations by increasing the number of health care professionals.

THE HPOG UNIVERSITY PARTNERSHIP RESEARCH GRANT

In 2011, North Dakota State University School of Nursing (NDSU SON) and CCCC collaborated on a four-year Health Professions Occupations University Partnership (HPOG UP) research grant to study the Next Steps Program's outcomes (Forster and Mueggenborg 2015). The first goal of this partnership was to engage in evaluation and research projects that explored how to encourage interest in health careers among American Indian youth and college students. The second goal was to discover best practices for supporting the recruitment and retention of American Indian people into professional nursing programs in North Dakota (Meit, TenBroeck, and Miesfeld 2015).

INTERDISCIPLINARY PROJECTS

While many American Indian students want to pursue college, they are less prepared than any other racial or ethnic group in the United States, according to the ACT data. In 2013, more than half (52 percent) of the roughly 14,000 American Indian students who completed the ACT met none of the four college benchmarks, which attempted to

Table 7.1 Number of American Indian Students Enrolled, Completed, and Employed in Their Chosen Occupation

Occupation	Total enrolled	Gender Male	Gender Female	Age (mean)[a]	Total completed	Gender Male	Gender Female	Age (mean)[a]	Total employed	Gender Male	Gender Female	Age (mean)[a]
Registered nurses	39	2	37	34 (24–53)	28	1	27	33 (24–50)	22	0	22	34 (24–50)
Licensed practical nurses	69	3	66	33 (22–59)	65	2	63	33 (22–59)	64	2	62	33 (22–59)
Social work	15	0	15	35 (27–48)	11	0	11	34 (27–48)	9	0	9	34 (27–48)
Dietitian	15	1	14	39 (25–63)	12	1	11	37 (25–63)	2	1	1	34 (25–63)
Certified nurse aids	121	6	115	31 (19–66)	93	5	88	30 (19–66)	87	5	82	30 (19–66)
Health information technology	4	0	4	37 (30–43)	2	0	2	38 (35–41)	2	0	2	38 (34–41)
Certified medical assistant	5	1	4	37 (25–46)	4	1	3	39 (25–46)	2	0	2	42 (42–42)
Emergency medical technician	1	0	1	31	1	0	1	31	1	0	1	31
Total	269	13	256	35	216	10	206	34	189	8	181	35

[a] Age range is given in parentheses.
SOURCE: Next Steps HPOG PRS system.

measure students' probability of earning Cs or higher in four postsecondary core subjects: English, reading, mathematics, and science. Only 10 percent of the American Indian test takers met all four benchmarks (Bidwell 2014). Although 60 percent of U.S. high school students continued to college, only 17 percent of American Indian students were able to continue their education because they contend with many challenges that average students do not encounter: the lack of awareness of many health careers, inability to navigate higher education systems especially if they are first-generation students, inadequate preparation in sciences and mathematics, financial barriers, and lack of role models and mentors from similar cultural backgrounds (Oliff 2017; Suez Mittman and Sullivan 2011). Additional challenges include geographic isolation of reservations, lack of cultural inclusion off the reservations, and lack of internet access at home for online courses (Oliff 2017; Tapia 2017). According to the 2018 *Broadband Deployment Report*, 85 percent of the 1.7 million American Indians living on rural reservations lack access to high-speed internet (Federal Communications Commission 2018).

Considering the underrepresentation of American Indians in health professions, limited preparation in STEM, along with the challenges American Indians encounter, a multifaceted approach was used to study the recruitment of American Indian students into health professions. As part of this grant, several educational efforts were initiated to increase awareness and interest in health professions: HPER 172 Introduction to Community and Public Health Course, Photovoice Project, Health Careers 4 U (HC4U) Summer Program, and Health Careers Edventures. Educational interventions that focus on health career opportunities have been successful in encouraging the pursuit of health careers by minority students (Brooks et al. 2013; Gefter et al. 2018; Grumbach and Mendoza 2008; Sequist 2009).

HPER 172 INTRODUCTION TO COMMUNITY AND PUBLIC HEALTH COURSE

Cankdeska Cikana Community College continued its partnership with Icahn School of Medicine at Mount Sinai and Columbia University Mailman School of Public Health of New York City and later with NDSU SON to provide a college-level course titled HPER 172 Introduction to Community and Public Health. This three-credit summer course addressed public health issues at the international, national, state, and Tribal Nation levels. Previous papers have described the course content and format (Austin et al. 2019; Heuer et al. 2016; Weintraub et al. 2015). This course was conducted using an interdisciplinary, interactive approach, with medical students, residents, and public health students from Icahn and Columbia, along with faculty and staff from all four educational institutions. Additionally, multiple guest speakers, many of whom were American Indian professionals, were invited to share their personal and professional experiences in achieving their careers. Many of the speakers shared their personal and professional stories, which included their successes and challenges as they transitioned into area universities and completed their professional degrees (Austin et al. 2019; Heuer et al. 2016; Weintraub et al. 2015).

Course objectives, along with CCCC students' satisfaction with the course content and educators, were evaluated on a five-point Likert scale. The students consistently rated 4.0 or above for meeting the objectives and overall satisfaction with the course.

During the four years of the HPOG UP grant, 57 American Indian students enrolled, and 51 completed the course.[1] Initially, the course was designed for high school and college students, but some of the enrolled participants included older-than-average students and elders who wanted to learn about public health issues. Of the 51 participants, 13 were older than average or elders. Thirty (59 percent) were female, whereas 21 (41 percent) were male. Two students had their GEDs and 5 were enrolled in GED courses; one student had previously completed a bachelor's degree. Twenty students completed their associate's degree at CCCC, and 8 of these students continued their education at area Tribal Colleges or universities. Five were retired. Educational information was missing on 20 students who completed the course.

Students' knowledge of public health issues increased after their participation in the course. Their knowledge of health careers also increased, and they indicated they were more likely to pursue health careers after completing this course. Over half of the students believed they could improve the health of their community (NDSU SON and CCCC 2013, 2014, 2015, 2016). Students interested in health careers listed nursing, medicine, pharmacist, dentist, physical therapist, social worker, and emergency medical technician as their preferred choices.

HPER 172 INTRODUCTION TO COMMUNITY AND PUBLIC HEALTH COURSE PHOTOVOICE PROJECT

In 2014 and 2015, CCCC and NDSU SON implemented community-based participatory research photovoice projects to enable the HPER 172 students to learn about a specific research method while studying how the environment impacts their health (Schell et al. 2009). The students participated in a presentation on photography and utilization of digital cameras. They were given one week to take pictures that promoted or challenged good health practices on their rural tribal nation. After the students submitted their photos, they were randomly placed into focus groups with facilitators who asked them questions about each of their pictures (Weintraub et al. 2015). Themes were identified from the focus groups.

Community-based participatory research is grounded in real-world context and identifies important problems and implements solutions that benefit members of the community (Cook 2008; Hergenrather et al. 2009; Stedman-Smith et al. 2012). Both photovoice projects increased the students' awareness of environmental factors that impact the health of American Indians residing on Spirit Lake Tribal Nation. The students who participated in these two projects applied the theoretical concepts they learned in the HPER 172 course about environmental health. Each year, some of their pictures, along with unidentified quotes describing the pictures, were displayed in the CCCC People's Choice Art Shows.

HEALTH CAREERS 4 U SUMMER PROGRAM

With the goal of strengthening career pathways for American Indian health professions, CCCC recognized the need for a youth program aimed at increasing interest in health careers. The college continued its partnership with Icahn School of Medicine Mailman School of Public

238 Heuer et al.

Health and later NDUS SON to develop Health Careers for U (HC4U), a one-week educational program for students aged 11–14. The curriculum focused on the main concepts of healthy living, exercise, safety, and professional career opportunities. The HC4U Program included workshops, physical fitness activities, and professional community speakers (NDSU SON and CCCC 2013, 2014, 2015, 2016; Weintraub et al. 2015). CCCC staff taught the students how to develop public service announcement (PSA) videos and posters. Students were placed in small groups, and they chose and researched their topics, wrote and acted out their scripts, shot the scenes, and edited the video until there was a master cut. While some group members were working on the video PSA, others developed a visual poster with the same message. The final day of HC4U, families and Tribal members were invited for a lunch and a program that showcased "HC4U What Is It About?," a video of student activities during the week; displayed students' PSAs and posters, and honored their participation in the program (Weintraub et al. 2015).

One hundred and thirty-one students[2] participated in the summer programs. Students completed daily evaluations based on a three-point scale that measured how they liked the planned daily activities, change in knowledge level, comfort level, participation interest, and staff interaction. Four open-ended questions gave students the opportunity to share one thing they learned that day, their favorite and least favorite activity, and anything that could have been done to make the day better.

The evaluation results were consistently positive over four years. The top health careers of interest listed by the students were medicine, nursing, veterinary, dietitian, and emergency medical technician. Over half of the students said they learned more than they expected. Their general knowledge increased in the following areas: public service announcements, healthy eating, emergency services, and various health careers. Most of the students enjoyed the activities and would recommend the HC4U Program to their friends. Over two-thirds of the students reported they would participate in future HC4U Programs.

HEALTH CAREERS EDVENTURES

American Indian students older than age 14 were no longer eligible to enroll in the HC4U Program, but they still wanted to participate in health-related activities while continuing to learn about various health professions. As a result, CCCC and NDSU SON developed the Health Careers Edventure Program for 15-to-19-year-old American Indian students on Spirit Lake Nation. This program aimed to teach students about educational pathways to various health careers at Tribal Colleges, state colleges, and universities. The curriculum focused on traditional healing, educational and employment skills, interview skills, physical activities, hands-on skills lab activities (e.g., taking blood pressure, making hand lotion in the pharmacy concept lab), and patient simulation scenarios. Other learning experiences included immersing the students in various campus activities so they could learn about student life and explore student associations on the campuses. The second year of the program, students volunteered for a day at the Spirit Lake Nation Casino and assisted staff in laundry, housekeeping, and maintenance (NDSU SON and CCCC 2015, 2016).

Sixteen American Indian students enrolled both years, but 10 attended and completed in 2014 and 8 completed in 2015. Twenty-eight percent of the participants were male and 72 percent were female.[3] The program evaluations from these two summer programs were overwhelmingly positive. Top health careers of interest were nursing, medicine, and veterinary. Students were excited to tour universities and participate in hands-on experiences in the skills labs (e.g., nursing, veterinarian, pharmacy) and patient simulator scenarios. Through their participation in multiple patient simulator scenarios, students learned how to assess respirations and heart sounds and participated in patient codes. They enjoyed extracurricular activities (e.g., movies, basketball, shopping), as well as many of the non-health-care-related educational activities. The days were long and filled with 8–10 activities per day, and some evaluation comments reflected the need to scale back the number of events.

YOUTH EDUCATION AND EMPLOYMENT SURVEY

According to the U.S. Department of Education, college enrollment among American Indian/Alaskan Native students decreased by 26 percent, from 179,000 to 132,000 between 2000 and 2010 (National Center for Educational Statistics 2017), and Native Americans have the highest unemployment rates of any racial or ethnic group in the United States (Bureau of Labor Statistics 2016). To gain an understanding of the transition of American Indian high school students into higher education and/or employment, NDSU SON and CCCC collaborated with Dr. Phillip Young P. Hong and his team from Loyola University, Illinois, to use the Perceived Education Barrier Scale and the Perceived Employment Barrier Scale (Hong, Polanin, and Pigott 2012) to conduct the Youth Education and Employment Survey. The purpose of this study was to assess American Indian eleventh- and twelfth-grade students' hope for obtaining their goals in higher education and employment.

A total of 515 students completed the survey from 12 high schools located on or near the four North Dakota Tribal Nations. The overall survey response rate was 64 percent based on the total number of students enrolled in eleventh and twelfth grade at participating schools compared to the number of students who participated the day of the survey (NDSU SON and CCCC 2015, 2016).

Individual reports were developed that compared each school's results to the Tribal Nation or reservations and all 12 schools. Results for the Spirit Lake Nation included the four individual schools' results, tribal nation aggregate, and all schools' data. The results were based on mean or average ($\bar{x}$) scores to ensure that all schools of varying size received an individualized report of their results. In addition, the use of mean or average scores provided a standard way of viewing results across all schools, regardless of size. Forty percent of the "all schools" students were interested in health careers: nursing, medicine, social worker, sports medicine, and physical therapist (Heuer et al. 2016).[4]

NURSING RECRUITMENT/RETENTION PROJECTS

Three million nurses compose the largest segment of the health care workforce in the United States, and the nursing profession is the fastest growing occupation in the country. Despite the growth, the demand for nurses is outpacing the supply. The Bureau of Labor Statistics (2019) projects the employment of registered nurses to grow 15 percent by 2026, which is higher than the average for all occupations. Primary reasons for this looming nursing shortage are the increased emphasis on preventive care, heightened rates of chronic conditions, and the aging of the baby boomer generation along with their need for additional health care services. According to the National Council on Aging (2018), about 80 percent of elders have one chronic disease, and 68 percent have at least two chronic conditions.

In 2017, North Dakotans aged 65 and older represented 15 percent of the total population. By 2025, 18 percent of the state's population is expected to be over 65, and many will be diagnosed with one or more chronic diseases such as obesity, diabetes, or mental illness (North Dakota Compass 2019). In addition to the aging population, the North Dakota nursing shortage will continue to be affected by four main drivers: 1) bottleneck of entry into nursing programs, 2) barriers to expanding nursing programs, 3) retention of North Dakota nurses in the state, and 4) need for immigration of nurses into the state (Moulton 2017).

While North Dakota leaders and administrators search for innovative recruitment strategies to increase the nursing workforce, the American Indian population continues to be overlooked. In 2010, North Dakota's nursing workforce lacked the racial and ethnic diversity that reflected the largest minority population, American Indians (Heuer, Moulton, and Klug 2013). As a result, multidimensional educational and research methodologies were implemented to identify best practices for supporting the recruitment and retention of American Indian students into the profession of nursing. This section highlights a variety of nursing projects that were undertaken, including a nursing school survey, a health care facility survey, the North Dakota American Indian Nursing Demographic Study, American Indian Annual Nursing Conferences, Voices of American Indians in Nursing Research study/videos, and an oral history of American Indian nurses research project/ documentary.

NORTH DAKOTA NURSING SCHOOL SURVEY

In 2012, NDSU SON and the Center for Nursing collaborated to develop a nursing program survey that assessed the characteristics of North Dakota nursing programs and identified trends of American Indian student enrollment and retention. Before this survey, there was only anecdotal information regarding enrollment and retention data for American Indian students. Survey questions focused on American Indian student enrollment, university support programs, nursing program support services, and recruitment and retention strategies for American Indian students. Invitations to participate in the study were distributed to all nursing program directors from the 10 higher education institutions that offered practical nursing degrees and the 14 institutions that offered registered nurse degrees (NDSU SON and CCCC 2013, 2014).

The survey was completed by 10 nursing program administrators. Two programs offered only practical nursing degrees, four offered both licensed practical nurses (LPNs) and registered nurse (RN) degrees, and four offered only bachelor of science nursing degrees. The number of applications ranged from 5 to 269, median of 57.5. The number of American Indian applications ranged from 1 to 35, median of 5, with one school not reporting.

The number of students accepted annually ranged from 5 to 112, median of 53.5. The number of American Indian students accepted yearly ranged from 1 to 18, median of 3, one program not reporting. The number of students currently enrolled ranged from 11 to 274, median of 69. The number of American Indian students currently enrolled ranged from 0 to 37, median of 2. The number of American Indian students who graduated in the past five years ranged from 0 to 42, median of 7.5, with four programs not reporting.

Nine institutions offered nonnursing tutoring services, and seven offered tutoring for nursing classes. Six institutions offered social support for American Indian students, while four nursing programs did. Eight institutions and four nursing programs offered financial assistance for American Indian students.

HEALTH CARE FACILITY SURVEY

To better understand the perspectives of health care administrators and directors of nursing, the 2012 Health Care Facility Survey was developed in collaboration with the North Dakota Center for Nursing. The survey included questions that focused on the number of full-time nurses, vacancies, salaries, retention of nurses, scholarship or educational loan programs, recruitment, and retention of American Indian nurses (NDSU SON and CCCC 2013, 2014).

Approximately 200 North Dakota health care facilities were invited to participate in the study. Twenty-six hospitals and 51 long-term care facilities returned their surveys for a 39 percent return rate. Hospitals in general had more vacancies per full-time equivalents than long-term care facilities and took longer to fill these positions. This was especially true of RNs (median vacancies per FTE: 0.09 to 0.00, $p = 0.061$; median weeks to fill a vacancy: 6.0 to 3.0, $p = 0.055$).

Compared to urban long-term care facilities, those in rural areas have a much higher need for LPNs (19 percent) and RNs (4 percent). It also takes rural long-term care facilities much longer to fill LPN positions (nine weeks longer) and RN positions (one week longer). Starting salaries for LPNs are about the same, but average LPN salaries are more in rural areas ($20 compared to $19). For RNs, rural starting salaries ($22) are much less than urban ($24), while their average salaries are about the same.

Location, pay, and atmosphere were the key reasons nurses remained working at particular facilities. As for location, they wanted to work close to home and be near their families. They wanted to be properly compensated for their education and work. Finally, the facility atmosphere was a multifaceted reason given for retention. This included having opportunities for professional growth, job safety, and an enjoyable, stress-reduced environment that included a team or family-oriented approach. Long-term care facilities attracted workers who preferred a work location where they could develop a closer relationship with patients. About half of the facilities surveyed offer links to nursing schools or loan repayment programs. Few facilities provided special recruitment or retention programs designed for American Indian nurses.

NORTH DAKOTA AMERICAN INDIAN NURSING DEMOGRAPHIC STUDY

To gain an understanding of the North Dakota American Indian nursing workforce, NDSU SON, North Dakota Center for Nursing, RAIN Program, and NDSU Department of Agricultural and Biosystems Engineering partnered to conduct a demographic study using a geographical information system. The purpose of this project was to annually evaluate the numbers and distribution of American Indian nurses across the state. Only the American Indian nurses who resided and were employed in North Dakota were included in this study.

North Dakota consists of 53 counties, including 4 urban, 12 rural, and 37 frontier counties (Center for Rural Health 2011, 2019). Data sets included the 2010 North Dakota census, annual population estimates by the Census Bureau, annual North Dakota Nursing Licensure, and the Tiger/Line shapefiles from census.gov for geographical information system mapping. The North Dakota Board of Nursing data set contained only the ethnicity, licensure/certification (advanced practice, RN, or LPN), and North Dakota county employment (NDSU SON and CCCC 2013, 2014, 2015, 2016).

The study was limited to the American Indian nurses self-reporting their ethnicity. Nurses only have one opportunity to self-report their ethnicity, when they apply for their license the first time. Additionally, the study only reflects the American Indian nurses who reside and are employed in North Dakota. There may be others who reside in North Dakota but work in a neighboring state.

From 2010 to 2016, there was an increase of 94 American Indian nurses in North Dakota. American Indian nurse practitioners had an increase of 6, registered nurses increased by 53, and licensed practical nurses increased by 35 (Wamono, Heuer, and Moulton 2016).

AMERICAN INDIAN ANNUAL NURSING CONFERENCES

Four annual nursing conferences were offered to the Next Steps students, nursing administration, nurse educators, practicing nurses, health care employers, and social workers in North Dakota and eastern Minnesota. NDSU SON, RAIN Program, CCCC, and North Dakota Center for Nursing collaborated to develop, implement, and evaluate the four conferences, which aimed to develop strategies for the recruitment and retention of American Indian students into the nursing profession. National, regional, and local speakers were secured as presenters. Selection depended on conference topics, speakers' expertise, and speakers' ability to inspire students and others in the audience.

The American Indian culture was integrated into conferences through the presence of an American Indian conference facilitator, the posting and removal of flags by veterans, inclusion of an American Indian drum group, opening/closing prayers, and a gift of a star quilt to the president of the educational institution in honor of his/her support of American Indian education and programs. Each year, participants' evaluations of the conference objectives, speakers, topics, and cultural activities were very positive (NDSU SON and CCCC 2013, 2014, 2015, 2016). Each conference included a community-based participatory evaluation/research component.

The number of participants in the four conferences was 217.[5] From the evaluation/research data collection, one of the main themes was the difficulty of recruiting and retaining American Indian students into nursing and other health professions because of social determinants and the lack of role models. Thus, projects were developed that focused on the recruitment and retention of American Indians in nursing and incorporated American Indian role models in the recruitment and retention messaging.

VOICES OF AMERICAN INDIANS IN NURSING RESEARCH STUDY/VIDEOS

To address the issue of a lack of role models for American Indian students and young adults, NDSU SON, NDSU Agriculture Communication, and the RAIN Program implemented a research and video project that focused on the recruitment and retention of American Indians into nursing. American Indians in the Voices of American Indian Nurses represent the five Tribal Nations/reservations in North Dakota. Participants included 11 American Indian nurses, 27 student nurses, four mentors, two Next Steps staff, and two RAIN staff.

The videos tell the stories of many American Indian nurses and student nurses who overcame obstacles to complete their nursing programs and achieve health care careers. They provide encouragement for others faced with similar challenges (NDSU SON and CCCC 2014, 2015, 2016).

At the 2013 American Indian Nursing conference, participants had an opportunity to watch and evaluate one video and offer suggestions for improvement. Forty-three participants completed the evaluations, and overall, feedback was very positive: on a scale of 1 (low) to 10 (high), the average rating overall was 9.3. The comments from the open-ended questions were used to revise the videos.

Six videos were completed; four focused on the successful attributes of the Next Steps and RAIN Programs, and the other two featured American Indian RNs and LPNs.[6] North Dakota Nursing Programs can use any of these videos for recruitment and/or retention of American Indian students in their programs. The Next Steps Program job placement specialist has used these videos at recruitment events.

ORAL HISTORY OF AMERICAN INDIAN NURSES RESEARCH PROJECT/DOCUMENTARY

The 2013 conference participants who evaluated the short video draft suggested more in-depth interviews to fully tell the stories of American Indian nurses. They also commented that American Indians are practically invisible in the mass media, and when they are portrayed they are generally depicted in stereotypical or historical images (Leavitt et al. 2015). Because of these comments, NDSU SON, CCCC, Kat Communication, and RAIN Program staff partnered to develop the American Indian Nursing Oral History Study. The interviews explored the nurses' personal stories, highlighting the transitions they experienced through their educational programs and nursing careers. The interviews were videotaped, and edited portions were used to develop the documentary titled *Essence of Healing: The Journey of American Indian Nurses* (NDSU SON and CCCC 2015, 2016).

The film showcased the lives of 14 American Indian nurses who live and work in the upper Great Plains. While their lives and stories were different, their past life experiences and American Indian heritage made them extraordinary healers.

The purpose of the film was twofold. First, it intended to evoke pride among American Indian people and to convey honor within American Indian communities by expanding understanding both within American Indian communities and the institutions and organizations in the public that educate, employ, or interact with American Indian nurses. Second, it was a valuable recruitment tool to inspire choice by informing and educating the public, especially those that influence and support students (e.g., families, elders, schools, communities).

Two hundred individuals attended the premiere at North Dakota Heritage Center in Bismarck, and 44 of the attendees completed the evaluations for a 22 percent return rate. Ninety-eight percent of the respondents rated the quality of the film, content presented, and overall presentation with a four or higher on each question using the 1-to-5 Likert scale.

MEDIA AND EDUCATIONAL DISSEMINATION OF THE DOCUMENTARY

The documentary *Essence of Healing: The Journey of American Indian Nurses* is the only film that showcases the lives of American Indian nurses in the upper Midwest.[7] A global multimedia awareness campaign was developed to promote the film's distribution in multiple media markets (Hyatt 2017; Lee 2017). This 58-minute film has been released on DVD. Some of the major media and educational milestones are discussed below.

Awards and Film Festivals. The documentary received the 2017 Sigma Theta Tau International (STTI) Nursing Media Award at the group's 44th biennial convention in Indianapolis, Indiana, in October 2017. STTI is an International Honor Society of Nursing that advances world health and celebrates nursing excellence in scholarship, leadership, and service. The organization reports more than 135,000 active members in 85 countries. STTI honors health care professionals for their contributions to professional excellence.

It was awarded the Best Service Film Award from the 42nd American Indian Film Festival in San Francisco in November 2017, which is the world's longest-running exposition showcasing independent films of U.S. American Indians and First Nations peoples of Canada. During the past 42 years, the American Indian Film Institute has celebrated generations of Indian filmmakers, performing artists, and audiences with the best of the most current Indian cinema.

In addition, the documentary has received nine awards, was selected as a finalist or semifinalist in 3 festivals, and was screened at 11 film festivals.

GoodHealthTV®. For one year, starting during Nurses Week in May 2016 and ending during Nurses Week in May 2017, short clips from *The Essence of Healing: Journey of American Indian Nurses* were shown on GoodHealthTV®. These two- to three-minute videos were for the recruitment and retention of American Indian students into nursing. GoodHealthTV® is the nation's premiere health and wellness education network and was created to entertain, engage, and educate viewers when they are most receptive to health and wellness education. It is played in the IHS clinics and tribal colleges and thus is an opportunity for patients and family members to learn about nursing from an American Indian nurse.

Prairie Public Broadcasting. Prairie Public Broadcasting is an award-winning radio, television, and public media service that educates, involves, and inspires the people of the prairie region. According to the program manager, Prairie Public Television will air the documentary over the next two years.

Native American Calling—Your National Electron Taking Circle. The national live call-in broadcast Native America Calling covered the documentary on its radio show, which was broadcast on over 70 stations.

***Essence of Healing: The Journey of American Indian Nurses* e-Campus Courses.** To nurture interest and provide educational information for prospective nursing students, Kat Communication and

NDSU SON partnered to develop access to two free, interactive, online educational programs focused on career preparation and career choices for students in grades 6–8 and 9–12. The goal of these two courses is to expose students in middle and high school to nursing as a future career. These courses are based on the profession of nursing and pathways into nursing; they feature stories of American Indian nurses in North Dakota and their experiences in school and work. Both online courses are divided into eight modules comprising educational videos, teacher-led and web-based games, and journal entries and forum questions that allow students to reflect on the given module and activities. These two online programs are designed to be used within existing classroom curriculum or as a guided activity for individual students. While the programs use nursing careers as examples, the information will be useful to all students as they prepare for high school and life after high school.

The e-Campus course was piloted with 10 American Indian high school students. Overall, the students' responses were extremely positive. The students said the course was interesting, and they learned a lot about nursing. Fifty-four percent of the students thought the course was easy to use. Students ranked the video clips, forums, and readings as their favorite parts of the e-Campus. Fifty-four percent stated they were very likely or somewhat likely to consider nursing as a career choice. Sixty-four percent of the students were extremely likely or very likely to recommend the e-Campus program to friends, and 37 percent reported somewhat likely.

LESSONS LEARNED

There is strong and significant interest among the Native population for health career pathways, and particularly for the nursing profession, that are rooted in cultural values of compassion, generosity, and helping others. Those pathways are never straight and clear, but with adequate resources, good information, and strong collaborations, successful student outcomes are accomplished. Sufficient and adequate resources to "follow" students throughout their respective pathways are essential, and although funding is the key, role models and mentoring are equally relevant.

The projects discussed reflect cross-cultural exchange that is mutually beneficial. For example, the Mt. Sinai medical students expressed how much they learned from living and working on a reservation and that it greatly contributed to their development as clinicians. Several have maintained relationships with the Dakota families they met and connected with while on the reservation. Likewise, the Native students enrolled in the various courses and programs were willing to share their experiences and engage in discussions about their culture with faculty and students.

Knowledge and understanding of "public or community health"— what it means, how it impacts the individual, and what can be done to change or improve health statistics—was expanded and enhanced via the various courses and activities.

While trying to establish a data set, the ratios of American Indian nurses to population in urban, rural, and frontier counties could not be studied because of the small numbers, which is a continuing issue for American Indian/Alaska Native populations. American Indian/Alaska Natives in the United States are less than 1 percent of the country's population, and therefore data and statistics are minimal. More recently there has been a much greater emphasis on these data sets by tribal leaders and communities to assure better representation that is based on actual numbers, and because of the small size of most Tribes, the use of trends analysis is more the norm. The projects described in this chapter showcase how partnerships help develop infrastructure where none existed. Finding community-based nurse researchers is a goal for many tribal communities.

Each of the projects that were part of this work included outcomes measures that were tracked and reported. Goals were set, progress was tracked, and results were quantified. In general, the desired outcomes were achieved at the project level. However, impact of the project over time remains unknown. The original project design did not include longitudinal tracking of participants that would have gathered additional information about future career choice and whether or not participation in the programs ultimately resulted in pursuit of a health care career or a course change in plans for the future. While we can measure specific outcomes, we cannot measure the impact that program participation had on individual lives over time.

Notes

Funded by Administration for Children and Families, U.S. Department of Health and Human Services (Grant 90FY0005). The University Partnership Research Grants for Health Professional Opportunity Grant, No. 90PH0019, Office of Planning, Research and Evaluation, Administration for Children and Families.

The authors would like to thank the following individuals for their participation with this project: Barb Anderson, BSW, Program Coordinator, University of North Dakota Recruitment/Retention of American Indians in Nursing Program; Larry Anderson, Next Steps Job Specialist; MaDonna Azure, MS, RN, former Next Steps Director; Chris Burd, PhD, RN, former Next Steps Co-Director; Linda Cushman, Columbia University Mailman School of Public Health of New York City; Phillip G. Longie, BS, Next Steps Director; Jon Rip, MD, MPH, Icahn School of Medicine at Mount Sinai; Ann Wadsworth, Next Steps Assistant Director; Deb Wilson, MS, Director, University of North Dakota Recruitment/Retention of American Indians in Nursing Program; and Danielle J. Myers-Wilson, MA, Next Steps Program Evaluation Coordinator.

1. 2012, N = 11; 2013, N = 12; 2014, N = 19; 2015, N = 9.
2. 2012, N = 22; 2013, N = 21; 2014, N = 40; 2015, N = 48.
3. Males, N = 5; females, N = 13.
4. Education and Employment Hope (Self-Reliance) Assessment of High School Junior and Seniors on North Dakota American Indian Reservations reports can be viewed at https://www.ndsu.edu/nursing/fargo_people/loretta_heuer/ (accessed August 13, 2019).
5. 2012, N = 49; 2013, N = 62; 2014, N = 51; 2015, N = 55.
6. The videos are available at https://www.ndsu.edu/nursing/fargo_people/loretta _heuer/ (accessed August 13, 2019).
7. The trailer for *The Essence of Healing* is available at https://www.youtube.com/ watch?v=qfO0KwOAE9s (accessed August 13, 2019).

References

Austin, Charlette, Emily Berg, Loretta Heuer, Linda Cushman, Cynthia Lindquist, and Jonathan Ripp. 2019. "Public Health and Health Professional Education at Tribal College: A Collaborative Immersion Program in Rural North Dakota." *Rural and Remote Health*, https://www.rrh.org.au/ journal/early_abstract/5020 (accessed June 25, 2019).

Bidwell, Allie. 2014. "Are American Indian Students the Least Prepared for College?" *U.S. News and World Report*. https://www.usnews.com/ news/blogs/data-mine/2014/03/13/are-american-indian-students-the-least -prepared-for-college (accessed November 14, 2018).

Brooks, Alyssa, Shakira Washington, Bradley Boekeloo, Brian Gilchrist, and Min Qi Wang. 2013. "Relationship of Personal Health Experiences with Interest in Health Careers among Youth from an Underserved Area." *Journal of Allied Health* 42(3): 135–140.

Bureau of Labor Statistics. 2016. "Labor Force Characteristics by Race and Ethnicity, 2015 BLS Reports." Washington, DC: Bureau of Labor Statistics. https://www.bls.gov/opub/reports/race-and-ethnicity/2015/home.htm (accessed June 3, 2019).

———. 2018. "Economy at a Glance: North Dakota." Washington, DC: Bureau of Labor Statistics. https://www.bls.gov/eag/eag.nd.htm (accessed May 9, 2019).

———. 2019. "Registered Nurses. Occupational Outlook Handbook." Washington, DC: Bureau of Labor Statistics. https://www.bls.gov/ooh/healthcare/registered-nurses.htm (accessed June 14, 2019).

Center for Rural Health. 2011. "North Dakota County Classification. University of North Dakota, School of Medicine & Health Sciences." https://ruralhealth.und.edu/assets/1378-5863/nd-county-classification.pdf (accessed August 13, 2019).

———. 2019. "North Dakota Frontier Counties." University of North Dakota, School of Medicine & Health Sciences. https://ruralhealth.und.edu/assets/2783-10703/nd-frontier.pdf (accessed August 13, 2019).

Cook, Won Kim. 2008. "Integrating Research and Action: A Systematic Review of Community-Based Participatory Research to Address Health Disparities in Environmental and Occupational Health in the USA." *Journal of Epidemiology and Community Health* 62(8): 668–676.

Emerson, Blair. 2017. "Native American Student Graduation Rates Lag Behind." *Bismark Tribune*, October 11. http://bismarcktribune.com/news/local/education/native-american-student-graduation-rates-lag-behind/article_669579ad-f197-5567-a2e7-f570cbdbb829.html (accessed November 16, 2018).

Federal Communications Commission. 2018. *Broadband Deployment Report No. Fcci 18-10*. Washington, DC: Federal Communications Commission. https://www.fcc.gov/reports-research/reports/broadband-progress-reports/2018-broadband-deployment-report (accessed November 16, 2018).

Forster, Hilary, and Mary Mueggenborg. 2015. *The HPOG University Partnership Research Grants*. OPRE 2015-84. Washington, DC: Office of Planning, Research and Evaluation, Administration for Children and Families, U.S. Department of Health and Human Services. https://www.acf.hhs.gov/sites/default/files/opre/cross_project_brief_hpogup_final_91115_reformatted_508_b2.pdf (accessed November 16, 2018).

Gefter, Liana, Judy Spahr, John Gruber, Sandra Ross, Laurie Watson, and

Barry Mann. 2018. "Addressing Health Disparities with School-Based Out-reach: The Health Career Academy Program." *Journal of Racial and Ethnic Health Disparities* 5(4): 700–711.

Grumbach, Kevin, and Rosalia Mendoza. 2008. "Disparities in Human Resources: Addressing the Lack of Diversity in the Health Professions." *Health Affairs* 27(2): 413–422.

Hergenrather, Kenneth C., Scott D. Rhodes, Chris Cowan, Gerta Bardhoshi, and Sara Pula. 2009. "Photovoice as Community-Based Participatory Research: A Qualitative Review." *American Journal of Health Behavior* 33(6): 686–698.

Heuer, Loretta, Patricia Moulton, and Marilyn G. Klug. (2013). "Community/ Academic Partnership Promoting Recruitment and Retention of American Indians into Nursing." North Dakota American Indian Nursing Workforce SON 2013-01 Practice Brief. https://www.ndsu.edu/fileadmin/nursing/ documents/HPOG_2013_Practice_Brief_.pdf (accessed June 14, 2019).

Heuer, Loretta, Mariella Young, Christine Leilani, Cynthia Lindquist, Marilyn G. Klug, Ann Wadsworth, and Jonathan Ripp. 2016. "The Impact of an Educational Intervention on American Indian Students' Interest in the Health Professions." *Journal of American Indian Higher Education* 27(4). https://tribalcollegejournal.org/impact-educational-intervention-american -indian-students-interest-health-professions/ (accessed November 20, 2018).

Holm, Jeffrey E., Nancy Vogeltanz-Holm, Dmitri Poltavski, and Leander McDonald. 2010. "Assessing Health Status, Behavioral Risks, and Health Disparities in American Indians Living on the Northern Plains of the U.S." *Public Health Reports* 125(1): 68–78.

Hong, Philip Young P., Joshua R. Polanin, and Terri D. Pigott. 2012. "Validation of the Employment Hope Scale: Measuring Psychological Self-Sufficiency among Low-Income Jobseekers." *Research on Social Work Practice* 22(3): 323–332.

Hyatt, Kim. 2017. "Award-Winning Documentary Aims to Recruit, Retain American Indian Nurses." *Bismarck Tribune*, December 21. http://bismarck tribune.com/news/state-and-regional/award-winning-documentary-aims -to-recruit-retain-american-indian-nurses/article_a25e38ef-fa5f-5907-ae9a -7ef42a884d00.html (accessed November 21, 2018).

Indian Health Service (IHS). 2015. *IHS Recruitment*. Rockford, MD: Indian Health Service. https://www.ihs.gov/dhps/programperformancedata/ recruitment/ (accessed November 21, 2018).

———. 2018. *Disparities*. Rockford, MD: Indian Health Service. https://www .ihs.gov/newsroom/factsheets/disparities/ (accessed June 12, 2019).

Leavitt, Peter A., Rebecca Covarrubias, Yvonne A. Perez, and Stephanie A.

Fryberg. 2015. "'Frozen in Time': The Impact of Native American Media Representations on Identity and Self-Understanding." *Journal of Social Issues* 71(1): 39–53.

Lee, Tanya H. 2017. "American Indian Nurses: Healing Grounded in Native Values." *Indian Country Today*, August 29. https://indiancountrymedia network.com/culture/health-wellness/american-indian-nurses-healing -grounded-native-values/ (accessed November 21, 2018).

Lindquist, Cynthia. 2016. "American Indian Voice: A National Perspective." In *Overcoming Educational Racism in the Community College: Creating Pathways to Success for Minority and Impoverished Student Populations,* Angela Long, ed. Virginia: Stylus, pp. 127–140.

Meit, Michael, Shannon TenBroeck, and Noelle Miesfeld. 2015. *Cankdeska Cikana Community College Tribal Health Profession Opportunity Grants (HPOG) Program—Overview and Preliminary Outcomes.* OPRE 2015-91. Washington, DC: Office of Planning, Research and Evaluation, Administration for Children and Families, U.S. Department of Health and Human Services: NORC at the University of Chicago, Red Star Innovations, National Indian Health Board. http://www.acf.hhs.gov/sites/default/files/ opre/year_4_practice_brief_cccc_9_21_15_b508pdf.pdf (accessed May 9, 2019).

Moulton, Patricia L. 2012. "North Dakota Nursing Needs Study: 2011 Licensed Nurse Supply Analysis." North Dakota Center for Nursing Research Publication No. 3. Fargo: North Dakota Center for Nursing. http://www.ndcenter fornursing.org/wp-content/uploads/2013/01/Licensed-Nurse-Results-2011 .pdf (accessed May 9, 2019).

———. 2017. North Dakota's Nursing Shortage Taskforce. Slide presentation. https://slideplayer.com/slide/16674763/ (accessed May 9, 2019).

National Center for Educational Statistics. 2017. "Undergraduate Enrollment." *The Condition of Education.* Washington, DC: National Center for Educational Statistics. https://nces.ed.gov/programs/coe/indicator_cha.asp (accessed May 9, 2019).

National Council on Aging. 2018. "Chronic Disease Management." Washington, DC: National Council on Aging. https://www.ncoa.org/healthy-aging/ chronic-disease/ (accessed May 9, 2019).

North Dakota Census Office. 2015. "Growing ND by the Numbers: Native American Population in North Dakota." December. Bismarck: North Dakota Census Office. https://www.commerce.nd.gov/uploads/8/Census NewsletterDec2015.pdf (accessed May 9, 2019).

North Dakota Compass. 2019. "North Dakota Population Trends." https:// www.ndcompass.org/trends/Population_Trends_June_12_2019.pdf (accessed June 14, 2019).

North Dakota Indian Affairs Commission. 2010. Statistics. Bismarck: North Dakota Indian Affairs Commission. http://www.nd.gov/indianaffairs/?id=76 (accessed May 9, 2019).

North Dakota State University School of Nursing (NDSU SON) and Cankdeska Cikana Community College (CCCC). 2013. "Building, Filling, and Proving the Nursing Pipeline: Efforts to Increase American Indian Involvement in North Dakota Healthcare Careers." Year 1 (2012–2013). https://www.ndsu.edu/fileadmin/nursing/documents/NursingPipelinePublication_032414HighRes.pdf (accessed May 9, 2019).

———. 2014. "Building, Filling, and Proving the Nursing Pipeline: Efforts to Increase American Indian Involvement in North Dakota Healthcare Careers." Year 2 (2013–2014) https://www.ndsu.edu/fileadmin/nursing/documents/NDS121002_NursingPublicationYear2_092314_HighRes.pdf (accessed May 9, 2019).

———. 2015. "Building, Filling, and Proving the Nursing Pipeline: Efforts to Increase American Indian Involvement in North Dakota Healthcare Careers." Year 3 (2014–2015). https://www.ndsu.edu/fileadmin/nursing/documents/NDS141004_HPOGYR3_060315_HR.pdf (accessed May 9, 2019).

———. 2016. "Building, Filling, and Proving the Nursing Pipeline: Efforts to Increase American Indian Involvement in North Dakota Healthcare Careers." Year 4 (2015–2016). https://www.ndsu.edu/fileadmin/nursing/documents/NDS151001_HPOG_DocumentYear4.pdf (accessed May 9, 2019).

Oliff, Helen. 2017. "Graduation Rates and American Indian Education." Addison, TX: Partnership with Native Americans. http://blog.nativepartnership.org/graduation-rates-american-indian-education/ (accessed May 9, 2019).

Schell, Kara, Alana Feguson, Rita Hamoline, Jennifer Shea, and Roanne Tomas-Maclean. 2009. "Photovoice as a Teaching Tool: Learning by Doing with Visual Methods." *International Journal of Teaching and Learning in Higher Education* 21(3): 340–352.

Sequist, Thomas D. 2009. "Health Careers for Native American Students: Challenges and Opportunities for Enrichment Program Design." *Journal of Interprofessional Care* 21(2): 20–30.

Stedman-Smith, Maggie, Patricia M. McGovern, Cynthia J. Peden-McAlpine, Linda R. Kingery, and Kathryn J. Draeger. 2012. "Photovoice in the Red River Basin of North: A Systematic Evaluation of a Community-Academic Partnership." *Health Promotion Practice* 13(5): 599–607.

Suez Mittman, Ilana, and Louis W. Sullivan. 2011. "Forming State Collaborations to Diversify the Nation's Health Workforce: The Experience of the Sullivan Alliance to Transform the Health Professions." *Journal of Genetic Counseling* 20(6): 547–555.

Tapia, Rafael. 2017. "Challenges to Education within Native American Communities." Addison, TX: Partnership with Native Americans.

University of North Dakota College of Nursing. 2011. "UND RAIN Program to Partner with Cankdeska Cikana Community College." *University Letter*, University of North Dakota. http://undnews.areavoices.com/2011/02/24/und-rain-program-to-partner-with-cankdeska-cikana-community-college/ http://blogs.und.edu/uletter/2011/02/und-rain-program-to-partner-with-cankdeska-cikana-community-college/ (accessed May 9, 2019).

U.S. Census Bureau. 2015. "North Dakota American Indian Health Profile: Population." Washington, DC: Census Bureau. https://www.ndhealth.gov/HealthData/CommunityHealthProfiles/American%20Indian%20Community%20Profile.pdf (accessed May 9, 2019).

———. 2016. "2012–2016 American Community Survey 5-Year Estimates." American Fact Finder. Washington, DC: Census Bureau. https://factfinder.census.gov/faces/tableservices/jsf/pages/productview.xhtml?src=bkmk (accessed May 9, 2019).

U.S. Department of the Interior. 2014. *2013 American Indian Population and Labor Force Report*. Washington, DC: Department of the Interior.

Wamono, Anthony, Loretta Jean Heuer, and Patricia Moulton. 2016. "North Dakota Nursing Demographic Mapping Study." Unpublished paper.

Weintraub, Jennifer, Julia Walker, Loretta Heuer, Marisa Oishi, Khushbu Upadhyay, Vivian Huang, Cynthia Lindquist, Linda F. Cushman, and Jonathan Ripp. 2015. "Developing Capacity for the American Indian Health Professional Workforce: An Academic-Community Partnership in Spirit Lake, North Dakota." *Annals of Global Health* 81(2): 283–289.

8

The Importance of Social Support for Low-Income Job Seekers

Cheryl A. Hyde
Karin M. Eyrich-Garg
Temple University

The conventional focus of many job training programs is to increase the human capital of participants so they can compete more effectively in the labor market. The acquisition of more education, work experience, technical expertise, and "soft" skills (such as interviewing and self-presentation) are critical, but they may not be sufficient for labor market success. This is particularly true for low-income and chronically unemployed individuals, who, despite participation in job training programs, often do not secure employment that will support them and their families. Consequently, these individuals move from various forms of public assistance to dead-end jobs, and sometimes back again. Neither option offers much financial security, let alone meets the overarching goal of many training programs—that of "participant economic self-sufficiency" (Brodsky and Ovwigho 2002; Cooney 2010; Gray 2005; Dworsky and Courtney 2007; Hong, Sheriff, and Naeger 2009; Kim 2009; Levine 2013; Seefeldt 2017; Turner, Danziger, and Seefeldt 2006). Structural barriers, such as the scarcity of jobs, may be mentioned as contributing factors to troubling labor market outcomes, but greater emphasis typically is placed on the training participant's motivation, behavior, and/or skill acquisition. In other words, inadequate human capital ultimately is believed to account for poor employment outcomes.

While matching one's human capital with employers' job requirements is essential, there are countless other factors that impact training and employment success (Barrera, Caples, and Tein 2001; Cleaveland 2002; Cooney 2010; Gingrich 2010). In this chapter, we examine the social support of low-income participants in a federally funded health professions training program in order to understand the impact of this relational context. What is the extent of their social support, and did participation in the training program bolster this assistance? Given our findings, we delineate implications for workforce development programs, including those supported by the Health Profession Opportunity Grants (HPOG) program.

SOCIAL SUPPORT

Social support, specifically group and network membership, is a primary means of estimating one's social capital, which concerns the presence and value of relationships generated through various forms of social participation (Grootaert et al. 2004; Lin 2000). The kind and quality of resources and support generated by one's actual and potential social capital can influence further accumulation of human capital—an individual's skill sets and knowledge levels (Brass et al. 2004; Casciano and Massey 2008; Flap and Boxman 2001; Ioannides and Topa 2010; McDonald, Benton, and Warner 2012; Phillips 2010; Migheli 2011). Conventionally, human capital is measured or approximated by level of education, training, and workforce experience (e.g., Becker 1964; Mincer 1958), though there also are efforts to recognize the value of "accumulated wisdom" and "commonsense" factors (Bottone and Sena 2011; Marimon and Quadrini 2011). Various forms of social capital allow individuals to more readily acquire and more effectively utilize their human capital.

There is considerable research on the relationship between social capital, specifically social support networks and group memberships, and labor market success across a variety of locations and sectors (for example, see Gezinski [2011]; Stoloff, Glanville, and Bienenstock [1999]; O'Connor [2013]; Tassier and Menczer [2007]). Networks and groups filter information and resource access, serving as critical conduits for job opportunities (Bertrand, Luttmer, and Mullainathan 2000; Chapple 2002; Marin 2012, 2013). These memberships, however, do not need to be solely employment focused. Network and group diversity, and on a broader level social capital that "bridges" an individual's group(s) to other groups, are key. The early work of Granovetter (1973) on "the strength of weak ties" suggested that network connections could vary in size and strength and were most useful when they facilitated the expansion of opportunity pathways or resource options. Certain types of networks, such as friendship based, can have the added benefit of enhancing labor force participation (Aguilera 2002). There also is evidence that jobs, or more precisely the workplace, provide individuals with access to new or enhanced groups and networks that help them accumulate more social capital over time (Brand and Burgard 2008; Dahlin, Kelly, and Moen 2008). Conversely, individuals experiencing periods of unemployment lose network ties and opportunities (Brand and Burgard 2008).

Potential and actual social support networks, and hence social capital, typically vary over the life course as life events, such as parenthood or retirement, result in access to new networks and groups and perhaps the loss of others (Brand and Burgard 2008; Fiori and Jager 2012; McDonald and Mair 2010). Network development also differs by cultural attributes. Men and women create, access, and pursue different kinds of networks, with the former more likely to build social capital resources that result in accumulated opportunities and eventually greater career options (McDonald 2011; McDonald, Lin, and Ao 2009; Parks-Yancy, DiTomaso, and Post 2006; Stoloff, Glanville, and Bienenstock 1999). Upper- and middle-class individuals have more robust, diverse, and resource-rich networks than do working- or lower-class individuals who tend to have smaller, more insular networks (Dahlin, Kelly, and Moen 2008; Horvat, Weininger, and Lareau 2003). Further, Desmond (2012) found that in high-poverty areas, individuals developed "disposable" ties with relatively new and unfamiliar acquaintances in order to obtain resources in times of crisis. Such connections, however, were "brittle and fleeting" and resulted in instability and mistrust over time.

In this chapter, we focus on the social support networks and primary group memberships of participants in the Health Information Professions (HIP) Career Pathway Initiative, which is part of the HPOG program. We examine this aspect of their social capital to determine if it expanded while they were in the training program.

TRAINING PROGRAM PARTNER

Our HPOG training program partner was the HIP program, which was coordinated and staffed primarily by the Center for Social Policy and Community Development at Temple University. Program partners included District 1199C Training and Upgrade Fund (partnership between National Union of Hospital and Healthcare Employees) and 50 acute care hospitals, Philadelphia Workforce Investment Board, Philadelphia Department of Public Welfare, Philadelphia Workforce Development, and area health care/medical employers. The focus on health profession training was in response to labor market predictions that the health/medical sector, particularly health informatics, would experience substantial employment growth over the next few years and offer good opportunities for employment with decent wages and benefits. Health sector jobs tend to be concentrated in urban areas, which makes health job training initiatives a potentially important antipoverty measure (Cheung and Aiken 2006; Nelson and Wolf-Powers 2010).

HIP was designed and run as a five-tier training program in various aspects of health information management:

- Tier 1: Medical office and accounts/electronic health records
- Tier 2: Coding specialist—AHIMA certification
- Tier 3: Associate's degree (with transferable credits) from the Community College of Philadelphia with transferable credits to Temple University
- Tier 4: Bachelor Degree in health information management from Temple University
- Tier 5: Master's degree in health informatics from Temple University.

Individuals could enter at any tier for which they were qualified. For example, a student would receive tuition and other assistance if she were accepted into the health information management major (Tier 4) at Temple University. Although the tier program was designed for participants to move from one tier to the next, most HIP participants completed only one tier and then pursued employment; the most common progression was Tier 1 to Tier 2 so that needed certifications could be obtained. Using a participant-centered approach, HIP offered, in addition to the employment training or tuition reimbursement (depending on the tier), career coaching, child care and transportation assistance, interviewing techniques, and job placement/internship guidance.

For our research, we focused solely on Tier 1 participants. To qualify for HIP/Tier 1, individuals had to pass basic math and writing literacy tests (at the 8th grade level); participate in a series of interviews and orientation sessions that assessed motivation, engagement, and self-presentation; and have no criminal background. The primary target population was Temporary Assistance for Needy Families (TANF) recipients, although the program expanded its pool to individuals at or below 250 percent of the federal poverty line. Two years into the initiative, the "Bridge to HIP" program was instituted for potential enrollees who did not pass the literacy test(s) but otherwise were eligible for Tier 1. This program provided intensive math and reading tutoring so that these individuals could then qualify for Tier 1. A total of 263 students in 13 cohorts completed Tier 1 over the five-year period from June 2010 to August 2015. Program staff included two course instructors who taught medical billing classes, two career coaches who worked with participants while they attended classes, two career placement coordinators who worked with participants once they had completed the training classes, a "Bridge to HIP" staff person, a program coordinator, and a program evaluator.

METHODS

Because our research began after several Tier 1 cohorts had completed the training program, we were able to follow only 181 participants in 8 cohorts from June 2013 to February 2016. Data were obtained through several sources as follows:

Training participant interviews. Individual interviews ($N = 181$) were conducted at program intake, exit, six months postexit and one year postexit. Unless otherwise noted, data used in this analysis are from program intake and six months postexit. The interview protocol has two components, the Arizona Social Support Interview Schedule (ASSIS) (Barrera 1980) and the Social Environment Questionnaire (SEQ). The

ASSIS measures perceived and actual network size, satisfaction with support, and need for support across seven domains (intimate interaction, material aid, advice, positive feedback, physical assistance, social participation, and negative interactions). The SEQ, designed specifically for this study, was composed of items from various social capital and community attribute engagement protocols (Christakopoulou, Dawson, and Gari 2001; Grootaert et al. 2004; Long and Perkins 2003; Roper Center for Public Opinion Research 2001; Smith, Hout, and Marsden 2013; U.S. Census Bureau 2012). Interviews averaged 90 minutes in length and were taped and transcribed.

Alumni focus group interviews. Eight focus groups were held with program alumni (N = 72). These group interviews covered how and why they joined the training program, feedback on the training program, current employment and educational activities, and current challenges and concerns. The focus groups were designed to be conversational. Each focus group lasted about two hours. The interviews were audio taped and transcribed; detailed observation notes were done.

Staff interviews. In-depth interviews were conducted with nine HIP staff members. These interviews focused on what the staff viewed as the strengths, accomplishments, challenges, and barriers of the training program participants, and reflections on the design and implementation of the training program. All interviews, which were 60–90 minutes in duration, were taped and transcribed.

For all interviews, quantitative data were cleaned and entered into SPSS for analysis. Qualitative data were thematically coded and analyzed per the constant comparative method (Charmaz 2006; Corbin and Strauss 2008; Cresswell 2007). All respondents were deidentified; any training participant and staff names used in publications and presentations are pseudonyms.

FINDINGS

Respondent characteristics are presented in Table 8.1. At intake, the sample was primarily African American women, half of whom have

Table 8.1 Respondent Characteristics at Intake (N = 181)

Item	Respondents
Age ± SD	36.74 ± 10.64
Female (%)	80.2
Race (%)	
White/Caucasian	5.5
Black/African American	83.4
Asian American/Pacific Islander	3.9
Hispanic/Latino	3.9
Other	3.0
Education completed (%)	
< High school	1.7
High school diploma or GED	30.4
Some college	56.5
College degree	10.5
Advanced degree	1.1

SOURCE: Authors' calculations.

some college education. The mean age was 37 (focus groups participants were older, with mean age of 48).

Group memberships are important aspects of network—and more broadly social capital—formation. Data on group and organizational membership at time of intake and six months postexit are presented in Table 8.2. At intake and again at six months postexit, the most frequently mentioned membership was in a religious group/organization. No other organization comes close in terms of respondent membership. There were two important changes: membership in professional or business associations rose from 6.6 percent (intake) to 31.3 percent (6 months postexit), and membership in a group that meets exclusively on the internet grew from 8.8 percent (intake) to 19.6 percent (six months postexit). Both of these increases can be attributed to maintaining membership and participating in several medical coding certification associations necessary for employment. Most of the respondents' primary groups had memberships that were all or most of the same race and gender; there was some variation with similar education (see Figure 8.1).

Findings for the social support networks of program participants at the time of intake and six months postexit are presented in Table 8.3. Potential networks are those individuals whom the respondent might

Table 8.2 Respondent Social Participation in Groups or Organizations at Intake and Six Months Postexit

Item	Intake (%) (N = 181)	Exit + 6 months (%) (N = 112)
Member of religious community	55.2	57.1
Attending religious services: (N = 168)		
< Few times per year	19.0	18.0
A few times per year	23.2	25.2
1–2 times per month	14.9	18.0
Almost every week	11.9	9.9
Every week	31.0	28.8
Attending non-worship activities in past six months (Time 1, N = 100; Time 3, N = 64)	57.0	54.7
Participated in/members of:		
Outdoor activity club/adult sports club	8.3	9.0
Youth organization	13.3	15.2
Parents' association (PTA/PTO, school service group)	21.0	18.8
Veteran's group	1.1	3.6
Neighborhood association/block group/crime watch	15.6	15.2
Charity, service club, or fraternal organization	12.2	13.5
Labor or workers' union	5.0	7.2
Professional or business association	6.6	31.3
Ethnic, nationality, or civil rights organization	6.1	12.5
Other public interest groups/political action groups	9.9	8.1
Literary, art, discussion or study group	23.2	13.5
Other hobby group or societies	11.7	9.0
Support or self-help groups (e.g., AA, Al-Anon)	10.5	7.2
Group that meets exclusively on internet	8.8	19.6
Other kinds of clubs or organizations	13.9	10.8
Primary group works with other groups in the neighborhood? (Time 1, N = 122; Time 3, N = 88)	74.6	70.5
Primary group works with other groups outside the neighborhood? (Time 1, N = 117; Time 3, N = 87)	74.4	73.5

SOURCE: Authors' calculations.

**Figure 8.1 Respondents' Primary Social Group—Percentage of Group
Members with Same Race, Gender, or Education**

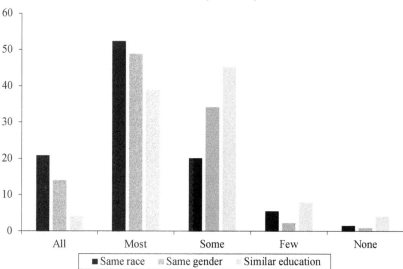

SOURCE: Authors' calculations.

call upon for various forms of assistance. Used networks are those individuals who were called upon within the 30 days prior to the interview. The average total network for the respondents was 9.46 persons at intake and 9.93 persons at six months postexit, which means that respondents essentially added (on average) half a person to their networks during and immediately after the training program. Used networks were comparable for both points in time at 8.06 and 8.52 individuals, respectively, again indicating limited growth in the size of total networks that were accessed in the month prior to the interview. Social participation constituted the single largest type of potential and used networks.

Figure 8.2 presents data on who the members were in these networks at six months postexit. Respondents overwhelmingly relied on friends and then various family members for support, as this example illustrates:

> When it comes to taking classes on Tuesdays and Thursdays, my mom is primarily the one I rely on to pick my kids up. She keeps them while I'm in class because I don't get out of work until 5:30. Regularly, she's the one that picks my son up from school. —Arlene

Table 8.3 Average Number of Individuals in Potential and Used Support Networks by Type of Network at Intake and Six Months Postexit

Type of network	N	Intake			Six months postexit	
		Potential	Used		Potential	Used
		Mean no. of individuals	Mean no. of individuals	N	Mean no. of individuals	Mean no. of individuals
Total network	180	9.5 (3.7)	8.1 (3.4)	112	9.9 (4.6)	8.5 (3.9)
Intimate interaction	180	3.2 (2.1)	2.7 (2.0)	112	3.3 (2.1)	2.9 (1.9)
Material aid	180	3.1 (2.1)	1.6 (1.6)	112	3.1 (2.2)	1.3 (1.6)
Advice	180	3.1 (2.0)	2.4 (1.9)	112	3.2 (2.1)	2.4 (1.7)
Positive feedback	180	4.1 (2.3)	3.5 (2.2)	112	3.8 (2.4)	3.1 (2.2)
Favors/help	180	3.1 (2.3)	2.4 (1.9)	112	3.5 (2.1)	2.8 (2.0)
Employment	151	2.1 (1.6)	1.5 (1.6)	112	2.5 (1.6)	1.6 (1.5)
Social participation	180	4.6 (3.0)	4.0 (3.0)	112	4.4 (2.6)	3.9 (2.5)
Negative interactions	180	2.1 (1.6)	1.6 (1.4)	112	2.1 (1.9)	1.7 (1.8)

NOTE: Standard deviations in parentheses.
SOURCE: Authors' calculations.

Given that religious organizations were the primary membership groups for these respondents, it is interesting to note that religious leaders and members are not represented to the degree one might expect in these networks. Also note that the only HIP-related network members were the career coaches, who were named by 19 of the 112 respondents.

Staff noticed the variations in levels of support as well as the quality of support for training participants:

> But what I've seen is that it [family support] is usually a very broad range. You have some students who are very supported, have a lot of people in their corner, you know what I mean? To support, to help them get through things. There are students who have no job, no income, and we're like, "Well, how are you getting through?"

Figure 8.2 Members of Respondent Networks by Number of Times Mentioned by Respondents, Six Months Postexit

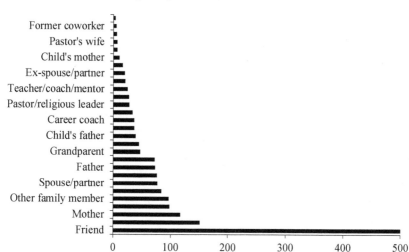

SOURCE: Authors' calculations.

And they're like, "Well, my fiancé is really adamant that I finish this program," or "My mother is gonna help me with my child and we're living with her and she's really being supportive." You know? And then you have the other side of the spectrum where, you know, you have students who have no support, nobody, no one cares. And they sometimes struggle, you know, a little bit when it gets to the point where we're getting close, that we're getting further into the training and, you know, you're starting to lose some of your, your, I keep calling it oomph. But you know, you're losing some of your determination. And the students who have support systems kind of have people to kind of say, "Keep going, keep pushing, we got your back, we're here for you." —Don, career coach

Other staff suggested that some networks, such as familial ones, actually were *impediments* to participant success:

On my caseload it's always drama with the extended family members. So you really have a couple of close family members that they're close to. Again even with those family members there's issues. So communication issues, conflict, there's a lot of conflict going on. —Sarah, career coach

You know, sometimes they [training participants] are the one person trying to do something positive, and they're also the person in their family who are taking care of the mother, have a brother who's an alcoholic, have somebody else who's dealing with something or other. —Serena, Bridge coordinator

Of particular concern in our study was the connection between networks and employment status. Table 8.4 presents the employment status of participants at six months postexit. Just over one-third of the respondents were actively looking for employment. Almost half of the respondents were employed in health sector jobs, though according to the respondents, few obtained positions in medical billing or coding:

It took a while, but finally my Career Placement Counselor—I was still working as a stylist—she called me, and I was very frustrated. This was in 2013. She asked what I was doing, and I told her I hate my job. She told me she'd get me out of there. AmeriHealth was hiring. So, I went in there, and that's where I've been. It's been about a year and a half now. . . . I'm working in customer service. I work with members, and doctors, and providers. I help people who are recently enrolled into the health insurance company. It's a Medicaid funded program, so I'm using all of the things I learned on a daily basis. The salary is decent. It's very challenging because there are a lot of time restraints on calls and stuff like that. It's [a] stable job, even though it's not in what I was trained for. —Karen

Referring again to Table 8.3, at intake the respondents' employment networks were just over 2.0 (potential) and 1.5 (used) individuals, suggesting that participants had only 2.0 individuals they thought they

Table 8.4 Employment Status of Participants at Six Months Postexit (N = 112)

Status	Frequency (%)
Transitioned from unemployment to health sector job	37.5
Transitioned from non-health-sector job to health sector job	8.0
Actively seeking employment	38.4
Employed in non-health-sector job	9.1
Continuing education	3.6
Caring for family member and not employed	2.7

SOURCE: Authors' calculations.

could count on and fewer than 2.0 individuals who they engaged with regarding employment. At six months postexit employment networks were only slightly larger at 2.5 (potential) individuals and 1.6 (used) individuals. This suggests that employment network development or enhancement did not happen during the training program. Indeed, one source of frustration among participants was the perceived lack of assistance in terms of employment networking done by HIP staff:

> I was under the expectation that after graduation, or during that time, they would have me matched with an internship. It never happened. So, I found some other things to do. —Joe

> I think that in terms of job placement, I think that some things should've been more available, especially, excuse me, this being a program run out of [university]. Temple has a big umbrella. This is medical billing and coding. They have a hospital. No one in my team to my understanding was even—or how they do the job placement was place with a facility, a hospital, with Temple, one or two out of each cohort. I think they could've been more ready, should've been more prepared to place us coming out. —Yolanda

> I was under the impression when I joined Cohort 10 that at the end there would be interviews lined up; that the career placement folks had the inside with different companies. But, it was more or less that you go and you find positions. The ones that they did have—the pay was so low that I had to tell my career coach that I cannot work for that pay. It was really low. I have a mortgage and big bills. —Maryanne

> Back in the day when I went through similar programs they had job placement. After you finish a program, they call you up and tell you to meet with the manager somewhere. You went, and you got the job. That's the only part that's missing from this program, the job placement side of it. They should base it on your merits, and send you out, and vouch for you to an employer. "She was excellent. Give her the job." None of that. —Ethel

> I'm actually a temp, and I got it through a temp program. And so now I'm actually looking for full-time. . . . I was looking the whole time, but I'm looking through Temple since I'm up here. [interviewer: Have you reached back out to the HIP program?] Actually, Betty is my placement coordinator, but they haven't really been that helpful. I like the program, that's not it, I just feel like

*they should have a better way of setting you up with a job after-
wards, or at least finding a way to get paid. —Connie*

These comments suggest that participants had unfilled expectations
regarding assistance in securing employment. Some of these expectations are based on the belief that the university system would or should
be a source of predetermined jobs and that HIP staff would make the
connections:

*It was presented like, all right, boom, as soon as you finish, boom,
it's a job. Boom, right here, bang-bang-bang-bang-bang. All right,
sounds good. All right, cool. I'm interested. And then it's like, all
right, I done went through like five, six interviews and nothing.
—Moe*

Program staff, however, viewed the networking for jobs differently
and placed responsibility on the program participants. In some cases,
staff encouraged participants to develop the skill of networking:

*Well, number one, I think it builds their confidence to be able to
talk to people to build networks. A lot of times the students don't
have people they can—they don't network at all, you know? And
one of the things that I do talk to them about is the importance of
networking, the importance of building your network. And one of
the main things I say to them is, if you consider the people who you
surround yourself with, if you're the smartest, the most successful,
the most driven person in that group, then you need to expand your
horizons to get more people into your network to help pull you up.
—Sarah, career coach*

A more common view, however, was that staff were quite critical of
participants' networking capabilities:

*Employment, oh man, they don't have any idea about what to do
with employment networks. . . . They're clueless. —Joanna, career
placement coordinator*

*[Many students have] good social support, but they suck at social
networking. Like, they're horrible at it. They're very insular. They
often, you know, I push them to like to connect with people and
build professional networks. It's not that they don't know how;
it's just that they don't want to. . . . They're insecure. They lack
confidence. They're very hesitant to connect to people who aren't
from their own community or aren't from their own racial group or
gender group or religious group. It just ends up being very hard to*

get them to see that they have to go beyond your social identity in order to connect with people that could be really valuable to them. A lot of them just don't do it. They make excuses for why they don't do. They just don't do it. —Karen, program coordinator

In interviews, participants mentioned that the class instructors and career coaches were helpful, largely because they felt motivated by them and that they were invested in their success:

So, there were instructors that were very dedicated to what they were doing, very regimented. But they pushed you, and they helped you along. They never—it definitely was no student left behind. . . . They were there to help you along, and well, if you can't do it, stay after with me, and we'll talk about what's going on. So you would see the care. So they were very dedicated to what they were doing. —Janet

Yet, as noted above, only a few participants named the coaches as members of their posttraining networks. In contrast, the work of the career placement coordinators was viewed with disappointment, largely because the facilitating of employment pathways and opportunities was seen as inadequate.

DISCUSSION

We have presented data on group membership and social support networks for low-income urban residents in a health professions training program. To summarize, their primary group memberships, the most popular of which was in a religious organization, were largely homogeneous in terms of race, gender, and education. Their social support networks were small at the outset and expanded only slightly while going through the training program. Training participants relied heavily on friends for assistance. Few respondents included training program staff in their six-month postexit networks.

Our research suggests that the respondents have generated bonding social capital that is small and homogeneous in scope. Attention is on primary group memberships and friends in a small support network. There is little evidence of creating either bridging or linking social capital, though one positive change was the increased membership in professional/business associations and internet groups postexit, both of which were attributable to accessing medical coding and health profession sites. Nonetheless, largely absent from their networks are individuals who could help with the generation of bridging or linking capital, something critical for improved access to employment and career opportunities after training. These findings are consistent with other studies of economically vulnerable individuals and communities—largely insular worlds in which trust and relationships are with a small number of similarly situated individuals and connections with opportunity pathways and institutions virtually nonexistent (Desmond 2012; Van Eijk 2010; Levine 2013; Seefeldt 2017; Smallacombe 2006).

Training participants and program staff had different views on networking. The participants wanted more help from the program in making employment connections—a desire that echoes some of best practices in the employment training literature (Hendra et al. 2016; King 2014; Strawn 2010). In contrast, staff viewed the lack of employment networking as a *participant* skill deficit. While some staff indicated that they encouraged participants to network, there was little evidence that networking strategies were taught or that the staff helped to create networks for participants to access. In other words, staff focused largely on an "improve human capital" approach rather than expanding their approaches to include viable social network development.

LESSONS LEARNED

How can the findings about the social support of low-income participants in a job training program inform future development of similar initiatives? Our recommendations are grounded in the need to incorporate social capital development into workforce training programs rather than rely solely or primarily on human capital development. Programs need to understand the relational context of participants, and then help them strategically expand connections.

Networking is not just a key strategy in finding employment but also a skill that needs to be learned and honed. Rather than only encouraging participants to network, program staff need to develop or codevelop networks and then assist participants in accessing them, and include presentation and follow-up strategies. Participants may not access networks because, as our findings suggest, they don't have networks with sufficient scope or depth. Relying primarily on participants to network is likely a setup for failure in the form of unemployment or underemployment. Events such as job fairs or employer "meet and greets," as examples, would have aided this study's participants. Partnering with churches (primary group membership) in the catchment area to hold employment events could be critically important. In other words, training programs need to incorporate network development and access as one of their component strategies. This also necessitates significant employer engagement, a hallmark in successful sector-based training programs. It was not apparent that cultivating such employer relations occurred within the HIP program.

Our study's participants interacted with, and felt differently about, the career coaches compared to the career placement coordinators. The former worked with the participants over an extended period of time and in the process developed closer relationships with them. In contrast, the latter had relatively little time with the participants, as they worked with them during a smaller window between the conclusion of classes and program exit. In their networks, the only staff mentioned were the career coaches, probably because of the closer ties that were developed within the program. Programs may want to adopt more of a casework model in which a participant is assigned to one staff person from intake to exit. Given the dearth of social support networks, having a staff person invested in their success through the program's duration may prove to be an important motivator, as well as resource, for participants. We also anticipate that program staff would be more likely to appear in a participant's social support network.

Training programs also may need to consider the extent to which a participant's existing network is a help or a hindrance. Staff noted that in some cases, family or friends served to sabotage (intentionally or not) a participant's efforts. Evaluation of the quality or nature of networks, not just their existence, needs to be part of the broader work with training participants. At strategic times during the training program, it may be that family, rather than individual, engagement is needed for participant success.

The training participants in our study engaged in a rigorous program in order to acquire knowledge and skills needed for medical coding and electronic billing jobs. And while some achieved employment success, most of the participants did not find jobs in the areas for which they had trained. Based on our research, we suggest that labor market success can't rely solely on the individual. Rather, context matters, and in our case, that context was group memberships and social support networks. In addition to the development of human capital, job training programs also need to facilitate social capital development, specifically the "bridging" or "linking" kind that connects network-poor individuals with opportunity pathways.

References

Aguilera, Michael Bernabé. 2002. "The Impact of Social Capital on Labor Force Participation: Evidence from the 2000 Social Capital Benchmark Survey." *Social Science Quarterly* 83(3): 853–874.

Barrera, Manuel. 1980. "A Method for the Assessment of Social Support Networks in Community Survey Research." *Connections* 3(3): 8–13.

Barrera, Manuel, Heather Caples, and Jenn-Yun Tein. 2001. "The Psychological Sense of Economic Hardship: Measurement Models, Validity, and Cross-Ethnic Equivalence for Urban Families." *American Journal of Community Psychology* 29(3): 493–517.

Becker, Gary. 1964. *Human Capital: A Theoretical and Empirical Analysis with Special Reference to Education*, 3rd ed. Chicago: University of Chicago Press.

Bertrand, Marianne, Erzo F. P. Luttmer, and Sendhil Mullainathan. 2000. "Network Effects and Welfare Cultures." *Quarterly Journal of Economics* 115(3): 1019–1055.

Bottone, Germana, and Vania Sena. 2011. "Human Capital: Theoretical and Empirical Insights." *American Journal of Economics and Sociology* 70(2): 401–423.

Brand, Jennie E., and Sarah A. Burgard. 2008. "Job Displacement and Social Participation over the Lifecourse: Findings for a Cohort of Joiners." *Social Forces* 87(1): 211–242.

Brass, Daniel J., Joesph Galaskiewicz, Heinrich R. Greve, and Wenpin Tsai. 2004. "Taking Stock of Networks and Organizations: A Multilevel Perspective." *Academy of Management Journal* 47(6): 795–817.

Brodsky, Anne E., and Pamela Caudill Ovwigho. 2002. "Swimming against the Tide: Connecting Low-Income Women to Living Wage Jobs." *Journal of Poverty* 6(3): 63–88.

Casciano, Rebecca, and Douglas S. Massey. 2008. "Neighborhoods, Employment, and Welfare Use: Assessing the Influence of Neighborhood Socioeconomic Composition." *Social Science Research* 37(2): 544–558.

Chapple, Karen. 2002. "'I Name It and I Claim It—In the Name of Jesus, This Job Is Mine': Job Search, Networks, and Careers for Low-Income Women." *Economic Development Quarterly* 16(4): 294–313.

Charmaz, Kathy. 2006. *Constructing Grounded Theory: A Practical Guide through Qualitative Analysis*. Thousand Oaks, CA: Sage.

Cheung, Robin, and Linda H. Aiken. 2006. "Hospital Initiatives to Support a Better-Educated Workforce." *Journal of Nursing Administration* 36(7/8): 357–362.

Christakopoulou, Sophia, Jon Dawson, and Aikaterini Gari. 2001. "The Community Well-Being Questionnaire: Theoretical Context and Initial Assessment of Its Reliability and Validity." *Social Indicators Research* 56(3): 321–351.

Cleaveland, Chad. 2002. "Why Don't These People Just Get a Job? Fragile Work Attachment in a Cohort of Welfare Recipients." *Social Work Abstracts* 38(3): 1318.

Cooney, Kate. 2010. "The Promise and Pitfalls of Employer-Linked Job Training for Disadvantaged Workers." *Administration in Social Work* 34(1): 27–48.

Corbin, Juliet, and Anselm Strauss. 2008. *Basics of Qualitative Research*. 3rd ed. Thousand Oaks, CA: Sage.

Cresswell, John. 2007. *Qualitative Inquiry and Research Design: Choosing among Five Approaches*. 2nd ed. Thousand Oaks, CA: Sage.

Dahlin, Eric, Erin Kelly, and Phyllis Moen. 2008. "Is Work the New Neighborhood? Social Ties in the Workplace, Family, and Neighborhood." *Sociological Quarterly* 49(4): 719–736.

Desmond, Matthew. 2012. "Disposable Ties and the Urban Poor." *American Journal of Sociology* 117(5): 1295–1335.

Dworsky, Amy, and Mark E. Courtney. 2007. "Barriers to Employment among TANF Applicants and Their Consequences for Self-Sufficiency." *Families in Society* 88(3): 379–389.

Fiori, Katherine L., and Justin Jager. 2012. "The Impact of Social Support Networks on Mental and Physical Health in the Transition to Older Adulthood: A Longitudinal, Pattern-Centered Approach." *International Journal of Behavioral Development* 36(2): 117–129.

Flap, Renk, and Ed Boxman. 2001. "Getting Started: The Influence of Social Capital on the Start of the Occupational Career." In *Social Capital: Theory and Research*, Nan Lin, Karen Cook, and Ronald S. Burt, eds. New York: Aldine de Gruyter, pp. 159–184.

Gezinski, Lindsay Blair. 2011. "Mediating Impact of Social Capital and Human Capital on Employment Outcome among Single Women Who Use Welfare: A Structural Equation Model." PhD diss., Ohio State University.

Gingrich, Luanne Good. 2010. "Single Mothers, Work(fare), and Managed Precariousness." *Journal of Progressive Human Services* 21(2): 107–135.

Granovetter, Mark S. 1973. "The Strength of Weak Ties." *American Journal of Sociology* 78(6): 1360–1380.

Gray, Karen A. 2005. "Women Who Succeeded in Leaving Public Assistance for a Living-Wage Job." *Qualitative Social Work* 4(3): 309–326.

Grootaert, Christiaan, Deepa Narayan, Veronica Nyhan Jones, and Michael Woolcock. 2004. "Measuring Social Capital: An Integrated Questionnaire." World Bank Working Paper No. 18. Washington, DC: World Bank.

Hendra, Richard, David H. Greenberg, Gayle Hamilton, Ari Oppenheim, Alexandra Pennington, Kelsey Schaberg, and Betsy L. Tessler. 2016. *Encouraging Evidence on a Sector-Focused Advancement Strategy: Two-Year Impacts from the WorkAdvance Demonstration.* New York: MDRC.

Hong, Philip Young P., Vamadu A. Sheriff, and Sandra R. Naeger. 2009. "A Bottom-Up Definition of Self-Sufficiency: Voices from Low-Income Job-seekers." *Qualitative Social Work* 8(3): 357–376.

Horvat, Erin McNamara, Elliot B. Weininger, and Annette Lareau. 2003. "From Social Ties to Social Capital: Class Differences in the Relations between Schools and Parent Networks." *American Educational Research Journal* 40(2): 319–351.

Ioannides, Yannis M., and Giorgio Topa. 2010. "Neighborhood Effects: Accomplishments and Looking beyond Them." *Journal of Regional Science* 50(1): 343–362.

Kim, Jeounghee. 2009. "Does Job Training Yield Positive Outcomes for Women on Public Assistance?" *Journal of Policy Practice* 8: 204–223.

King, Christopher T. 2014. "Sectoral Workforce and Related Strategies: What We Know… And What We Need to Know." In *Connecting People to Work: Workforce Intermediaries and Sector Strategies*, Maureen Conway and Robert P. Giloth, eds. New York: American Assembly, pp. 209–238.

Levine, Judith. 2013. *Ain't No Trust: How Bosses, Boyfriends, and Bureaucrats Fail Low-Income Mothers and Why It Matters.* Berkeley: University of California Press.

Lin, Nan. 2000. "Inequality in Social Capital." *Contemporary Sociology* 29(6): 785–795.

Long, D. Adam, and Douglas D. Perkins. 2003. "Confirmatory Factor Analysis of the Sense of Community Index and Development of a Brief SCI." *Journal of Community Psychology* 31(3): 279–296.

Marimon, Ramon, and Vincenzo Quadrini. 2011. "Competition, Human Capital, and Income Inequality with Limited Commitment." *Journal of Economic Theory* 146(3): 976–1008.

Marin, Alexandra. 2012. "Don't Mention It: Why People Don't Share Job Information, When They Do, and Why It Matters." *Social Networks* 34: 181–192.

———. 2013. "Who Can Tell? Network Diversity, Within-Industry Networks, and Opportunities to Share Job Information." *Sociological Forum* 28(2): 350–372.

McDonald, Steve. 2011. "What's in the 'Old Boys' Networks? Accessing Social Capital in Gendered and Racialized Networks." *Social Network* 33: 317–330.

McDonald, Steve, Richard A. Benton, and David F. Warner. 2012. "Dual Embeddedness: Informal Job Matching and Labor Market Institutions in the United States and Germany." *Social Forces* 91(1): 75–97.

McDonald, Steve, Nan Lin, and Dan Ao. 2009. "Networks of Opportunity: Gender, Race, and Job Leads." *Social Problems* 56(3): 385–402.

McDonald, Steve, and Christine A. Mair. 2010. "Social Capital across the Life Course: Age and Gendered Patterns of Network Resources." *Sociological Forum* 25(2): 335–359.

Migheli, Matteo. 2011. "Capabilities and Functionings: The Role of Social Capital for Accessing New Capabilities." *Review of Political Economy* 23(1): 133–142.

Mincer, Jacob. 1958. "Investment in Human Capital and Personal Income Distribution." *Journal of Political Economy* 66(4): 281–302.

Nelson, Maria, and Laura Wolf-Powers. 2010. "Chains and Ladders: Exploring the Opportunities for Workforce Development and Poverty Reduction in the Hospital Sector." *Economic Development Quarterly* 24(1): 33–44.

O'Connor, Lindsey Trimble. 2013. "Ask and You Shall Receive: Social Network Contacts' Provision of Help during the Job Search." *Social Networks* 35: 593–603.

Parks-Yancey, Rochelle, Nancy DiTomaso, and Corinne Post. 2006. "The Social Capital Resources of Gender and Class Groups." *Sociological Spectrum* 26(1): 85–113.

Phillips, Rosemary F. 2010. "Initiatives to Support Disadvantaged Young People: Enhancing Social Capital and Acknowledging Personal Capital." *Journal of Youth Studies* 13(4): 489–504.

Roper Center for Public Opinion Research. 2001. *Social Capital Benchmark Survey*. Storrs: University of Connecticut.

Seefeldt, Kristin S. 2017. *Abandoned Families: Social Isolation in the Twenty-First Century*. New York: Russell Sage Foundation.

Smallacombe, Patricia Stern. 2006. "Rootedness, Isolation, and Social Capital in an Inner-City White Neighborhood." In *Social Capital in the City: Community and Civic Life in Philadelphia*. Richardson Dilworth, ed. Philadelphia: Temple University Press, pp. 177–195.

Smith, Tom W., Michael Hout, and Peter V. Marsden. 2013. *General Social Surveys, 1972–2012: Cumulative Codebook*. Chicago: National Opinion Research Center.

Stoloff, Jennifer A., Jennifer L. Glanville, and Elisa Jayne Bienenstock. 1999. "Women's Participation in the Labor Force: The Role of Social Networks." *Social Networks* 21: 91–108.

Strawn, Julie. 2010. *Farther, Faster: Six Promising Programs Show How Career Pathways Bridges Help Basic Skills Students Earn Credentials That Matter*. Washington, DC: Center for Law and Social Policy, Center for Postsecondary and Economic Success.

Tassier, Troy, and Filippo Menczer. 2007. "Social Network Structure, Segregation, and Equality in a Labor Market with Referral Hiring." *Journal of Economic Behavior and Organization* 66(3–4): 514–528.

Turner, Lesley J., Sheldon Danziger, and Kristin S. Seefeldt. 2006. "Failing the Transition from Welfare to Work: Women Chronically Disconnected from Employment and Cash Welfare." *Social Science Quarterly* 87(2): 227–249.

U.S. Census Bureau. 2012. Selected Household Characteristics. *2012 American Community Survey*. Washington, DC: U.S. Census Bureau. http://factfinder2.census.gov/faces/tableservices/jsf/pages/productview.xhtml?pid=ACS_12_1YR_CP04&prodType=table (accessed May 15, 2019).

Van Eijk, Gwen. 2010. "Does Living in a Poor Neighborhood Result in Network Poverty? A Study on Local Networks, Locality-Based Relationships and Neighbourhood Settings." *Journal of Housing and the Built Environment* 25: 467–480.

9
Implementing Career Pathway Training with a Family Focus

The Two-Generation Approach of the Community Action Project of Tulsa, Oklahoma

Teresa Eckrich Sommer
Terri Sabol
Patricia Lindsay Chase-Lansdale
Northwestern University

Christopher T. King
University of Texas at Austin

Innovative workforce development strategies aimed at preparing low-income adults for career employment in the twenty-first century economy are expanding across the United States. Indeed, this volume focuses on sector-based career pathway training programs, one of the most promising new approaches. This chapter presents the implementation and evaluation of Career*Advance*®, a career pathway training program with an explicit focus on low-income families with young children. Career*Advance*® combines high-quality early childhood services for children with career training and employment supports for their parents. Career pathway training programs targeted to families seek to increase parent education, employment, and earnings, and in turn to improve children's development.

The Community Action Project of Tulsa County, Oklahoma (CAP Tulsa), an antipoverty agency, is at the forefront of innovation in workforce development for low-income parents. CAP Tulsa's Career*Advance*® program takes a two-generation human capital approach, promoting the education and skills of parents and children together. The program recruits parents from CAP Tulsa's high-quality, no-cost early childhood education centers and prepares them for health care careers, a growth sector of the local economy. Career*Advance*® also offers support services to parents, including career coaching, peer supports, employment services, and financial assistance.

The Health Profession Opportunity Grants 1.0 program provided CAP Tulsa with an unprecedented opportunity to bring Career*Advance*® to scale, expanding from 40 to over 300 families served.[1] CAP Tulsa is the only HPOG grantee with an intervention designed explicitly to serve parents, and Career*Advance*® is the only sectoral career pathway program under study that offers human capital services to parents *and* children simultaneously.

The purpose of this chapter is to provide an overview of the Career*Advance*® program; offer preliminary findings, including program participants' experiences and reactions to the innovation; and discuss how CAP Tulsa has evolved in its two-generation approach. The chapter concludes with insights for program administrators and policymakers interested in promoting sector-based career pathway programs for families.

BACKGROUND

Head Start is the largest federally funded early childhood education program targeted to low-income children and takes a whole-family approach, making it a promising platform for testing a two-generation human capital approach. Community colleges (and their nonprofit, technical school counterparts) are increasingly serving student parents with similar sociodemographic characteristics of Head Start parents. Many student parents in community colleges have young children, and 15 percent are single parents (Horn, Nevill, and Griffith 2006).

Community colleges often have had disappointing results in helping low-income student parents overcome barriers and reach their educational goals (Goldrick-Rab and Sorenson 2010; Miller, Gault, and Thorman 2011). For example, among unmarried parents who started postsecondary education in 1995–1996, fewer than 17 percent attained an associate's or bachelor's degree within six years (Goldrick-Rab and Sorenson 2010). Workforce programs also struggle to address common barriers faced by low-income parents, such as access to quality, reliable child care, social isolation, and few financial resources (Gardner, Brooks-Gunn, and Chase-Lansdale 2017).

Workforce training programs aimed specifically at young, low-income parents on public assistance were launched in the 1980s and 1990s. Yet these programs (e.g., Project Redirection; New Chance Demonstration; Teenage Parent Demonstration; and Learning, Earning, and Parenting Program) were largely ineffective in promoting GED attainment, employment, or exits from welfare (Granger and Cytron 1999; Heckman 2000). Similarly, workforce development programs for the broader population of economically disadvantaged adults that began in the same era (such as JTPA) also had lackluster effects on parent human capital (Bloom et al. 1993; Heckman, LaLonde, and Smith 1999).

Yet, an expanding innovation in the field of job training programs—sector-based career pathway training—has shown promise for low-income adults (King and Prince 2015). Sector-based career pathway training programs have produced positive impacts on educational persistence and certification, and they have improved earnings and income—especially when combined with financial incentives and wraparound support services (Esyster, Anderson, and Durham 2013; Holzer 2009). The effectiveness of career pathway training targeted specifically to parents with young children is unknown.

Why would such an approach be effective? First and foremost, parenthood is no longer viewed as a barrier but rather as an advantage to parent participation in workforce training. Parents who see their children thriving and learning in school may become inspired to pursue their own educational goals (Gelber and Isen 2013; Love et al. 2013; Sommer et al. 2012). Early childhood education programs have also been recognized as an ideal platform for serving parents and children together (Chase-Lansdale and Brooks-Gunn 2014).

Second, a two-generation approach addresses logistical challenges parents commonly face. Coordinated parent and child school schedules can help parents balance the competing demands of school, work, and the care of young children. Offering child care before and after school also ensures that children are fully cared for while parents attend classes and training.

Third, career pathway training programs with close ties to employers and employment can help reduce parental stress and financial worry and make finding career employment more likely (Chase-

Lansdale, Sommer, Sabol, Brooks-Gunn et al. 2019). Career employment increases attachment to work and likely leads to increasing wages over time, and which may in turn expand available resources at home that benefit children.

Fourth, early childhood education programs can help address social isolation by strengthening social capital (Small 2009; Sommer et al. 2016). Early childhood education centers can serve as safe, trusted communities that support the best interests of children and offer opportunities for social connection among parents, teachers, and staff (Chase-Lansdale and Brooks-Gunn 2014).

Finally, two-generation interventions may increase service efficiencies. Community-based partnerships that align programming and draw on the specialized expertise and organizational structures already in place are well positioned to target and streamline services. High-quality early childhood education centers, such as Head Start, with embedded family support services are likely to be well equipped to help parents set goals, access emergency assistance and other financial supports, and address a broad range of family needs (e.g., housing and mental health services). Likewise, innovative and well-funded community colleges are likely to have the expertise and resources to support occupational skills training, employment services, and academic issues (e.g., tutoring, academic and career coaching).

THE CAREER*ADVANCE*® PROGRAM MODEL

CAP Tulsa became the Head Start and Early Head Start grantee for the majority of Tulsa County in 1998 (King et al. 2009). A decade later, through the visionary leadership of CAP Tulsa's Executive Director Steven Dow, the agency expanded its investments to include a more intensive focus on the education and employment of the parents of children participating in its early childhood education centers. CAP Tulsa began enrolling parents in Career*Advance*® in 2009 and dramatically expanded its reach in 2010 with HPOG 1.0 funds (CAP Tulsa also received HPOG 2.0 funds in 2015). Below we describe the Career*Advance*® program's key components during the HPOG 1.0 grant period.

Early childhood education. CAP Tulsa serves over 2,000 children each year through Head Start, Early Head Start, and Oklahoma's state-funded early education program, in addition to a smaller (250 children) home visiting program. The agency's early education centers are of unusually high quality. Teachers have bachelor's degrees and engage in high-quality teacher-child interactions as measured by the CLASS assessment system. CAP Tulsa's early childhood education services also have been shown to increase school readiness in the short term and reduce grade retention and chronic absenteeism in elementary and middle school (Gormley, Phillips, and Gayer 2008; Phillips, Gormley, and Anderson 2016).

Sector-based career training. CAP Tulsa's two-generation human capital approach uses a sector-based approach to improve parents' chances for securing stable employment and higher wages by identifying and targeting promising areas of the local economy. Market analyses of Tulsa identified health care as a growth sector (Glover, King, and Carter Smith 2012). Through cross-agency partnerships with Tulsa Community College and Tulsa Technology Center, CAP Tulsa purchased entry-level certification classes and paid full tuition, fees, and related school costs for parents accepted into the program.

Stackable credentials. CAP Tulsa offers credentialing at multiple levels in the nursing and health information technology fields in partnership with two local colleges. The goal is for parents to obtain career employment with family-supporting wages, job stability, and opportunities for career advancement and wage growth (King et al. 2009). For example, a parent might pursue short-term certification, such as a nursing assistant training earning only $9–$12 per hour, in order to minimize time demands on the family when a child is very young. The parent may then progress to a more challenging and time-intensive college-level training, such as a licensed nurse practitioner making $16–$20 per hour, when a child enters elementary school.

Employment services. Partnerships with local health care employers in search of job candidates are also a key component of the program. Under HPOG 1.0, CAP Tulsa began with a workforce intermediary or partner to match the needs of employers with the skills of workers, in the form of the local workforce board (Chase-Lansdale and Brooks-Gunn 2014; Giloth 2004).

Training and certification geared toward the needs of the local employers may be more likely to lead to stable employment and higher earnings than just "getting any job" (Holzer and Martinson 2005; Jenkins 2006). Yet this strategy can be challenging for a special population, such as parents of young children, in which employer demands and family needs must be considered. CAP Tulsa has developed several key supportive program elements, such as coaching, peer supports, and financial incentives, to help parents manage competing demands.

Coaching and peer support. Early education programs such as Head Start are well designed to support parents. CAP Tulsa families were already receiving family support services, including referrals to community-based services (e.g., housing and mental health services) and emergency assistance and other financial supports. The Career*Advance®* program added academic coaches as a supplement to CAP Tulsa's Family Support services. Career coaches hold individualized sessions with parents to address barriers, offer problem-solving strategies and social support, and develop a career advancement plan. The plan helps parents learn goal setting, planning, and accountability skills, which may promote self-efficacy and attachment to careers.

Meetings with small groups of Head Start parents (15 each) allow for frequent (weekly) exposure and interaction among parents. Led by career coaches employed by CAP Tulsa, these meetings help parents develop career-related skills, such as job interview skills and business etiquette, and provide advising on college readiness, course selection, and career counseling. Peer groups also discuss self-empowerment and self-advocacy, stress management, and nutrition. Central to both coaching and peer supports is the building of social capital among parents and staff, increasing social connection and support for addressing their near- and far-term needs (Small 2009; Sommer et al. 2016).

Incentives and other financial supports. Career*Advance®* is intentionally structured to reduce the financial burden of returning to school by offering tuition-free classes, free books and materials (such as stethoscopes and scrubs), and incentives for participation. These supports are meant to offset the costs of returning to school, including the loss of income when parents either reduce work hours or exit the labor force to focus on their education. Moreover, many low-income students who enroll in postsecondary education incur significant debt, even with scholarships and grants (Goldrick-Rab and Sorenson 2010), and often leave before completing a degree, which likely would have led to higher earnings. To help offset the range of financial concerns, Career*Advance*® participants can earn up to $3,000 annually for regular attendance in classes and peer group meetings, achieving certification or employment milestones, gaining at least six credit hours, and maintaining a 3.0 grade point average. Parents also receive vouchers to pay for after-hour child care for children enrolled in CAP Tulsa's early childhood education centers, children on CAP Tulsa's waiting list, or older siblings.

THE EFFECTS OF TWO-GENERATION HUMAN CAPITAL PROGRAMS ON PARENTS AND CHILDREN IN HEAD START

To date, there have been few studies of the effectiveness of two-generation human capital program models. One randomized control evaluation studied the Enhanced Early Head Start's influence on parents' human capital but did not involve intensive or on-site services for parents: parents were referred to existing community-based services and expected to access them on their own. The experiment showed no significant differences between treatment and control groups in parenting, employment, education, earnings, or child development three years after program start. Possible explanations for the lack of impacts include the low-intensity program model for parents, which typically involved simple referrals to other services without follow-up, combined with varying levels of expertise and comfort among the Early Head Start staff in supporting parent human capital services (Hsueh and Farrell 2012).

CAP Tulsa's Career*Advance*® program employs an alternative, more intensive model involving support services provided by staff with specialized expertise on-site at Head Start centers, the intentional alignment and coordination of services for parents and children, and mutually beneficial Head Start and community college partnerships. A descriptive analysis of persistence and completion among the first

Career*Advance*® program entrants (N = 92) showed promise for parents: 76 percent of program enrollees attained at least one health care certificate 16 months after enrollment (two consecutive semesters with or without a summer break), and 58 percent remained in the program 16 months after program start. Of those who left the program during the first 16 months, 68 percent attained a work-applicable certificate (Sabol et al. 2015).

Recent Evaluation of Career*Advance*®

The most recent evaluation of Career*Advance*® examined the one-year effects of program participation on parent human capital, parent psychological well-being, and children's Head Start attendance. The study used quasi-experimental methods to estimate the average treatment effect of Career*Advance*® combined with quality early childhood education (e.g., Head Start) among a total sample of almost 300 families, including program enrollees and a matched-comparison group who received early education services only (Chase-Lansdale, Sommer, Sabol, Chor et al. 2019; Sommer et al. 2019). The evaluation measured the added effect of parent career pathway training to high-quality early learning services, which included center-based care for children, emergency financial services for families, and goal setting for parents. The study found that one year of Career*Advance*® participation promoted parents' career certificate attainment and employment in the health care sector and boosted parent psychological well-being. Career*Advance*® also improved children's Head Start attendance and reduced chronic absenteeism. The findings, all of which are statistically significant, are described in more detail below.

Almost two-thirds (61 percent) of Career*Advance*® enrollees achieved at least one health care certification in one year compared to 4 percent of the matched-comparison group. These rates are high, even when compared to national rates over a much longer time frame among all community college students, of whom 53 percent achieved a certificate or degree within six years of community college enrollment (Nelson, Froehner, and Gault 2013). Career*Advance*® certification rates are also favorable when compared with similar career training programs (Card, Kluve, and Weber 2015). For example, experimental studies of WorkAdvance, a program with intensive support services that was largely serving student parents, found that the program increased credential attainment by 25 percentage points compared to the control group (Hendra et al. 2016), a much smaller gain than experienced by Career*Advance*® enrollees.

Career*Advance*® also improved sector-based employment: 51 percent of parents in the program were employed in the health care sector compared to 27 percent in the matched-comparison group. Participation in Career*Advance*® did not have a significant effect on hourly earnings, yet the Career*Advance*® group also did not report higher levels of material hardship. This may have occurred because the program offered financial incentives of, on average, about $1,800 per year that may have offset the income loss over the course of the year among this group (about $1,300 per year).

Career*Advance*® parents also reported higher levels of commitment to work, greater levels of self-efficacy, and higher levels of optimism one year after program entry compared to the matched-comparison group (Chase-Lansdale et al. 2019). Parents also did not report higher levels of perceived stress or psychological stress after one year of Career*Advance*® participation combined with Head Start services.

Average rates of children's Head Start attendance were 5.13 percent higher in the Career*Advance*® group than the matched comparison group after one semester (Sommer et al., forthcoming). This translates into Career*Advance*® children attending Head Start about five more days than matched comparison children over one semester. Career*Advance*® participation was also associated with significant reductions in children's chronic absence. The proportion of children who were chronically absent among the Career*Advance*® group was 37 percent compared to 59 percent among the matched comparison group, a 22 percentage point difference.

EXPLORING POSSIBLE MECHANISMS FOR EFFECTS OF CAREER*ADVANCE*®

Unpacking Effects on Parents

Descriptive data from annual focus groups with parents who both continued in and exited the Career*Advance*® program during HPOG

I–funded years suggest ways in which program services may have worked together to support the success of enrollees. The positive effects of Career*Advance*® on parent human capital and psychological well-being may be the result of the program's intensive financial and support services. Participants can comment on the utility of program elements, which can give program designers and organizations insights, even when they do not have a formal evaluation of the effectiveness of individual elements.

The Career*Advance*® program's coordinated parent-child schedules may have helped parents solve some of the logistical challenges parents commonly face, including the coordination of schedules:

> *I like how they've made the program fit around the youngest child's schedule . . . how they've tailored it to fit around those hours, which really would tailor around all school-age children's hours. So only during clinical times do you have to really worry about before and after care. But for the most part, all of us can still take the kids, kiss them goodbye, do our thing, and then be there to pick them up.*[2]

Likewise, as intended, the small groups of parents who enrolled together in community college classes seemed to build social connection and support for balancing school, work, and the care of young children with limited financial resources. Parents discussed ways in which they helped each other with homework, transportation, child care, and daily encouragement. The support of their peers may have played an important role in program persistence (and ultimately program completion):

> *I know if I tried to leave this program, I would have some people on my phone. And that's the good thing about us being, that's the one good thing about us being a small group of people. If one of us tried to leave it, oh, we gonna be on that phone quick, "Wait a minute what are you doing?"*

One-on-one and group coaching also offered concrete solutions and motivation when parents faced educational barriers:

> *I took [the GED test] like twice and I could never pass it. And I just felt so dumb that I was like, there is no need for me to take the GED test. How hard is it to take the GED test and I keep failing it so I must be dumb. And I just kept feeling that way. I will give up. But my Career Coach and GED instructor, "Don't give up, never give up." And I'm not a give-upper. I like to challenge myself. And you know they talked and talked to me and "just take your time."*

Because I like to rush also. And that was my problem. I want to get it, get it done. So, I stayed there for a while and took it the third time and there I went. I passed it. I just had to do it, just take my time.

Coaches and peers together seemed to offer a breadth and depth of support not experienced by many Career*Advance*® participants in previous college experiences or by comparison group members:

My favorite part is so much support we're getting. We can pretty much call [the coach] anytime. . . . We constantly have the support not only from our classmates but also from our teachers and our coach. . . . When I was in community college before, it was just me against the world basically, you know. So, if I dropped out, nobody cared. It was just, I was only disappointing myself. Now if anybody is missing too much class, we'd call them and are like, you know, "Where are you at? Come to class."

Free tuition and financial incentives importantly seemed to counter the many financial burdens faced by parents, including past student loan debt and reduced earnings when returning to school. Numerous parents reported that without free tuition, they would not have been able to enroll in Career*Advance*®. Financial supports were often the most highly rated:

Tuition was number one because of school getting paid for, and the second thing would be the child care so I can go to school.

The tuition finding is supported by information gleaned from site visits indicating that a significant number of Career*Advance*® participants entered the program with student debt incurred from their previous attempts to obtain postsecondary credentials that may have made them ineligible for federal educational loan assistance (Glover, King, and Carter Smith 2012).[3]

Effects on Children

We hypothesize that improvements in parents' human capital and psychological well-being are also likely to lead to improvements in children's development in the short and long term, including academic success and social competence (Duncan, Ziol-Guest, and Kalil 2010; Yoshikawa, Weisner, and Lowe 2006). Parents with more education and skills may provide more cognitively stimulating home environments, which may boost children's literacy, numeracy, and other cognitive domains (Crosnoe and Kalil 2010). They also may serve as better academic role models, have higher expectations for their children, and become better advocates for their children's schooling, which may in turn promote children's motivation and cognitive and social skills (Davis-Kean 2005; Kalil and Crosnoe 2009; Klebanov and Brooks-Gunn 2006).

Analysis of the impacts of Career*Advance*® on children's outcomes is forthcoming. Preliminary results from focus groups with participants in the program suggest possible associations between improved parent human capital and children's development. For example, the skills parents developed in training may have increased parents' engagement with their children's schooling and confidence in supporting their learning.

> *I have found, on a positive note, what school has done in our house is . . . like, my nine-year-old has always struggled in math. And I have always struggled in math. It's never been a strong suit. I've always told her that, you know, sorry I can't really help you. And she's relied on that, "Well mommy can't help me. She doesn't get numbers . . ." Well, when I got put in this math tutoring class, I felt like I could then relate to her more, and I felt like it was empowering me because it was giving me those skills that I left behind somewhere in high school and junior high. And so when I would get home, for the first couple of weeks, I'd be like, "I can help you." She's like, "No you can't, you don't know how to do this", and I was like, "No, really, I know how to do it now." So, I feel like, I wasn't getting so upset with her because now I know the material and understand it and I'm getting it. So, it's helping her to feel better about herself, and I feel better about myself because for all those years, it was embarrassing to tell your nine-year-old, "Sorry I can't help you with this because I don't know it myself." So, I feel like that's been a positive—that I can guide them better now, that I have the information, I can help them better.*

Parents also identified ways that they served as academic role models for their children.

> *I'm the first person to even go to school. So, it feels good to me to just know that I'm gonna make a better, like pave a better path for my son. The chances of him going to school if I complete school are so much higher. And that's, you know, not only will I create a better life for him as a child, but it'll give him some encourage-*

*ment and motivation, and I can be a better role model for him to go
to school when he's older. So it makes me feel a lot better, I think.*

Role modeling by parents may shape children's expectations for
themselves, which in turn could motivate parents to pursue more education and further advance their careers. These bidirectional benefits to
parents and children could lead to greater collective benefits for parents
and children than those accrued by separate, uncoordinated human capital services to parents and children, although further study is needed.

Other Evidence

Other early evidence on the effectiveness of two-generation human
capital models for families with children enrolled in early education
services like Head Start is also emerging. A recent article in the *Russell Sage Foundation Journal of the Social Sciences* by coauthors of
this chapter (Sommer et al. 2018) advocates for federal investment in
two-generation human capital approaches as a way to reduce poverty
among children in the near and long term. An analysis of a program
model that recruits parents of children enrolled in Head Start services
for career pathway training across a range of promising career fields
(such as health care, information technology, and manufacturing) estimates average benefit-cost ratios of 1.3 within 5 years and 7.9 within 10
years (assuming 10 percent of parents of children enrolled in Head Start
services participated in career training [Sommer et al. 2018]). These
estimates are based only on increased earnings and thus underestimate
other societal benefits, such as reduced use of public benefit programs
and increased tax revenue.

THE IMPLEMENTATION AND EVOLUTION OF
CAREER*ADVANCE*®

The Ray Marshall Center at the University of Texas at Austin and
Northwestern University's Institute for Policy Research partnered to
study the implementation of Career*Advance*® under an HPOG University Partnership research grant. The evaluation involved monthly calls
between researchers and program staff and quarterly meetings among

all community partners led by CAP Tulsa. It also included semiannual focus groups and interviews with service delivery staff and program leaders at both CAP Tulsa and partner agencies (such as Tulsa Community College and Union Public Schools Adult Education program) and parents (enrolled, exited, and matched-comparison parents).

Studying the implementation of Career*Advance*® provides insights into the complexities of serving parents and children at the same time, and reveals benefits and challenges at the agency, participant, and partner levels. Several themes emerged across these levels, including the importance of a well-defined and operational two-generation organizational mission; the value to participants of key supportive elements; the necessity of close ties with employers; and the importance of sustained, mutually beneficial partnerships. For each theme, we explore lessons for the field.

Operationalizing a Two-Generation Mission

Early in its tenure as the Head Start and Early Head Start delegate of Tulsa County, CAP Tulsa began considering organizational strategies that reflected the critical role parents' education and family income play in promoting children's well-being. The agency, with the support of local philanthropy, responded by developing a two-generation strategy that took shape through Career*Advance*®. Over the years, CAP Tulsa has continued to adjust its services and partnerships to maximize its ability to operationalize a two-generation mission. Ongoing programmatic questions include whom best to serve and for how long.

Whom to serve

Initially, CAP Tulsa focused on services for parents who were prepared for college-level coursework. Yet, this group turned out to include no more than 10 percent of parents with children enrolled in CAP Tulsa's early childhood education services. The agency later added pre-college programming, including English as a Second Language (ESL), GED, and developmental education services as part of a pipeline of preparation for Career*Advance*® (Sommer et al. 2016).

ESL services have become especially important, given the growing number of immigrant families in Tulsa, Oklahoma. CAP Tulsa's two-generation ESL program recruits parents of children enrolled in

Head Start and delivers an ESL curriculum that is contextualized to child development and children's early school experiences. A recent descriptive study of the program (Sommer et al. 2018) finds that parents advanced their English language skills at higher rates than parents in traditional community-based ESL programs. Parents in the program moved on average from beginning to high intermediate levels based on National Reporting System benchmarks. The program also supported parents' focus on their children, including an improved sense of parents' agency in their children's school and other child-related domains. It is too early to tell whether parents in the ESL program will later enter Career*Advance*®, as the impacts of CAP Tulsa's two-generation ESL program on parent and child outcomes are under study.

How long to serve

Under HPOG 1.0, CAP Tulsa supported parents' desired highest level of certification within the health care career field, such as licensed registered nurse, yet found this approach too expensive and time consuming, given the four to five years it often took parents to achieve their goal. CAP Tulsa, under HPOG 2.0, now offers one year of career training and an additional year of support services after parents are employed. Whether to target parent-centered services beyond children's participation in each childhood education programming, and whether to focus on short-term certification or to support high levels of career advancement are both ongoing questions. Further program innovation and evaluation is warranted.

Under HPOG 1.0 and ongoing, CAP Tulsa's two-generation approach has expanded beyond its model two-generation program Career*Advance*® to the agency as a whole. CAP Tulsa continually seeks new ways to promote children's development across all types of programming, especially through coordinated, aligned, and mutually reinforcing services for parents and children. For example, Family Support services focus not just on goal setting but also on building parents' executive functioning as a means to improving skills across domains, including work, parenting, and family functioning. Likewise, home visiting incorporates simultaneous and connected parent and child skill building. CAP Tulsa continually seeks innovative ways to advance parent and child well-being at the same time.

Supportive Services for Parents

Descriptions from program participants over many years suggest that the Career*Advance*® program's combination of coaching, peer services, and financial supports (including incentives and wraparound child care) are critically important to parents' ability to persist in the program. Other programmatic elements may also prove valuable. For example, CAP Tulsa is implementing new strategies to further align parent and child curricular elements. The agency is testing an increased focus on parenting topics (including child discipline and strategies for balancing work, family, and school) as part of the program's training services. It has also developed new peer partner meeting curriculum that gives parents the opportunity to use meeting time while children are in care (up to two hours per week) to address self-defined needs (e.g., household errands or doctor's appointment). Additional research on the implementation of these approaches will suggest whether they should be continued.

Employers and the Sequencing of Work and School

The original Career*Advance*® program was designed with career employment in mind. The agency chose to support parents' education and employment in the viable and growing health care career field in Tulsa, and one that could afford parents the opportunity to earn stackable credentials. The option to build career skills over time is especially attractive to parents of young children, who may need to move in and out of work and school in accordance with the shifting financial and care needs of their family.

Over time, the program has deepened its relationship with employers in a number of ways. A workforce intermediary (Giloth 2004) was part of the original HPOG 1.0 design. Under HPOG 2.0, Tulsa County WorkAdvance (TCW), a leading-edge, sector-based workforce development organization, serves this function while also taking the lead role in screening, training, and supporting Career*Advance*® participants in their first year of employment. While academic and career coaching were originally provided in-house by CAP Tulsa's academic coaches who were based in the agency's early childhood education center, employment and career coaching is now offered at TCW by workforce training and employment experts who help enrollees gain and retain career jobs during their first year after certification. Academic coaching remains within CAP Tulsa's early childhood education centers and serves as a key bridge between early childhood education services and workforce training and employment supports.

Sustained, Mutually Beneficial Partnerships

Community-based partnerships are central to most two-generation human capital programs. The number and intensity of CAP Tulsa's partnerships and CAP Tulsa's role in leading them have evolved over time. Tulsa Community College was the Career*Advance*® program's initial education partner for parents ready for college-level training. However, when Tulsa Community College dropped its certified nursing assistant program and CAP Tulsa increased its focus on shorter-term certification programs, Tulsa Technology Center became the primary education partner for the agency. This partnership provided benefits for both organizations. Guaranteed classes, regardless of enrollment levels, provided a secure funding source for Tulsa Technology Center. College classes in which CAP Tulsa could participate in teacher selection and enroll only CAP Tulsa parents allowed for better matching of instructor skills and parents served and afforded parents sustained opportunities for social connection among parents of children enrolled in CAP Tulsa's early childhood education programs. The agency's current partnership with TCW offers additional cross-agency benefits, including new cross-organizational knowledge and strategies. For example, TCW has learned to be more family friendly in the way it operates and has expanded its knowledge of quality, affordable, and local child care options for parents. TCW staff have also developed a better understanding of the ways in which parents may pursue education and employment discontinuously, balancing income, education, and family care needs. Likewise, CAP Tulsa has learned from its partnership with TCW how to successfully engage employers and support parents' sustained career employment.

It is challenging to know whether offering the same combination of services at another community-based organization, and in close partnership with early childhood education services, would produce effects similar to those seen in the first year of program participation.

The choice of a two-generation lead agency is likely to depend on the service delivery capacity and leadership in a given community. For example, at the time of the inception of Career*Advance*®, no publicly funded organization (such as the local workforce board, Tulsa Community College, or Tulsa Technology Center) or nonprofit (such as the local Goodwill agency) appeared sufficiently well positioned to lead a two-generation strategy. Yet community circumstances may change, and new leaders may present themselves.

An understanding of the time and intensity needed to support the cross-community goal of investing in the human capital of parents and children is also still emerging. Initial insights from CAP Tulsa's experiences suggest that a lead agency with the experience and the motivation to invest in services that support both generations is a necessary starting point. Yet, whether the primary agency can change over time, and whether an early childhood education provider should take a lead role, is an open question. As federal funding under HPOG 2.0 wraps up (in September 2020), CAP Tulsa is considering whether a different or broader constellation of partnerships, perhaps with a new lead agency, could sustain a two-generation intervention.

CONCLUSION

Aligning Head Start services for children with sectoral career pathway training programs for their parents addresses two of the most significant barriers student parents face (Adams, Spaulding, and Heller 2015): achieving educational credentials in a timely manner that produce earnings benefits in the near term and long term, and cost-effectively caring for their children with quality educational services while parents are enrolled in school and working (Attewell, Savill-Smith, and Douch 2009). Historically, workforce development strategies in the United States have not systematically addressed these concerns, nor have most early education programs typically addressed parents' education and workforce needs, tending to focus much more on parenting and basic literacy. In fact, most colleges and traditional workforce programs are largely unaware of the parental status and related needs of their students (King et al. 2009; Miller, Gault, and Thorman

2011), suggesting the potential benefits to community colleges and technical centers of learning how to better serve the growing population of student parents.

The two-generation field is still in its early stages, and more model testing is needed. Yet, career pathway training programs with a family-centered approach hold promise for supporting the human capital outcomes of parents and children. HPOG University Partnership funding provided an exceptional opportunity for CAP Tulsa, its partners, and Career*Advance*® participants to take risks and try a new approach to career pathway training designed specifically for families with young children. This chapter illustrates the innovative thinking that went into the design, implementation, and evaluation of the Career*Advance*® program. It represents a first step in, hopefully, a much longer trajectory of workforce training and employment strategies that improve outcomes for low-income families with young children.

Notes

1. In 2010, ACF awarded the first round of five-year HPOG grants (HPOG 1.0) to 32 organizations in 23 states, including five tribal organizations, with approximately $67 million disbursed each year through fiscal year 2015. It awarded a second round of five-year grants in 2015 to 32 organizations across 21 states (HPOG 2.0).
2. The quotes in this chapter are all from focus groups conducted by research team members with program participants.
3. Unfortunately, we cannot accurately estimate the number of participants with outstanding unpaid student debt from our data. The share of participants with at least some college education at enrollment has ranged from as low as 20 percent to as high as 60 percent under HPOG 1.0 (Christensen, Juniper, and King 2015). Analysis of national U.S. Department of Education data by Miller (2012) for the Student Parent Success Initiative indicates that student parents are more likely than others to drop out and to have unpaid college debt without obtaining postsecondary degrees and that the problems are even more severe for single student parents.

References

Adams, Gina, Shayne Spaulding, and Caroline Heller. 2015. *Bridging the Gap: Exploring the Intersection of Workforce Development and Child Care.* Washington, DC: Urban Institute.

Attewell, Jill, Carol Savill-Smith, and Rebecca Douch. 2009. *The Impact of Mobile Learning: Examining What It Means for Teaching and Learning.* London: Learning and Skills Development Agency.

Bloom, Howard S., Larry L. Orr, George Cave, Stephen H. Bell, and Fred Doolittle. 1993. *The National JTPA Study: Title II-A Impacts on Earnings and Employment at 18 Months.* https://files.eric.ed.gov/fulltext/ED357261.pdf (accessed May 7, 2019).

Card, David, Jochen Kluve, and Andrea Weber. 2015. "What Works? A Meta-analysis of Recent Active Labor Market Program Evaluations." NBER Working Paper No. 21431. Cambridge, MA: National Bureau of Economic Research.

Chase-Lansdale, P. Lindsay, and Jeanne Brooks-Gunn. 2014. "Two-Generation Programs in the Twenty-First Century." *Future Child* 24(1): 13–39.

Chase-Lansdale, P. Lindsay, Teresa Eckrich Sommer, Terri J. Sabol, Jeanne Brooks-Gunn, Hirokazu Yoshikawa, Christopher T. King, and Amanda Morris. 2019. "The Effects of a Two-Generation Human Capital Intervention on Low-Income Parent and Their Young Child in Head Start." *Journal of Family Psychology* 33(4): 433–443.

Chase-Lansdale P. Lindsay, Teresa Eckrich Sommer, Terri J. Sabol, Elise Chor, Jeanne Brooks-Gunn, Hirokazu Yoshikawa, Christopher King, and Amanda Morris. 2019. "What Are the Effects of a Two-Generation Human Capital Program on Low-Income Parents' Education, Employment and Psychological Well-Being?" Two-Generation Programs: Policy Brief No. 1. Washington, DC: Ascend at the Aspen Institute. https://ascend.aspeninstitute.org/resources/cap-tulsa-careeradvance-impact-analysis-2019/ (accessed May 7, 2019).

Christensen, Kristen, Cynthia Juniper, and Christopher King. 2015. *Career*Advance® *Implementation Study Findings through July 2015.* Austin, TX: Ray Marshall Center for the Study of Human Resources, Lyndon B. Johnson School of Public Affairs, University of Texas. http://raymarshallcenter.org/2016/02/29/careeradvance-implementation-study-findings-through-july-2015/ (accessed November 15, 2018).

Crosnoe, Robert, and Ariel Kalil. 2010. "Educational Progress and Parenting among Mexican Immigrant Mothers of Young Children." *Journal of Marriage and Family* 72(4): 976–990.

Davis-Kean, Pamela E. 2005. "The Influence of Parent Education and Family Income on Child Achievement: The Indirect Role of Parental Expectations and the Home Environment." *Journal of Family Psychology* 19(2): 294–304.

Duncan, Greg J., Kathleen M. Ziol-Guest, and Ariel Kalil. 2010. "Early-Childhood Poverty and Adult Attainment, Behavior, and Health." *Child Development* 81(1): 306–325.

Eyster, Lauren, Theresa Anderson, and Christin Durham. 2013. "Innovations and Future Directions for Workforce Development in the Post-Recession Era." Washington, DC: Urban Institute.

Gardner, Margo, Jeanne Brooks-Gunn, and P. Lindsay Chase-Lansdale. 2017. "The Two-Generation Approach to Building Human Capital: Past, Present, and Future." In *Wiley Handbook of Early Childhood Development Programs, Practices, and Policies: Theory-Based and Empirically-Supported Strategies for Promoting Young Children's Growth in the United States*, Elizabeth Votruba-Drzal and Eric Dearing, eds. Hoboken, NJ: John Wiley & Sons, pp. 330–362.

Gelber, Alexander, and Adam Isen. 2013. "Children's Schooling and Parents' Investment in Children: Evidence from the Head Start Impact Study." NBER Working Paper No. 17704. Cambridge, MA: National Bureau of Economic Research.

Giloth, Robert P. 2004. *Workforce Intermediaries for the Twenty-First Century*. Philadelphia: Temple University Press.

Glover, Robert W., Christopher T. King, and Tara Carter Smith. 2012. *Expanding the CareerAdvance® Program in Tulsa, Oklahoma*. Austin, TX: Ray Marshall Center for the Study of Human Resources, Lyndon B. Johnson School of Public Affairs, University of Texas.

Goldrick-Rab, Sara, and Kia Sorensen. 2010. "Unmarried Parents in College." *The Future of Children* 20(2): 179–203.

Gormley, William T., Deborah Phillips, and Ted Gayer. 2008. "Preschool Programs Can Boost School Readiness." *Science* 320(5884): 1723–1724.

Granger, Robert C., and Rachel Cytron. 1999. "Teenage Parent Programs: A Synthesis of the Long-Term Effects of the New Chance Demonstration, Ohio's Learning, Earning, and Parenting Program, and the Teenage Parent Demonstration." *Evaluation Review* 23(2): 107–145.

Heckman, James J. 2000. "Policies to Foster Human Capital." *Research in Economics* 54(1): 3–56.

Heckman, James J., Robert LaLonde, and Jeffrey Smith. 1999. "The Economics and Econometrics of Active Labor Market Programs." In *Handbook of Labor Economics*, vol. 3, Orley Ashenfelter and David Card, eds. Amsterdam: North Holland.

Hendra, Richard, David H. Greenberg, Gayle Hamilton, Ari Oppenheim, Alexandra Pennington, Kelsey Schaberg, and Betsy L. Tessler. 2016. *Encouraging Evidence on a Sector-Focused Advancement Strategy: Two-Year Impacts from the WorkAdvance Demonstration.* New York: MDRC.

Holzer, Harry J. 2009. "Workforce Development as an Antipoverty Strategy: What Do We Know? What Should We Do?" In *Changing Poverty, Changing Politics,* Maria Cancian and Sheldon Danziger, eds. New York: Russell Sage Foundation, pp. 301–329.

Holzer, Harry J., and Karin Martinson. 2005. *Can We Improve Job Retention and Advancement among Low-Income Working Parents?* Washington, DC: Urban Institute.

Horn, Laura, Stephanie Nevill, and James Griffith. 2006. *Profile of Undergraduates in US Postsecondary Education Institutions, 2003-04: With a Special Analysis of Community College Students.* Statistical Analysis Report. NCES 2006-184. Washington, DC: National Center for Education Statistics.

Hsueh, JoAnn, and Mary E. Farrell. 2012. *Enhanced Early Head Start with Employment Services: 42-Month Impacts from the Kansas and Missouri Sites of the Enhanced Services for the Hard-to-Employ Demonstration and Evaluation Project.* OPRE Report No. 2012-05. Washington, DC: Office of Planning, Research and Evaluation, Administration for Children and Families, U.S. Department of Health and Human Services.

Jenkins, Davis. 2006. *Career Pathways: Aligning Public Resources to Support Individual and Regional Economic Advancement in the Knowledge Economy.* Barrington, RI: Workforce Strategy Center.

Kalil, Ariel, and Robert Crosnoe. 2009. "Two Generations of Educational Progress in Latin American Immigrant Families in the U.S.: A Conceptual Framework for a New Policy Context." In *Immigration, Diversity, and Education,* Elena L. Grigorenko and Ruby Takanishi, eds. New York: Routledge/Taylor and Francis, pp. 188–204.

King, Christopher T., Robert W. Glover, Tara Smith, Rheagan Coffey, and Brian Levy. 2009. "The Career*Advance®* Pilot Project: Recommended Jobs Strategy for Families Served by the Community Action Project of Tulsa County." Austin, TX: Ray Marshall Center for the Study of Human Resources, Lyndon B. Johnson School of Public Affairs, University of Texas.

King, Christopher T., and Heath J. Prince. 2015. "Moving Sectoral and Career Pathway Programs from Promise to Scale." In *Transforming U.S. Workforce Development Policies for the 21st Century,* Carl Van Horn, Tammy Edwards, and Todd Greene, eds. Kalamazoo, MI: W.E. Upjohn Institute for Employment Research, pp. 195–229.

Klebanov, Pamela Kato, and Jeanne Brooks-Gunn. 2006. "Cumulative, Human Capital, and Psychological Risk in the Context of Early Intervention: Links with IQ at Ages 3, 5, and 8." *Annals of the New York Academy of Science* 1094(1): 63–82.

Love, John M., Rachel Chazen-Cohen, Helen Raikes, and Jeanne Brooks-Gunn. 2013. "What Makes a Difference? Early Head Start Evaluation Findings in a Developmental Context." *Monographs of the Society of Research in Child Development* 78(1): vii–viii.

Miller, Kevin. 2012. *Single Student Parents Face Financial Difficulties, Debt, without Adequate Aid.* Fact sheet. IWPR No. C394. Washington, DC: Institute for Women's Poverty Research.

Miller, Kevin, and Barbara Gault, and Abby Thorman. 2011. *Improving Child Care Access to Promote Postsecondary Success among Low-Income Parents.* Report No. C378. Washington, DC: Institute for Women's Policy Research. https://iwpr.org/publications/improving-child-care-access-to -promote-postsecondary-success-among-low-income-parents/ (accessed May 7, 2019).

Nelson, Bethany, Meghan Froehner, and Barbara Gault. 2013. "College Students with Children Are Common and Face Many Challenges in Completing Higher Education: Summary." Briefing paper. Washington, DC: https:// iwpr.org/publications/college-students-with-children-are-common-and -face-many-challenges-in-completing-higher-education-summary (accessed May 7, 2019).

Phillips, Deborah, William Gormley, and Sara Anderson. 2016. "The Effects of Tulsa's CAP Head Start Program on Middle-School Academic Outcomes and Progress." *Developmental Psychology* 52(8): 1247–1261.

Sabol, Terri J., Teresa Eckrich Sommer, Patricia Lindsay Chase-Lansdale, Jeanne Brooks-Gunn, Hirokazu Yoshikawa, Christopher T. King, and Emily C. Ross. 2015. "Parents' Persistence and Certification in a Two-Generation Education and Training Program." *Children and Youth Services Review* 58: 1–10.

Small, Mario L. 2009. *Unanticipated Gains: Origins of Network Inequality in Everyday Life.* New York: Oxford University Press.

Sommer, Teresa Eckrich, Patricia Lindsay Chase-Lansdale, Jeanne Brooks-Gunn, Margo Gardner, Diana Mendley Rauner, and Karen Freel. 2012. "Early Childhood Education Centers and Mothers' Postsecondary Attainment: A New Conceptual Framework for a Dual-Generation Education Intervention." *Teachers College Record* 114(10): 1–40.

Sommer, Teresa Eckrich, Celia J. Gomez, Hirokazu Yoshikawa, Terri J. Sabol, Elise Chor, Amy Sanchez, Patricia Lindsay Chase-Lansdale, and Jeanne Brooks-Gunn. 2018. "Head Start, Two-Generation ESL Services, and Parent Engagement." *Early Childhood Research Quarterly.* https://doi .org/10.1016/j.ecresq.2018.03.008 (accessed October 2, 2019).

Sommer, Teresa Eckrich, Terri J. Sabol, Patricia Lindsay Chase-Lansdale, and Jeanne Brooks-Gunn. 2016. "Two-Generation Educational Programs for Parents and Their Young Children." In *The Leading Edge of Early Childhood Education: Linking Science to Policy for a New Generation of Pre-Kindergarten*, Nonie K. Lesaux and Stephanie M. Jones, eds. Cambridge, MA: Harvard Education Press, pp. 135–158.

Sommer, Teresa Eckrich, William P. Schneider, Elise Chor, Terri J. Sabol, Patricia Lindsay Chase-Lansdale, Jeanne Brooks-Gunn. ...Christopher T. King. 2019. *The Effects of a Two-Generation Human Capital Program on Children's Attendance in Head Start.* Unpublished manuscript.

Sommer, Teresa Eckrich, William P. Schneider, Elise Chor, Terri J. Sabol, Patricia Lindsay Chase-Lansdale, Jeanne Brooks-Gunn, ...Christopher T. King. Forthcoming. *What Are the Effects of a Two-Generation Human Capital Program on Children's Attendance and Chronic Absence in Head Start?* Two-Generation Programs: Policy Brief No. 3. Washington DC: Ascend at the Aspen Institute.

Yoshikawa, Hirokazu, Thomas S. Weisner, and Edward D. Lowe. 2006. *Making It Work: Low-Wage Employment, Family Life, and Child Development.* New York: Russell Sage Foundation.

10
Psychological Self-Sufficiency

An Empowerment-Based Theory for Workforce Training and Adult Education

Philip Young P. Hong
Timothy O'Brien
Jang Ho Park
Rana Hong
Loyola University Chicago

Terri Pigott
Georgia State University

Brian Holland
American University and BLH Technologies

This chapter focuses on low-income workers and their job-seeking efforts in health professions during an economic downturn, when the health care sector experienced labor shortages or was in high demand for quality workers. Prior research on workforce development has been overly outcome driven and has given relatively less attention to the process of building psychological strength as one reaches the economic self-sufficiency (ESS) outcome (Harvey, P. Hong, and Kwaza 2010; P. Hong 2013). Little is known about what psychological prerequisites are needed to achieve desired economic outcomes when life risks and resilience counterbalance the path to success.

To fill this gap in the literature and in the mainstream workforce development practice, we partnered with two Health Profession Opportunity Grants (HPOG) grantees—Gateway Technical College in Kenosha, Wisconsin, and Southland Health Care Forum in Chicago Heights, Illinois—to generate evidence on low-income students' empowerment and transformative career pathways to becoming health professionals.

This research could serve as the basis for developing improved workforce development strategies for HPOG programs and other employment programs for low-income individuals and families.

The project examined the extent to which psychological self-sufficiency (PSS)—activation of one's internal psychological strength against her perception of the barriers to achieving career goals—affects one's employment placement and ESS outcome in the health professions (P. Hong 2013; P. Hong, Choi, and Key 2018). The guiding research question is, how is HPOG participants' PSS associated with their economic success? The four-year study collected and analyzed survey responses from participants in the two HPOG program sites that use a career pathway model. This project obtained site-specific contextual survey data to evaluate the empowerment-based workforce development models in the health professions by highlighting the process element of internal strength as it relates to HPOG outcomes. It merged this survey data with the national Performance Reporting System (PRS) administrative data to promote cross-project learning. Multimethod analyses of the data contributed to theory building in workforce development for low-income individuals.

MUTUALLY BENEFICIAL PARTNERSHIP

This section describes the HPOG partner characteristics and the emergence of a mutually beneficial partnership. Problems addressed by HPOG program partners and the problems proposed to be studied by Loyola University Chicago as the evaluation partner converged as the main focus of collaboration. The HPOG program aimed to provide low-income individuals with education, training, and support services that prepare them to enter and advance in the health care positions that provide good pay, experience labor shortages, and are in high demand. HPOG had five goals:

1) target skills and competencies demanded by the health care industry;

2) support career pathways (including articulated career ladders);

3) result in employer- or industry-recognized certificates or degrees;

4) combine support services with education and training services to help participants overcome barriers to employment, as necessary; and

5) provide training services at times and locations that were easily accessible to targeted populations (Anderson et al. 2014, p. 3).

The HPOG partners addressed two main problems:

1) Underpreparedness for the academic rigors of postsecondary education is becoming increasingly acute. High dropout rates, low test scores, and poor academic performance lead to low retention and completion.

2) Hospitals, home health care providers, community clinics, assisted living facilities, and insurance companies report problems with health care personnel recruitment and retention. Loyola, as the university partner, located perceived employment barriers and employment hope as the common missing link and the source of the problems identified by HPOG partners. Therefore, Loyola's research aimed to provide evidence for developing new approaches to address social service needs among low-income job seekers receiving employment services and training through HPOG. This knowledge base could serve as the foundation for adding to the empowerment tradition in workforce development.

HPOG Program Partner 1: Southland Health Care Forum

Southland Health Care Forum (Southland) provides allied health care occupational training for Temporary Assistance for Needy Families (TANF), low-income, at-risk, limited-English-speaking individuals, and disadvantaged adults (18 years and older), leading to employment in high-paying, high-demand health care careers. An HPOG project titled "Pathways to Health Care Occupations" was awarded to address the problem of critical shortages of health care workers—medical assistant (MA), certified nurse assistant (CNA), licensed practical nurse (LPN), and phlebotomist technician) in Cook and Will Counties in Illinois. There were over 1,200 vacancies in nursing, allied medical, laboratory, and medical office occupations in Chicago Southland hospitals, clinics, long-term care facilities, physicians' practices, dialysis centers, and diagnostic laboratories.

Since 2003, Southland has developed and delivered health care training programs that react to changing staffing needs and provide solutions to staffing shortages. It used an empowerment-based workforce development model to arm HPOG students with the inner power and belief that they can complete the program, obtain certification, and advance in their chosen profession. Southland offered a strong career pathway system to receive state certification, 120-hour internships, and job placement in the health care sector. To increase the numbers of qualified MAs and LPNs, Southland offered to meet high-demand health care occupational needs in the region in seven ways:

1) Enroll 55 MA and 20 CNA and LPN students annually.

2) Provide Online Work Readiness Assessment, Test for Adult Basic Education, basic skill modules, remediation, and classroom learning.

3) Connect students with clinical externship opportunities.

4) Provide support services.

5) Collaborate with Southland Health Careers and Prairie State College for CNA- and MA-track courses.

6) Collaborate with the Coalition of African American Nurses for LPN-track courses.

7) Collaborate with Medix for access to electronic health records.

To achieve these goals, Southland provided financial support for tuition, examinations, books, fees, training supplies, certification testing, drug screening, and criminal background checks for participants. The MA required 50 hours of coursework on medical terminology, insurance billing and coding, medical ethics, customer service, and legal implications of the administrative and clerical position; the electronic health records required 40 hours on the fundamentals of health information technology as it relates to electronic health records and health information exchange; the CNA required seven credit hours to gain basic skills necessary to give basic patient care in a nursing home or hospital; and phlebotomy technician required 90 hours of coursework to prepare students to collect blood specimens for the purpose of laboratory analysis.

Southland's applicants often face many barriers to successfully completing their training, typically related to students' lack of self-confidence and poor academic experiences prior to enrolling. Support services such as financial aid, child care services, case management, and referrals were available on an as-needed basis. For customer service skills the Employability Skills Series called "Working with People" was offered to help learners develop critical interpersonal skills essential for succeeding in the workforce (four to six hours). Video segments illustrated important problem-solving skills, conflict resolution techniques, and practical customer service skills in a real-life work setting. Also, a life skills course called "You Can Make It Happen: Nine Steps to Success" (20–25 hours) was designed to help individuals obtain a sense of self and which negative and positive experiences/relationships could affect their future. Students were urged to take control; through a series of steps, they created a vision and plan of the action necessary to establish schedules to persist in their quest for a better life.

HPOG Program Partner 2: Gateway Technical College

Gateway Technical College (Gateway) is part of the Wisconsin Technical College System and is an accredited postsecondary institution that grants technical diplomas and two-year associate's degrees. Established in 1911, Gateway serves the southeastern Wisconsin counties of Kenosha, Racine, and Walworth with a total population that exceeds 400,000; many of these residents work outside the district boundaries or commute to Illinois. Curriculum is developed collaboratively with industry partners and Gateway to provide sound teaching methodology. The HPOG project titled "The Gateway Health Professions Opportunities Program (HPOP)" was awarded, and it was administered as a comprehensive collaborative program that features adult basic education, college-level coursework within a health care career pathway, soft skills development, and case management services. Program services included classroom instruction, mentoring, mock interviewing, grooming, professionalism and ethics training, job shadowing, and health career exploration. All eligible individuals could receive financial aid, child care services, case management, and other support services. Support services for TANF recipients and other low-income individuals included transportation, dependent care, and temporary housing, which are necessary to participate in funded activities. The HPOP integrated academic instruction with occupational skills training in specific health care fields, linking opportunities to improve basic literacy and mathematics skills and obtain a high school education or GED with work-based learning in the health care industry.

Gateway provided training and support for career progression along the health care career pathways, as well as short-term skills certification or credentialing that enabled incumbent workers to advance along health care career ladders. These included licenses, certificates, diplomas, and degrees. Gateway's extensive health care career ladders include the allied health program and nursing programs, both with multiple layers of certificates, diplomas, and associate's degrees. A new health apprenticeship certificate was developed for those already holding a high school diploma or equivalent, or those finishing that portion of the HPOP. The certificate program became the entry point into the health care courses, providing support for the student on many levels.

The certificate had six three-credit courses to be completed in one semester and included courses in medical terminology, career exploration (clinical shadowing), introduction to the health care industry, general education remediation (focus on writing and math), introduction to Gateway, soft skills, and an assessment tool for English language learner students. Support services are in place at Gateway for English language learner students. Participants may obtain employment post-certification, or obtain employment and discontinue the program, obtain employment and continue in the program, or receive the certification and continue in the program. The accredited nursing program grants an associate's degree of nursing and prepares students for vocational licensure as LPNs and positions as CNAs. Gateway health care opportunities include community pharmacy technician, dental assistant, health information technology, health unit coordinator, medical assistant, medical billing clerk, medical transcription, nursing, nursing assistant, physical therapist assistant, radiography, and surgical technology.

University Research Partnership: Loyola University Chicago

Despite the numerous studies on economic vulnerability, the study of self-sufficiency is hindered by a lack of conceptual and measurement sophistication. First, the conceptual domains of self-sufficiency are usually ideologically imposed versus empirically derived. Second, the measurement of self-sufficiency focuses primarily on the economic dimension of the concept. Third, studies on self-sufficiency rarely consider the processes of psychological transformation. For the most part, self-sufficiency is removed from the human development and change process and examined largely as an economic outcome wherein people who receive public benefits will become independent from government support and find jobs to be able to afford their basic needs.

The added value of this university-community partnership was the examination of a nontangible process using psychological self-sufficiency (PSS) as the theoretical framework (P. Hong 2013; R. Hong et al. 2019). Represented by the process that moves from perceived employment barriers to employment hope, PSS embodies hope and resilience building against the odds of giving up and disengaging from the goal-directed process. Often, this is captured by the staff as they coach students to stay positive and motivated as they face the many challenges that arise during the program (P. Hong, Kim, et al., forthcoming).

In our preparation meetings with the two HPOG program partners, it was echoed that there is a great need for measuring and monitoring PSS as an empowerment process–based benchmark capturing individual transformation as it contributes to ESS. Funders seldom request reporting on this benchmark (Harvey, P. Hong, and Kwaza 2010), and HPOG programs had not developed an evaluation metric or system to adequately represent its work on empowering students who wrestle with day-to-day employment barriers and social exclusion; it was as though these psychological processes did not exist or had little to do with the outcomes. This could validate the anecdotal evidence suggesting the importance of relationship-based psychological capital development that the staff emphasized was key to sustaining career pathway development for low-income students (P. Hong, Kim, et al., forthcoming).

The two HPOG programs partnered with Loyola to examine how the development of PSS could help their training programs prepare participants and fill labor shortages within high-demand, well-paying positions in the health care sector. HPOG program partners wanted to know which specific program activities were associated with PSS as an empowerment process for students that would lead to their success outcomes in HPOG program delivery—achieve health care skills and competencies, support career pathways, attain industry-recognized certificates or degrees, utilize support services in education and training to help participants overcome barriers to employment, and provide training services at times and locations that are easily accessible to the targeted populations.

As for Loyola, the partnership allowed the university to gather time-series data at four time points based on the PRS data collection schedule, as shown in Figure 10.1. Administering the PSS survey that contains questions on PSS—perceived employment barriers, employ-

Figure 10.1 HPOG Performance Reporting System Data Collection Schedule

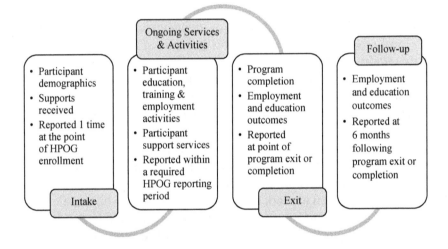

SOURCE: HPOG Performance Reporting System.

ment hope, and ESS—and other positive psychological attributes complemented the analyses using the PRS data that were already being collected. Comparing these data among the two different HPOG sites was useful for strengthening support for untapped resources within the career pathways model, upon which the HPOG program is based.

In this regard, Loyola University Chicago's main research goal was twofold: first, to validate the factor structure of PSS, comprising employment hope and perceived employment barriers; and second, to investigate the extent to which PSS is associated with ESS. The following key research questions were addressed:

1) How does PSS change over time during HPOG program participation?

2) How are PSS and ESS scores different between the two HPOG partners?

3) How is PSS associated with program completion and employment outcomes?

4) How does PSS affect ESS?

BACKGROUND LITERATURE

Evidence-based movement in public policy research has shifted the focus toward success outcomes, while many community-based practitioners have maintained the importance of process that leads to success (P. Hong 2013). Theory of change and logic models tend to omit the psychological process and transformation that provides the engine for any change at the individual, familial, and community systems. James G. March (1994) posited that decisions made based on analysis of cost and benefits may yield a good short-term outcome, but those made on the basis of identity provide long-term sustainable outcomes.

Rules prescribe, more or less precisely, what is appropriate action. They also, more or less precisely, tell actors where to look for precedents, who are the authoritative interpreters of different types of rules, and what the key interpretative traditions are. Still, the unambiguous authority of rules cannot be taken as given—it cannot be assumed that rules always dictate or guide behavior. Rather, it is necessary to understand the *processes* through which rules are translated into actual behavior and the factors that may strengthen or weaken the relation between rules and actions (March and Olsen, p. 7).

To focus on the identity—who job seekers are—and the process they take to become competent, work-ready candidates, vocational research provides a good background on the construct of hope. According to McWhirter, Hackett, and Bandalos (1998), three key models of career psychology were empirically supported—Betz and Fitzgerald's (1987) realism of career choice, Farmer's (1985) achievement motivation model, and Hackett and Betz's (1981) self-efficacy of career model. Lent, Brown, and Hackett's (1994) social cognitive career theory, which built on these prior models, "aimed at understanding the processes through which people develop educational/vocational interest make career-relevant choices, and achieve performances of varying quality in the educational and occupational pursuits" (Lent, Brown, and Hackett 2002, p. 62). Self-efficacy beliefs, outcome expectations, and goals are intricately related variables that serve as the foundational makeup of social cognitive career theory. It is posited that individuals are likely to develop career interests and make career choices, and succeed in tasks for which they have strong self-efficacy beliefs and outcome expectations, given that they have the necessary skills and environmental supports.

Emergence of positive psychology has provided balance between studying the human deficiencies and the optimal human functioning (Seligman 2002). This movement in psychology has contributed to the development of positive organizational behavior (POB; Luthans 2002a), which focuses on "a positive approach to developing and managing human resources in today's workplace" (Luthans et al. 2007, p. 542). Luthans (2002b) defined POB as "the study and application of positively oriented human resource strengths and psychological capacities that can be measured, developed, and effectively managed for performance improvement" (p. 59). Capturing individual-level POB constructs were the four elements of hope, (self-)efficacy, resilience, and optimism (HERO) that were termed positive psychological capital or PsyCap (Luthans, Youssef, and Avolio 2007). High levels of HERO (together as a higher-order construct) have been found to be associated with desired employee attitudes, behaviors, and performance (Avey et al. 2011).

These theories may have postulated applicability to the general population using multiple positive psychological traits, but some vocational psychologists and other researchers have focused on minorities with particular emphasis on hope. Beck et al. (1974) introduced the hopelessness scale to capture individual's level of pessimism of future outcomes, and McWhirter, Hackett, and Bandalos (1998) reported on career expectations among Mexican-American high school girls.

Diemer and Blustein (2007) developed a vocational hope and identity measure to be applied to urban adolescent career development and identified four constructs of future career identification, vocational identity, work role resilience, and salience of chosen career. Juntunen and Wettersten (2006) and Yakushko and Sokolova (2010) validated the measures of work hope among economically disadvantaged youth and the Ukrainian college students respectively. Snyder et al. (1991) and Babyak, Snyder, and Yoshinobu (1993) from psychology and Herth (1991) from nursing have contributed significantly to the growth of hope as a construct and measure to theorize its effects on various positive life outcomes—not limited to employment and career outcomes.

Along with the widespread utilization of hope measures as a protective factor, P. Hong, Sheriff, and Naeger (2009) derived this concept as being central to their research by way of a bottom-up approach to conceptualizing and theorizing self-sufficiency from the perspective of low-income job seekers. Extensive qualitative analyses of focus groups were conducted to develop a measure that captured the experiences of low-income job seekers and their understandings of self-sufficiency (P. Hong 2013). The result of these investigations led to development of the Employment Hope Scale (EHS; P. Hong and Choi 2013, 2017; P. Hong, Choi, and Polanin 2014; P. Hong, Polanin, and Pigott 2012; P. Hong et al. 2016) and the Perceived Employment Barrier Scale (PEBS; P. Hong et al. 2014; P. Hong, Song, et al. 2018).

Combining the EHS and PEBS, the PSS process was theorized to affect the ESS outcome (P. Hong 2013). PSS speaks to the undoing of the psychological barriers that drew political criticisms as the source of long-term stay on welfare. It is the switching of these barriers into the hopeful possibilities that generate the momentum for goal commitment, pursuit, and achievement (R. Hong et al. 2019). However, less attention has been given to this as part of the comprehensive action plan to promote the ESS outcome (Cooney 2006).

This process of developing PSS is theoretically supported by a concept called "mental contrasting," which involves concurrently focusing on a positive outcome and the obstacles that block the path to the outcome (Duckworth et al. 2011). By engaging in the process of contrasting the barrier-filled reality with the desired future outcome, one generates positive energy toward goals (Oettingen 2000; Oettingen, Pak, and Schnetter 2001). Perceiving barriers first as barriers is the starting point in this psychological process to transform the negative self-assessment into a positive one and channel this toward the desired future outcomes (P. Hong 2013).

STUDY METHODOLOGY

Data and Data Collection Strategy

This study examined adults receiving health care career pathway training and employment support at two HPOG partner sites. Approximately 834 respondents were recruited to participate in the survey. The PSS survey instrument was developed and approved by Loyola University Chicago's institutional review board. Program participants were asked to participate in surveys at four different time points (start of program, middle of program, end of program/employment, and six-month follow-up)—consistent with the HPOG partners' PRS scheduled data collection and entry (see Figure 10.1).

Loyola University Chicago researchers also conducted seven focus groups of staff, employers, alumni, and current students from the two HPOG program partner sites to supplement the quantitative data. They used this qualitative data to further examine the extent to which HPOG program participation affected PSS and to explore which key programmatic components of HPOG significantly influenced successful program completion and economic success.

Measures and Analyses

The PSS survey collected basic demographic information and measured employment-related intrapersonal and noncognitive skills, employment hope, and perceived barriers to employment.

The Short Employment Hope Scale (EHS-14) was used to measure the positive psychometric properties of PSS (P. Hong, Choi, and Polanin 2014). The 4-factor, 14-item Likert-type scale—ranging between 0 at the lower end and 10 at the higher end—has been found to have a high reliability and validity in the cross-national context (P. Hong et al. 2016). The four factors or subscales of EHS are 1) psychological empowerment, 2) futuristic self-motivation, 3) utilization of skills and resources, and 4) goal orientation (P. Hong, Choi, and Polanin 2014). The average score of EHS with 10 being the maximum possible score and 0 being the lowest possible score was used to denote employment hope.

The Perceived Employment Barrier Scale (PEBS) was used to measure the barriers among HPOG program participants (P. Hong et al. 2014). The 5-factor, 20-item Likert-type PEBS ranged between 1 at the lower end and 5 at the higher end with a high reliability and validity and robust cross-cultural applicability (P. Hong et al. 2018): 1) health and mental health barriers, 2) human capital barrier, 3) labor market exclusion barrier, 4) child care barrier, and 5) soft skills barrier (P. Hong et al. 2014). Each item measured the extent to which respondents personally perceived it to be a barrier to finding employment, and the average score of all 20 items was calculated to capture the overall level of perceived employment barrier.

PSS was measured by taking the difference score between the EHS and PEBS (P. Hong, Choi, and Key 2018). ESS was measured using the WEN ESS Scale to capture the multidimensionality of economic well-being (Gowdy and Pearlmutter 1993). This continuous measure includes various questions that fall under four factors: 1) autonomy and self-determination, 2) financial security and responsibility, 3) family and self-well-being, and 4) basic assets for community living.

As for the focus group data, the following questions were used as the guide:

1) HPOG program in general. "What are your overall feelings as you go through this HPOG program? Now that you are in a training program, how is it different from what you thought it would be?"

2) Goals. "What made you decide to pursue your education through HPOG? Talk about some of your goals. How has being in the HPOG program helped you develop your goals?"

3) Internal and external motivation. "What were your internal and external motivations initially in the program, and what has motivated you to keep going? How has being in the HPOG program changed the way you feel about yourself? How has the program changed how you consider your chances for getting a job?"

4) Barriers vs. support. "What do you think are the things that make it hard for you to get a job? What supports will help you get a job? Will these supports help you overcome the obstacles that were mentioned?"

5) Linkages. "How do goals, motivation, and barriers come together for you? How do you think hope plays a part in your training right now? Is hope from within or from other people?"

A series of rigorous statistical analyses for quantitative data were conducted to examine the relationship between PSS and ESS among HPOG program participants at the two program partner sites. Qualitative content analysis was further conducted to fully explicate the meaning of the texts in focus group data. After open coding, the information derived from the focus groups was segmented with the codes based on the meaning units, which were later semantically classified. Data reduction was then involved to identify and highlight the most relevant and meaningful descriptions of texts (Schreier 2012). To ensure trustworthiness throughout the study, the researchers used credibility, dependability, conformability, and transferability, following the suggestions of Lincoln and Guba (1985).

Sample Description of HPOG Students by Two HPOG Sites

Participants in the HPOG programs at Southland and Gateway could be characterized as low-income job seekers who lack education and skills, have limited human capital or have health problems, are challenged with a host of employment barriers, have lived in areas of concentrated poverty and joblessness, and subsequently have difficulty finding and keeping jobs.

Of 834 participants, 64.05 percent were working in jobs that they had been with for an average of 1,000 days at an average hourly rate of $10.80. As shown in Table 10.1, only 39.69 percent were employed in jobs that sponsored their health insurance, and 26.6 percent had jobs that provided a pension. Only 33.81 percent of workers were able to pay all their bills with their earned income. Nearly 70 percent had at least one child, and approximately 20 percent had more than three children. It was also revealed that a majority of participants (95.45 percent) had at least one other adult living in the household, and 91.21 percent had one or more earners living in the same household to help offset the cost

Table 10.1 Sample Characteristics

Characteristics	Southland (N = 386)		Gateway (N = 448)		Total (N = 834)	
	N / M	% / SD	N / M	% / SD	N / M	% / SD
Employed						
Yes	196	53.26	319	73.17	515	64.05
No	172	46.74	117	26.83	289	35.95
Employed days	916 (1,148)		1,152 (1,402)		1,043 (1,293)	
Hourly wage ($)	11.24 (5.59)		10.54 (3.31)		10.80 (4.30)	
Health insurance						
Yes	77	39.09	131	40.06	208	39.69
No	120	60.91	196	59.94	316	60.31
Pension						
Yes	45	23.44	92	28.48	137	26.60
No	147	76.56	231	71.52	378	73.40
Able to pay bills						
Yes	81	23.14	177	42.86	258	33.81
No	269	76.86	236	57.14	505	66.19
Children						
0	112	30.27	136	31.41	248	30.88
1	104	28.11	119	27.48	223	27.77
2	83	22.43	91	21.02	174	21.67
3 or above	71	19.19	87	20.09	158	19.68
Adult(s)						
0	14	3.71	23	5.26	37	4.55
1	172	45.62	179	40.96	351	43.12
2	113	29.97	149	34.10	262	32.19
3 or above	78	20.69	86	19.68	164	20.15
Earner(s)						
0	42	11.54	27	6.41	69	8.79
1	233	64.01	239	56.77	472	60.13
2	70	19.23	112	26.60	182	23.18
3 or above	19	5.22	43	10.21	62	7.90
House income	16,216 (14,606)		20,880 (19,351)		18,830 (17,567)	
Welfare benefit(s)						
Yes	211	56.87	191	44.32	402	50.12
No	160	43.13	240	55.68	400	49.88

(continued)

Table 10.1 (continued)

Characteristics	Southland (N = 386)		Gateway (N = 448)		Total (N = 834)	
	N / M	% / SD	N / M	% / SD	N / M	% / SD
Marital status						
Married, spouse present	40	10.64	82	19.07	122	15.14
Married, spouse absent	20	5.32	13	3.02	33	4.09
Never married	258	68.62	262	60.93	520	64.52
Separated	13	3.46	10	2.33	23	2.85
Divorced	41	10.90	60	13.95	101	12.53
Widowed	4	1.06	3	0.70	7	0.87
Housing						
Rental	144	44.86	246	60.59	390	53.65
Own home/condo	111	34.58	79	19.46	190	26.13
No home	4	1.25	12	2.96	16	2.02
Assisted housing	26	8.10	41	10.10	67	9.22
Other	36	11.21	28	6.90	64	8.80
Age (years)	31.48	(10.19)	30.39	(9.55)	30.94	(9.89)
Gender						
Male	32	8.74	26	7.37	58	8.07
Female	334	91.26	327	92.63	661	91.83
Race						
Native American or Alaska Native	–	–	2	0.56	2	0.28
Asian or Pacific Islander	1	0.28	2	0.56	3	0.42
Black or African American	246	68.72	115	32.39	361	50.63
White or European American	48	13.41	156	43.94	204	28.61
Nonwhite Hispanic	33	9.22	46	12.96	79	11.08
Bi-/multiracial	24	6.70	28	7.89	52	7.29
Other	6	1.68	6	1.69	12	1.68
Education level						
Less than high school	3	0.83	20	5.81	23	3.26
High school/GED	72	19.89	94	27.33	166	23.51
Some college but no degree	148	40.88	113	32.85	261	36.97
Diploma or certificate from voc., tech, etc.	74	20.44	75	21.80	149	21.10

Table 10.1 (continued)

	Southland (N = 386)		Gateway (N = 448)		Total (N = 834)	
Characteristics	N / M	% / SD	N / M	% / SD	N / M	% / SD
Associate's degree	27	7.46	25	7.27	52	7.37
Bachelor's degree	29	8.01	14	4.07	43	6.09
Master's degree	9	2.49	1	0.29	10	1.42
Professional school degree	–	–	2	0.58	2	0.28
Longest job experience (years)	3.93 (6.03)		4.57 (6.42)		4.24 (6.23)	

NOTE: M = Mean. SD = Standard Deviation.
SOURCE: Authors' calculations based on survey data.

of living. Just over half the participants received some type of public assistance, and nearly 65 percent had never been married before and 80 percent were single. As for housing, nearly 80 percent either rented or owned a home, and 2.02 percent had no stable housing. Participants were a little older than 30 years of age, mostly women (91.83 percent), and largely minority—50.63 percent black or African American, 11.08 percent nonwhite Hispanic, and 7.29 percent multiracial. About 23.51 percent had a high school degree or equivalent, and about 73 percent had some postsecondary education. Participants' longest job experience was on average 4.24 years.

While the two HPOG program partners were similar in many of the demographic information, some key differences between the two are noteworthy. Compared to Southland (53.26 percent), Gateway (73.17 percent) had far more students who were working during HPOG program participation, and they tended to have worked longer days in the current job at a lower hourly rate. Gateway participants (42.86 percent) viewed at a greater rate than Southland participants (23.14 percent) that they were able to pay all their bills with their earned income. Also, Gateway students had more earners in the household, and a greater percentage of them lived in a household with two or more additional earners. Gateway students found themselves in households with greater average annual incomes, and fewer of them (44.32 percent) received public assistance compared to Southland students (56.87 percent). Slightly more Gateway students (22.09 percent) were currently married compared to their counterparts at Southland (15.96 percent). Gateway showed more rental homes (60.59 percent) compared to Southland (44.86 percent), while its homeownership (19.46 percent) was much lower than Southland (34.58 percent). Age and gender distribution was roughly the same, but Gateway had a greater proportion of white students (43.94 percent) compared to Southland (13.41 percent).

STUDY FINDINGS

Quantitative Results

At the end of HPOG 1.0 program implementation in September 2016, 834 students (92 percent of all participating HPOG students at the partner sites) had completed the first survey, 577 (69 percent) the second survey, and 326 (56 percent) the third survey. Over the four survey points, about 70 percent reported having increased their employment hope, and 57 percent reported having decreased their perceived employment barriers. As hypothesized, results indicated that PSS significantly contributes to ESS—specifically, increases in PSS contributed significantly to the increase in ESS outcomes. This suggests that workforce development practitioners should focus on clients' PSS when working with them to achieve ESS outcomes. Specifics of these results are discussed below, based on the research questions as presented before.

Research Question 1: How does PSS and ESS change over time during HPOG program participation?

Table 10.2 shows changes in PSS score over time during HPOG program participation. There is an increase in the PSS score between Time 1 and 2, and it remains about the same at Time 3. However, there is a significant decrease at Time 4. This pattern is consistent with the over-time change in employment hope and all of its subscales. Interestingly, perceived employment barriers drops between Time 1 and 2 and between Time 3 and 4. Particularly, the score difference between Time 1 and Time 4 for child care and human capital barriers declined at a statistically significant level.

Table 10.2 Descriptive Statistics (Total Sample)

Construct	Time 1 M	Time 1 SD	Time 2 M	Time 2 SD	Time 3 M	Time 3 SD	Time 4 M	Time 4 SD	F
Psychological self-sufficiency (PSS)	7.40	1.48	7.58	1.40	7.57	1.49	7.12	1.92	4.27** (Diff T2,T3 > T4)
Employment hope scale (EHS)	9.23	1.09	9.32	1.00	9.34	1.00	8.82	1.62	7.53*** (Diff T1,T2,T3 > T4)
Factor 1: Psychological empowerment	9.35	1.16	9.38	1.19	9.42	1.13	8.90	1.82	5.47** (Diff T1,T2,T3 > T4)
Factor 2: Futuristic self-motivation	9.24	1.27	9.25	1.26	9.24	1.34	8.74	1.86	5.09** (Diff T1,T2,T3 > T4)
Factor 3: Utilization of skills and resources	8.97	1.44	9.18	1.25	9.24	1.14	8.82	1.70	5.97*** (Diff T2,T3 > T4)
Factor 4: Goal-orientation	9.37	1.16	9.44	1.02	9.41	1.13	8.76	1.96	10.41*** (Diff T1,T2,T3 > T4)
Perceived employment barriers (PEB)	1.84	0.88	1.75	0.89	1.77	0.96	1.69	0.91	1.69
Factor 1: Physical & mental health	1.44	1.07	1.41	1.05	1.46	1.11	1.46	1.06	0.23
Factor 2: Labor market exclusion	2.18	1.11	2.07	1.07	2.07	1.12	1.93	1.13	2.54
Factor 3: Child care	1.96	1.18	1.84	1.19	1.88	1.22	1.64	1.04	2.99* (Diff T1 > T4)
Factor 4: Human capital	2.08	1.12	1.95	1.13	1.97	1.16	1.82	1.10	2.88* (Diff T1 > T4)
Factor 5: Soft skills	1.62	0.97	1.55	0.94	1.56	1.00	1.62	0.99	0.82

NOTE: *significant at the 0.10 level; **significant at the 0.05 level; ***significant at the 0.01 level. Time 1 (N = 834), Time 2 (N = 605), Time 3 (N = 422), Time 4 (N = 108).
SOURCE: Authors' calculations based on survey data.

Table 10.3 Descriptive Statistics (Total Sample)

Construct	Time 1		Time 2		Time 3		Time 4		F
	M	SD	M	SD	M	SD	M	SD	
Economic self-sufficiency (ESS)	2.78	0.96	2.82	0.97	2.91	1.00	3.23	1.02	6.81*** (Diff T1,T2,T3 < T4)
Resilience (R)	3.40	0.71	3.43	0.74	3.45	0.72	3.18	0.77	3.72*
Self-efficacy (SEF)	4.42	0.53	4.45	0.53	4.46	0.57	4.10	0.67	11.92*** (Diff T1,T2,T3 > T4)

NOTE: *significant at the 0.10 level; **significant at the 0.05 level; ***significant at the 0.01 level. Time 1 (N = 834), Time 2 (N = 605), Time 3 (N = 422), Time 4 (N = 108).

SOURCE: Authors' calculations based on survey data.

As for ESS, it gradually increases over the course of program participation. Particularly, the Time 4 score is significantly greater than the earlier three time points (see Table 10.3). Overall resilience and self-efficacy marginally increased from Time 1 to Time 3 but saw a significant drop at Time 4.

Table 10.4 describes information drawn from the PRS data and compares the PSS scores over time by each of the psychologically related support services provided by HPOG. PSS scores were maintained higher during Times 1–3 for participants who received academic counseling and case management compared to those who did not, and the drop in score at Time 4 was smaller in magnitude but statistically significant for those who did not use academic counseling. PSS scores increased at a higher rate during Times 1–3 for participants who received career counseling and job search services compared to those who did not, and the drop in PSS score was statistically significant for those who did not receive this service. Only 14 cases received mentoring service, and the score drop at Time 4 was as much as three full PSS points. However, the nonrecipient of the mentoring services had Time 4 PSS score significantly lower than the previous Time 2 and 3 scores.

Research Question 2: How are PSS and ESS scores different between the two HPOG partners?

Tables 10.5 and 10.6 present the difference in the PSS score change over time between the two HPOG program partners. Both start relatively equal at Time 1—7.38 for Southland and 7.41 for Gateway—but Southland increases marginally at Time 2 and drops at Time 3 to further decrease at Time 4. Gateway increases between Time 1 and 2 and between Time 2 and 3, only to see the PSS score drop to 7.06 compared to 7.19 for Southland at Time 4.

Employment hope at Southland continued to stay consistently high between Time 1 and 3, but the score dropped significantly at Time 4. All four subscales saw a significant decrease at Time 4. Barriers decreased overall, and in particular, labor market exclusion and human capital barriers subscales decreased at a statistically significant level at Time 4. Figure 10.2 shows the trend analysis.

For Gateway, employment hope score was lower compared to Southland, but the over time change showed a similar increasing pattern with the score at Time 4 dropping significantly. Interestingly, only

Table 10.4 PSS Scores over Time by Support Services (Total Sample)

Construct	N	Time 1		Time 2		Time 3		Time 4		F
		M	SD	M	SD	M	SD	M	SD	
Academic counseling										
Yes	137	7.44	1.64	7.84	1.11	7.87	1.29	6.67	2.66	2.62
No	1,547	7.39	1.50	7.58	1.40	7.57	1.50	7.25	1.77	2.64*
Career counseling										
Yes	92	7.27	1.49	7.51	1.42	7.64	1.44	6.44	3.23	1.23
No	1,592	7.40	1.51	7.61	1.37	7.59	1.49	7.24	1.74	3.40*
										(Diff T2 > T4)
Case management										
Yes	143	7.41	1.62	7.76	1.25	7.77	1.35	6.67	2.66	2.11
No	1,541	7.39	1.50	7.59	1.39	7.58	1.50	7.25	1.77	2.82*
Job search										
Yes	53	7.27	1.70	7.38	1.56	7.51	1.73	5.81	3.84	1.03
No	1,631	7.39	1.50	7.61	1.37	7.60	1.48	7.24	1.77	3.67*
										(Diff T2,T3 > T4)
Mentoring										
Yes	14	7.11	1.55	7.00	0.87	7.25	0.72	4.25	6.72	0.79
No	1,670	7.39	1.50	7.61	1.38	7.60	1.49	7.23	1.76	3.81**
										(Diff T2,T3 > T4)

NOTE: *significant at the 0.10 level; **significant at the 0.05 level; ***significant at the 0.01 level. Time 1 (N = 710), Time 2 (N = 520), Time 3 (N = 355), Time 4 (N = 99).
SOURCE: Authors' calculations based on survey data.

Table 10.5 Descriptive Statistics (Southland)

Construct	Time 1 M	Time 1 SD	Time 2 M	Time 2 SD	Time 3 M	Time 3 SD	Time 4 M	Time 4 SD	F
Psychological self-sufficiency (PSS)	7.38	1.46	7.51	1.43	7.41	1.56	7.19	1.57	0.88
Employment hope scale (EHS)	9.38	0.93	9.40	0.94	9.34	1.00	8.87	1.24	4.76** (Diff T1,T2,T3 > T4)
Factor 1: Psychological empowerment	9.55	0.97	9.49	1.06	9.48	0.94	8.84	1.75	7.24*** (Diff T1,T2,T3 > T4)
Factor 2: Futuristic self-motivation	9.40	1.16	9.37	1.17	9.24	1.38	9.24	1.79	5.65*** (Diff T1,T2,T3 > T4)
Factor 3: Utilization of skills and resources	9.07	1.32	9.22	1.24	9.22	1.15	8.89	1.38	1.76*** (Diff T1,T2,T3 > T4)
Factor 4: Goal-orientation	9.50	0.99	9.50	0.99	9.38	1.18	8.99	1.65	4.05** (Diff T1,T2,T3 > T4)
Perceived employment barriers (PEB)	2.00	0.99	1.90	1.00	1.93	1.08	1.68	0.94	1.68
Factor 1: Physical & mental health	1.64	1.29	1.58	1.23	1.62	1.27	1.42	1.04	0.55
Factor 2: Labor market exclusion	2.42	1.13	2.32	1.13	2.32	1.19	1.94	1.19	2.79*
Factor 3: Child care	1.97	1.19	1.97	1.31	1.99	1.34	1.57	1.05	1.79
Factor 4: Human capital	2.32	1.26	2.10	1.22	2.14	1.26	1.79	0.99	3.77* (Diff T1 > T4)
Factor 5: Soft skills	1.73	1.11	1.64	1.03	1.69	1.11	1.67	1.07	0.39

NOTE: *significant at the 0.10 level; **significant at the 0.05 level; ***significant at the 0.01 level. Time 1 (N = 386), Time 2 (N = 288), Time 3 (N = 225), Time 4 (N = 54).
SOURCE: Authors' calculations based on survey data.

Table 10.6 Descriptive Statistics (Gateway)

Construct	Time 1		Time 2		Time 3		Time 4		F
	M	SD	M	SD	M	SD	M	SD	
Psychological self-sufficiency (PSS)	7.41	1.50	7.64	1.38	7.74	1.39	7.06	2.23	4.66** (Diff T2,T3 > T4)
Employment hope scale (EHS)	9.11	1.20	9.25	1.04	9.33	1.02	8.76	1.93	4.20** (Diff T2,T3 > T4)
Factor 1: Psychological empowerment	9.19	1.28	9.27	1.28	9.34	1.31	8.97	1.90	1.45
Factor 2: Futuristic self-motivation	9.11	1.35	9.15	1.32	9.24	1.30	8.80	1.95	1.54
Factor 3: Utilization of skills and resources	8.89	1.53	9.14	1.27	9.25	1.13	8.76	1.97	4.41** (Diff T3 > T4)
Factor 4: Goal-orientation	9.24	1.28	9.38	1.05	9.43	1.07	8.54	2.22	8.16*** (Diff T1,T2,T3 > T4)
Perceived employment barriers (PEB)	1.70	0.75	1.61	0.76	1.58	0.77	1.70	0.89	1.54
Factor 1: Physical & mental health	1.26	0.80	1.25	0.82	1.28	0.86	1.50	1.10	1.48
Factor 2: Labor market exclusion	1.98	1.06	1.85	0.96	1.79	0.96	1.93	1.08	2.00
Factor 3: Child care	1.95	1.17	1.73	1.05	1.75	1.05	1.70	1.04	3.34*
Factor 4: Human capital	1.88	0.94	1.81	1.03	1.78	1.00	1.84	1.20	0.60
Factor 5: Soft skills	1.53	0.82	1.47	0.85	1.41	0.84	1.57	0.91	1.16

NOTE: *significant at the 0.10 level; **significant at the 0.05 level; ***significant at the 0.01 level. Time 1 (N = 448), Time 2 (N = 317), Time 3 (N = 197), Time 4 (N = 54).
SOURCE: Authors' calculations based on survey data.

Figure 10.2 Descriptive Trend Analysis of Psychological Self-Sufficiency (Barriers and Hope) and Economic Self-Sufficiency at Southland

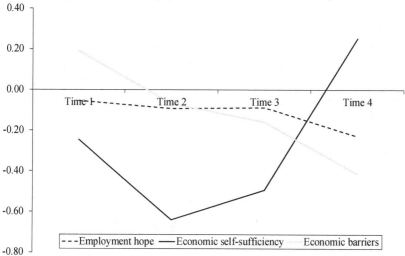

SOURCE: Authors' calculations based on survey data.

Figure 10.3 Descriptive Trend Analysis of Psychological Self-Sufficiency (Barriers and Hope) and Economic Self-Sufficiency at Gateway

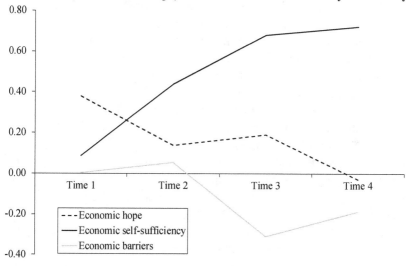

SOURCE: Authors' calculations based on survey data.

two of four subscales—utilization of skills and resources and goal orientation—saw significant decrease at Time 4. Child care barrier was the only subscale that decreased significantly at Time 4. Figure 10.3 shows the trend analysis.

As for ESS, Southland's score was lower (2.59) compared to Gateway (2.94) at Time 1 but displayed consistent increase to Time 4, with the Time 4 score being significantly larger than the previous three time points (see Table 10.7). A similar trend was observed for Gateway, and the Time 4 score (3.42) was greater than that of Southland's (3.11) (see Table 10.8). Resilience and self-efficacy were found to significantly decrease at Time 4 in the Southland sample but not at Gateway.

Research Question 3: How is PSS associated with program completion and employment outcomes?

This analysis used the PRS and PSS survey data. Table 10.9 first illustrates the change in PSS scores over time between those who were employed at exit and those who were not. The PSS score was higher at Time 3 for those who found employment at exit compared to their counterparts, and the drop in score at Time 4 was much greater at a statistically significant level for those who did not find employment at the time of exit.

When comparing those who were employed at a follow-up date with those who were not, PSS scores were greater at all time points for those who were employed compared to those who were not. The Time 1 and Time 3 PSS scores were particularly higher at a statistically significant level. Also, those who were not employed at follow-up had a significant drop in PSS score at Time 4.

Similarly for HPOG program completion, the PSS score at Time 1 was slightly higher for those who did complete compared to those who did not. The completed group maintained higher PSS scores throughout Times 1–4, and the Time 4 score in particular was statistically significantly higher for those who completed the HPOG program compared to those who did not. While the group that completed the program experienced very little reduction in the PSS score at Time 4, the amount of decrease was statistically significant for those who did not complete the program. The average hourly wage at follow-up was $13.35 for all HPOG participants at Southland and Gateway.

Table 10.7 Descriptive Statistics (Southland)

Construct	Time 1		Time 2		Time 3		Time 4		F
	M	SD	M	SD	M	SD	M	SD	
Economic self-sufficiency (ESS)	2.59	0.98	2.55	0.95	2.70	1.02	3.11	0.98	5.54*** (Diff T1,T2,T3 < T4)
Resilience (R)	3.53	0.66	3.53	0.74	3.48	0.75	3.08	0.81	6.73*** (Diff T1,T2,T3 > T4)
Self-efficacy (SEF)	4.51	0.52	4.52	0.54	4.49	0.56	3.89	0.71	21.16*** (Diff T1,T2,T3 > T4)

NOTE: *significant at the 0.10 level; **significant at the 0.05 level; ***significant at the 0.01 level. Time 1 (N = 386), Time 2 (N = 288), Time 3 (N = 225), Time 4 (N = 54).
SOURCE: Authors' calculations based on survey data.

Table 10.8 Descriptive Statistics (Gateway)

Construct	Time 1		Time 2		Time 3		Time 4		F
	M	SD	M	SD	M	SD	M	SD	
Economic self-sufficiency (ESS)	2.94	0.92	3.06	0.93	3.15	0.93	3.42	1.08	4.76** (Diff T1,T2 < T4)
Resilience (R)	3.28	0.74	3.34	0.73	3.42	0.69	3.33	0.69	1.16
Self-efficacy (SEF)	4.34	0.52	4.40	0.51	4.42	0.57	4.39	0.49	1.24

NOTE: *significant at the 0.10 level; **significant at the 0.05 level; ***significant at the 0.01 level. Time 1 (N = 448), Time 2 (N = 317), Time 3 (N = 197), Time 4 (N = 54).
SOURCE: Authors' calculations based on survey data.

330

Table 10.9 Descriptive Statistics (Total Sample)

Construct	N	Time 1 M	Time 1 SD	Time 2 M	Time 2 SD	Time 3 M	Time 3 SD	Time 4 M	Time 4 SD	F
Employed at exit		0.32(NS)		0.33(NS)		1.65(NS)		0.88(NS)		
Yes	584	7.42	1.57	7.63	1.49	7.78	1.38	7.37	1.92	1.86
No	1,100	7.38	1.47	7.59	1.31	7.50	1.53	7.02	1.91	3.14*
										(Diff T2,T3 > T4)
Health care employer		0.39(NS)		1.26(NS)		1.61(NS)		0.11(NS)		
Yes	446	7.43	1.67	7.73	1.49	7.81	1.43	7.20	2.11	2.17
No	1,238	7.38	1.45	7.56	1.33	7.52	1.50	7.16	1.82	2.28
Employed at follow-up date		2.16*		0.73(NS)		2.11*		1.43(NS)		
Yes	305	7.56	1.19	7.71	1.25	7.95	1.15	7.60	1.92	0.93
No	1,379	7.33	1.56	7.59	1.40	7.52	1.54	6.99	1.90	4.57**
										(Diff T2,T3 > T4)
Exited		0.87(NS)		0.22(NS)		1.88(NS)		1.47(NS)		
Yes	915	7.43	1.55	7.62	1.40	7.75	1.35	7.42	1.88	2.21
No	769	7.33	1.44	7.59	1.34	7.45	1.58	6.86	1.93	3.58*
										(Diff T2,T3 > T4)
HPOG completed		0.58(NS)		0.17(NS)		1.54(NS)		2.43*		
Yes	689	7.43	1.53	7.62	1.44	7.73	1.38	7.71	1.44	1.69
No	995	7.36	1.48	7.60	1.33	7.49	1.56	6.79	2.11	5.22**
										(Diff T1,T2,T3 > T4)

Hourly wage at follow-up   13.35 (6.43)

NOTE: *p < 0.05; **p < 0.01; ***p < 0.001; NS = not significant. Time 1 (N = 710), Time 2 (N = 520), Time 3 (N = 355), Time 4 (N = 99).
SOURCE: Authors' calculations based on survey data; HPOG Performance Reporting System.

Table 10.10 Descriptive Statistics (Southland)

Construct	N	Time 1		Time 2		Time 3		Time 4		F
		M	SD	M	SD	M	SD	M	SD	
Employed at exit										
Yes	34	7.56	1.30	7.75	1.75	7.87	0.72	7.88	1.23	0.13
No	720	7.35	1.49	7.56	1.34	7.43	1.57	7.17	1.62	1.35
Health care employer										
Yes	15	8.02	1.24	8.43	0.54	8.20	0.70	7.75	1.70	0.18
No	739	7.34	1.48	7.56	1.36	7.44	1.55	7.19	1.60	1.32
Employed at follow-up date										
Yes	87	7.72	1.19	7.61	1.49	7.62	1.30	7.89	1.40	0.11
No	667	7.30	1.51	7.56	1.34	7.43	1.58	7.10	1.61	1.80
Exited										
Yes	111	7.57	1.66	7.81	1.22	7.77	1.28	8.12	1.29	0.45
No	643	7.31	1.44	7.53	1.37	7.40	1.58	7.02	1.60	1.76
HPOG completed										
Yes	94	7.56	1.68	7.56	1.51	7.62	1.38	7.97	1.45	0.15
No	660	7.32	1.45	7.57	1.34	7.42	1.57	7.09	1.60	1.79
Hourly wage at follow-up				14.78 (7.06)						

NOTE: Time 1 (N = 307), Time 2 (N = 223), Time 3 (N = 173), Time 4 (N = 51).
SOURCE: Authors' calculations based on survey data; HPOG Performance Reporting System.

Examining the association between PSS and program completion and employment outcomes at each HPOG program level, the overall trend was mostly consistent but had some locally particular data patterns. As presented in Table 10.10, Southland's data showed that the PSS scores continued to rise for those who completed the program at all time points and maintained higher scores, particularly at Times 3 and 4. PSS was higher for those who were employed at exit, who had health care employment, and who were employed at follow-up during Times 1–4. It was interesting to find that the PSS scores did not experience a drop at Time 4 except for those who were employed in health care. Even in this case, the drop at Time 4 was not as large in magnitude compared to those who were not. The average hourly wage at follow-up was $14.78.

For Gateway, as shown in Table 10.11, the group that found employment at exit had a PSS score that was closely tied with its counterpart at Times 1 and 2, but the gap widened at Time 3, and the drop at Time 4 was not as precipitous compared to those who were not employed at exit. For health care employment, the gap started widening at Time 2 after starting at a similar point at Time 1, and the score at Time 4 ended up being higher than those who were not employed in health care. Those who were employed at follow-up started with a higher PSS score and maintained higher scores throughout program participation and at follow-up Time 4. The drop in PSS score at Time 4 was statistically significant in reference to its Time 2 and Time 3 scores for those who were not employed at follow-up. Program completion followed the same pattern as that of employment at exit, and those who did not complete experienced a significant decrease in the PSS score at Time 4 in comparison to its Time 1–3 PSS scores. The average hourly wage at follow-up was $12.75.

Research Question 4: How does PSS affect economic self-sufficiency (ESS)?

After validating the latent factor structure of the measurement model, the PSS theoretical model was tested using a structural equation modeling (SEM) technique (P. Hong, Choi, and Key 2018). As shown in Figure 10.4, all fit indices indicate that the hypothesized model has a good fit to the data, $\chi^2 = 304.287$, p $= 0.000$, df $= 63$, CFI $= 0.957$, TLI $= 0.947$, RMSEA $= 0.068$ [0.060 $-$ 0.075]. PEBS had a negative associa-

Table 10.11 Descriptive Statistics (Gateway)

Construct	N	Time 1 M	Time 1 SD	Time 2 M	Time 2 SD	Time 3 M	Time 3 SD	Time 4 M	Time 4 SD	F
Employed at exit										
Yes	550	7.41	1.59	7.63	1.49	7.77	1.42	7.33	1.97	1.78
No	380	7.43	1.45	7.65	1.24	7.67	1.42	6.13	3.17	3.35*
										(DiffT1,T2,T3 > T4)
Health care employer										
Yes	432	7.40	1.68	7.72	1.50	7.79	1.45	7.17	2.15	2.19
No	499	7.43	1.40	7.57	1.29	7.67	1.38	7.06	2.41	1.34
Employed at follow-up date										
Yes	218	7.61	1.19	7.74	1.17	8.11	1.05	7.50	2.08	1.75
No	712	7.36	1.60	7.61	1.45	7.62	1.49	6.81	2.33	3.10*
										(DiffT2,T3 > T4)
Exited										
Yes	804	7.41	1.53	7.60	1.42	7.75	1.37	7.28	1.95	2.35
No	126	7.46	1.47	7.85	1.20	7.67	1.62	3.53	5.69	5.43**
										(DiffT1,T2,T3 > T4)
HPOG completed										
Yes	595	7.41	1.51	7.63	1.43	7.75	1.38	7.66	1.46	1.80
No	335	7.43	1.54	7.65	1.33	7.68	1.52	5.84	3.14	5.89***
										(DiffT1,T2,T3 > T4)
Hourly wage at follow-up						12.75 (6.08)				

NOTE: Time 1 (N = 403), Time 2 (N = 297), Time 3 (N = 182), Time 4 (N = 48).
SOURCE: Authors' calculations based on survey data; HPOG Performance Reporting System.

Figure 10.4 Structural Equation Model of Psychological and Economic Self-Sufficiency

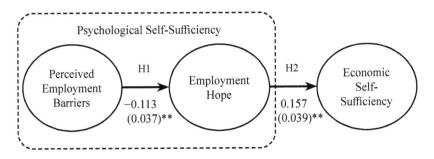

NOTE: Standardized errors are in parentheses.
SOURCE: Authors' calculations based on survey data.

tion with EHS, and EHS was positively associated with ESS. The Sobel test result indicated that EHS is a full mediator ($z = -2.43$, $p = 0.014$).

As reported in Figures 10.5 and 10.6, the PSS theoretical model for Southland had fit indices that indicated a good fit to the data, $\chi^2 = 158.341$, $p = 0.000$, df = 63, CFI = 0.963, TLI = 0.955, RMSEA [95 percent CI] = 0.063 [0.051 − 0.075]. PEBS had a negative relationship with EHS, and EHS was positively associated with ESS. The PSS theoretical model for Gateway had fit indices that also indicated a good fit to the data, $\chi^2 = 198.941$, $p = 0.000$, df = 63, CFI = 0.953, TLI = 0.942, RMSEA [95 percent CI] = 0.069 [0.059 − 0.080]. PEBS had a negative relationship with EHS, and EHS was positively associated with ESS. The Sobel test result indicated that EHS is a full mediator (Southland: $z = -1.96$, $p = 0.049$ and Gateway: $z = -2.31$, $p = 0.020$).

Qualitative Results

Based on focus groups at the two sites, students reported that the HPOG program has helped them overcome fear and build confidence and a sense of achievement in their pursuit of a health care career. They said the HPOG program was a once-in-a-lifetime opportunity that made a lasting impact on their lives. They underscored holistic staff support— characterized by accessibility, accountability, and encouragement—as a critical program component. Two categories emerged from the focus group with students: the meaning of the HPOG program and students'

Figure 10.5 Structural Equation Model of Psychological Self-Sufficiency and Economic Self-Sufficiency for Southland

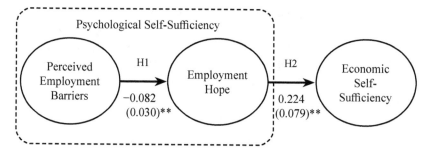

NOTE: Standardized errors are in parentheses.
SOURCE: Authors' calculations based on survey data.

Figure 10.6 Structural Equation Model of Psychological Self-Sufficiency and Economic Self-Sufficiency for Gateway

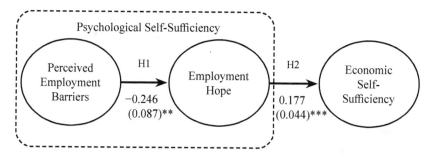

NOTE: Standardized errors are in parentheses.
SOURCE: Authors' calculations based on survey data.

internal strengths. Other findings involved staff's perspectives on the HPOG program, and staff's perspectives on hope and barriers were categorized from the focus groups with program staff, tutors, and advisors. Lastly, the focus groups with employers identified self-confidence and motivation as qualities of good employees.

Across all focus groups, intrinsic support of the HPOG program providers—namely, instructors, tutors, program staff, and peer groups—appears to increase and sustain PSS at the individual student level.

The meaning of the HPOG program among students

Participants identified four subcategories with regard to the meaning of the HPOG program—overcoming fear and confidence building, sense of achievement, giving opportunity, and staff support. Notably, nontraditional, close support from instructors, tutors, and program staff was described to have three core aspects to the supportive relationship—accessible, accountable, and encouraging. Below are excerpts from the focus group:

1) Overcoming fear and confidence building

I'm always learning. Always. Always. So that helps, it helps being on the job now. Because you can incorporate new, you know, and different things, and . . . it takes away a lot of fear of the unknown. That's what this program has done. Whereas if I came into school just on my own, I always found a reason to back out. Or, you know, it was always something. Whereas now I feel more accountable . . . it just makes it a little easier.

2) Sense of achievement

Not only did it help me, you know, with learning more, and obviously, being able to be marketable at some point, but it helped me on a very personal level as well. I don't think I would have been able to achieve [as] much [as] I have without HPOG.

3) Giving opportunity

I personally felt like it's a second chance. When life gets in the way. Like, you know, sometimes life gets in the way, where, some of us are older, so we probably had that opportunity before but we didn't take advantage of it. So, I feel like this is a second chance . . . to do it right.

4) Staff support

I think HPOP is just overall just a good support system. Period.

[T]hey know who you are, they get back to you right away, you don't have to wait in a long line to talk to them, you don't have to you know, wait days for a return phone call.

I bet if I email her, she'll have an answer probably in about 15 minutes—I say, "Do she sit on there and watch the pot?"

I felt like they hold you accountable. Like that accountability means soooo much. Like, being young and you have some work and school, and then some people have children, so when you meet with them they hold you accountable—what's your grade, how did you do on this test, and not only do they hold you accountable, but they encourage you at the same time.

I felt comfortable with her. I didn't feel rushed. She explained how to do my résumé.

Students' internal strengths

Confidence and hope were commented as internal strengths. In particular, participants described that hope is an inspiration to make a better life. Below is an excerpt from the focus group:

Well, I'm a whole lot more confident than I was before.

I think that hope is the beginning, is the start . . . it's the beginning, and then once that hope sets in, then you start believing, and then that's where it—and then you have that faith that you need to be able to feel that you can accomplish. After, after beginning with that hope.

Hope gives you that ambition to keep pushing forward. I think it's an inspiration, you know, to just make a better life for yourself in the future, have more income to be able to . . . afford to do what you want.

Only way you fail is not to try.

Staff's perspectives on the HPOG program

HPOG staff pointed out the positive impact of program structures on helping students. Below is an excerpt from the focus group:

We're giving them a process, a structure, a point of contact, and I think the students really embrace that—that from all the chaos in their background, they're coming to some place that actually has a plan to get from A to B. And I think that's kind of refreshing for some of the students to have that, for sometimes the very first time.

Furthermore, the function of peer support was constantly stressed. Togetherness and a cohort system were used to describe peer support in the HPOG program.

I think our class is really unique because we are together for six hours a day, and that's a lot of time to spend with people, and when we go to the nursing home we're working side by side, so we have to have that trust in each other to do that, but, you know, it took her a little bit, but she softened up.

One of the things that HPOP has brought to the table is that this might be the very first team that they've been on that's been successful, and a cohort that's kind of moved through a program and been successful. And I think that translates very effectively into the workplace.

Staff also identified the important function of a sense of belonging in the program to create a pride among students.

I think for many of them, it's that first sense of a community that they're part of and that they're proud of. Some of them are not proud of the communities that they come to Gateway from, yet they're on our campus as a community, and I think there's a sense of pride in that.

Staff's perspectives on hope and barriers

Staff said that goal attainment led to self-efficacy, and then self-efficacy increased the level of hope. Also, hope was described to function to mitigate the barriers. Below is an excerpt from the focus group:

I'm so thankful for this program, and when they start off like that right at the beginning, you just see the hope in their eyes now, that they can get through school and don't have to worry about certain barriers that would, you know, hold them back.

Self-efficacy comes from achieving goals like that, it's a mindset that people are doing things for them, and now they're doing something for themselves, and that self-efficacy piece, I think, raises their level of hope.

Four aspects of perceived barriers emerged: No role model, childcare, health issues, and balance between work and study.

I'm hearing their stories. So I think, too, this is their norm, this is their life, they don't know what it'll be like to be in a different situation. 'Cause it's all they've ever seen. And so I think that, it's just scary for them. Or, my mom didn't work, my grandma didn't work, my—this person doesn't work, so they haven't had the role model, they don't know what it looks like to go, to go out every day, to go seek that job, or, and those types of things.

And just as far as if they have to retake courses, sometimes, it's just, you know there's some issues with their child care, it could be numerous things, and they had to drop a class or withdraw, or didn't pass for some reason.

So one of those barriers may be that they have to work during the same time that those classes are being held.

Employers' expectations on employees

Employers in the focus groups identified three qualities for successful employees: high level of confidence, independent working, and high level of motivation. Below is an excerpt from the focus group:

I'm in home health care, so we are really looking for people that we are gonna be able to trust to be working independently, so we look for people that have good self-confidence, that are going to present well when they go in the customer's home, and that we are gonna trust to do what they're assigned to do.

I've been really impressed lately [with someone whom] I just hired in the last couple of months, and she is so motivated and wants to continue learning. She's an undergrad, loves her jobs, and just comes to me, probably weekly, and says, "What else can I do, what more can I do? I wanna learn how to do this, I wanna learn how to do that." Which I love, rather than the nurse that just goes out, does her business, and goes home. The motivation factor for me is really the key.

FURTHER RESEARCH USING PSS

This project examines the dynamics of low-wage labor market and workforce development as their outcomes are affected by the psychological process of program participants. The study focused on the PSS process as a precursor to the ESS outcome; the PSS process embodies both the individual and structural conditions that limit one's ability to enter and stay active in the labor market for low-income and low-skilled individuals. PSS could be mistaken for its primary focus on the surface to be about changing the individual psychological motivation as opposed to addressing the structural inequities that generate systemically limiting labor market conditions for low-income, low-skilled individuals (P. Hong 2013). Because PSS is a function of employment barriers both at the individual (i.e., health and mental health, child care, and soft skills) and structural (labor market exclusion and human capital) levels, it has the potential for suggesting a bottom-up program and policy recommendations (P. Hong et al. 2014).

First, findings on PSS increasing over time during program participation—both at Southland and Gateway—between Times 1 and 3 show that HPOG programming provides the support necessary to activate hope and minimize the perceived barriers. However, consistent findings on the significant decrease in the PSS score at Time 4 suggest HPOG program participants are vulnerable once they leave the supportive environment and enter into the precarious workplace norms, culture, and scheduling. PSS at Time 4 offers the opportunity to engage the employers to invest in the HPOG graduates during their onboarding process—so as to prevent PSS scores from decreasing among their new hires.

Second, associating PSS with HPOG program completion, employment, retention, and ESS could help promote program and policy development that fosters growth in PSS. This could help bridge the gap between perceived employment barriers and employment hope and have significant implications for how antipoverty policies are to be shaped in this country.

Third, because PSS affects ESS consistently in the Southland and Gateway samples, HPOG programs could be more intentional about investing in PSS in the program delivery. For instance, the use of support services by HPOG participants was associated with increase in PSS. However, this information says little about what quality service is standard for ensuring PSS to be strengthened during the course of program participation. Qualitative data support the importance of "soft touch" coaching and instruction, rules and boundaries of accountability, and peer support, all of which combine to provide a sense of belonging and make the journey all the more worthwhile. However, because there is no mechanism to invest in this seemingly central yet difficult to standardize relationship-based support system, it is seen as peripheral or left to the discretion of HPOG program specialists and support staff.

In response to this dilemma, at the request of HPOG partners and other community-based workforce development programs, the Loyola

University Chicago research team at the Center for Research on Self-Sufficiency (CROSS) developed a standardized curriculum aimed to empower the potential to achieve goals by way of channeling individual PSS toward the targeted goal—employment and career advancement. The CROSS research team named the program Transforming Impossible into Possible (TIP®) to represent its main focus on individual PSS as the process of transforming barriers (impossible) to hope (possible) (P. Hong 2016). Goal setting in TIP® does not use the traditional SMART (specific, measurable, attainable, relevant, and timely) goal method; rather, the nontraditional meaning-making and purpose-finding TIP 1 (true, intrinsic, purposeful) goal process, which is designed to reach the TIP 2 (tangible, intentional, practical) goal outcome. Delivered in a group setting, TIP® generates peer support and relationship-based strength to recognize and accept the barriers as such and activate hope to commit to actions that will overcome the barriers. TIP® could serve as a model to provide a standardized soft skills baseline on which HPOG programs could provide the training and education necessary to develop health care career skills and knowledge.

The partnership between two HPOG programs and Loyola University Chicago used PSS as an intermediate benchmark of success that leads to program completion, employment, and retention (P. Hong 2013). Other HPOG programs could consider using the Employment Hope Scale (EHS) and the Perceived Employment Barrier Scale (PEBS) to track PSS over time during program participation. Also, PSS to ESS can be adopted as the theory of change based on an empowerment perspective to frame program development and evaluation (P. Hong, Choi, and Key 2018).

PROGRAM AND POLICY IMPLICATIONS

At the program design stage, HPOG has been framed as an employment initiative for TANF participants and other low-income individuals. This approach, like other federal workforce development programs, leads to a set of endpoint outcomes where job placement is one critical metric for success and, in turn, the increase in employment wages (and decrease in TANF dependency) will generate self-sufficiency for the participant. The correlation between training and employment makes intuitive sense, when policy evaluation relies on a narrower definition of workforce development where coordination between institutional stakeholders (government agencies, educational partners, and employers) is horizontally aligned (Jacobs and Hawley 2009, p. 2544).

The assessment of HPOG, however, is better informed when using a process-oriented outcomes framework that examines the employability of program participants (P. Hong 2013). This shift in emphasis suggests a broader definition of workforce development to reflect the "set of processes that govern the identification, recruitment, assessment and training of job seekers into employment as well as the maintenance and advancement of these persons in their careers that enhance self-sufficiency and revitalize the communities in which these individuals live" (Holland 2015, p. 55). Using this lens, therefore, suggests that the process of workforce development also requires vertical directionality that must be evaluated as hard-to-serve populations move closer toward accessing the labor market as their barriers are addressed with interventions of a strong safety net and social network.

But this vertical workforce development activity also calls upon other interventions from workforce entities to assist in addressing the direct and indirect barriers that job seekers face as they aim to penetrate the labor market (Iversen and Armstrong 2006). Direct barriers are those impediments to employment that are related to employment, either by job history, experience, or skills capacity, as well as those challenges that address the means to access and means to employment (e.g., lack of or a poorly written résumé, limited knowledge of where to look for job opportunities, or not having the skills that are required for an occupation/industry). Indirect barriers are more environmentally based that prevent or inhibit the job seeker to enter and sustain employment (e.g., transportation, internet access, poor housing), as well as those noncognitive challenges that relate to social or family support (e.g., lack of dependent care, limited or no medical insurance to address chronic health concerns) that are specific to an individual job seeker on a case-by-case basis.

For HPOG participants, the barriers to employability are not cognitive, as a stand-alone reason for poor labor force participation, nor are their impediments indicative of a participant's putative laziness (as perceived by the general public) or that job opportunities are not available in the labor markets where HPOG grants have been awarded. This study points to a previously underreported finding about the supply side of the labor market, which is that HPOG participants often face deficits of PSS as a process, which yields to lack of hope and motivation to look for and enter work in the face of perceived barriers. The other yet unexplored demand-side disconnect has to do with the lack of investment by health care employers in a PSS-focused organizational culture to onboard and stabilize the newly hired HPOG and other entry-level employees (P. Hong 2019).

The perspective of implementation research here is useful to examine how horizontal and vertical workforce development policies are played out in the field. When juxtaposed against a horizontal workforce development evaluation methodology, the efforts of case managers for harder to serve populations will have job placement numbers predictably lower than initial project goals. These disappointing results, which often lead some critics to dismiss workforce development programs at large (as they see the public workforce system as designed to support a demand-driven pipeline of new job entrants for industry), are the result of two key factors. First, case managers are not well equipped in the assessment of PSS among job seekers, so referrals to employers will be made only when the case managers "cream" those job candidates who are closest to the labor market.

Second, the overemphasis of a demand-driven focus and incentives behind the public workforce system competes with a dual-customer approach: employment services are now considered universal, as the distinction between "core" and "intensive" services, as existing under the Workforce Investment Act of 1998, no longer exists (Holland 2016). These services are collapsed into career services without any requirement for sequencing of services under the Workforce Innovation and Opportunity Act of 2014, which supersedes the Workforce Investment Act of 1998.

In order to fill these gaps in current workforce development, the methodological approach deployed in this chapter to explore the vertical workforce development process has the potential to present PSS as the metrics for employability. PSS can be used as a conceptual and empirical bridge to improve the efficiency of workforce development programs to connect the job seeker with the other members of the workforce system. The success of workforce development under this alternative construct suggests that when more barriers are removed, job seekers move closer toward labor market participation, and that the role for government in workforce development (whether directly funded or channeled to nonprofit organizations) is to act as the facilitator of this employability by offering comprehensive services.

To this end, a probabilistic evaluation model might generate an algorithm with the results needed to demonstrate the effectiveness of addressing barriers and movement toward greater hope—by which PSS is a good process metric for capturing employability or job-readiness (P. Hong 2013). In turn, this employability index might be effectively deployed by case managers, who can then better assess and triage harder-to-serve populations in their caseloads. This vertical development approach can demonstrate how HPOG proved to be an innovative model of establishing a career pathway for TANF participants to move toward employability—while advancing their PSS—in a high-growth economic sector. HPOG, therefore, represents a pioneering effort to demonstrate the interrelationship between economic development, workforce development, and antipoverty policies in practice, even if they are often housed in silos by traditional evaluation research.

CONCLUSION

PSS promises to nurture positive characteristics, such as resilience, grit, sacrifice, and resolve as low-income job seekers strive for individualized employment goals (P. Hong 2016; P. Hong, Choi, and Key 2018; P. Hong, Kim, et al., forthcoming; R. Hong and P. Hong, forthcoming; R. Hong, et al. 2019; P. Hong, R. Hong, et al., forthcoming). These noncognitive behaviors reflect the inner strengths that help withstand and overcome employment barriers (Heckman 2012–13). The transformative decision to partake in this enduring process is rooted in the sense of purpose—the desire and effort that individuals put forth to accomplish their goals, make significant contributions to society, and maintain a meaningful existence. Psychological transformation has been the missing link in workforce development research and practice. This human-centered approach to building character, identity, motivation, and resilience is the key to sustaining long-term successful career pathways.

Our current research on low-income job seekers finds that the successful path to employment and retention requires these potential employees to tap into their deep-seated purpose as they embark on the journey toward their employment goals. This purpose can be contextualized differently for each individual but is unequivocally grounded in what we conceptualize as PSS, which comprises perceived barriers and hope (P. Hong 2013). Employment hope can serve as the motivating purpose toward one's goals despite many rejections and barriers in the low-wage labor market (P. Hong and Choi 2017). Developing employment hope is similar to the process of acquiring "possible selves" as goal-oriented road maps (Oyserman et al. 2004).

In workforce development, "nudging" (Thaler and Sunstein 2008) to empower individuals as "hoping" agents is a fairly common practice. However, this process is hardly considered central to the change that impacts the decisions and actions of individuals. Employment and career specialists often provide employment-hope-based coaching—a method of noncognitive nudging—but only as an add-on to other well-regarded, deliberate programs such as human capital development and labor force attachment approaches. The purpose-driven, noncognitive nudging has received relatively less attention compared to these dominant paradigms and subsequently has not been measured or evaluated in light of the tangible outcomes. Therefore, we challenge investigators to further examine the purpose-driven PSS as it contributes to the mainstream discourse on workforce development, career pathways, employer engagement, and system change at large.

References

Anderson, Theresa, Pamela Loprest, Teresa Derrick-Mills, Lauren Eyster, Elaine Morley, and Alan Werner. 2014. *Health Profession Opportunity Grants: Year Two Annual Report (2011–2012)*. OPRE Report No. 2014-03. Washington, DC: Office of Planning, Research and Evaluation, Administration for Children and Families, U.S. Department of Health and Human Services: Abt Associates and the Urban Institute.

Avey, James B., Rebecca Reichard, Fred Luthans, and Ketan Mhatre. 2011. "Meta-Analysis of the Impact of Positive Psychological Capital on Employee Attitudes, Behaviors, and Performance." *Human Resource Development Quarterly* 22(2): 127–152.

Babyak, Michael A., C. R. Snyder, and Lauren Yoshinobu. 1993. "Psychometric Properties of the Hope Scale: A Confirmatory Factor Analysis." *Journal of Research in Personality* 27(2): 154–169.

Beck, Aaron T., Arlene Weissman, David Lester, and Larry Trexler. 1974. "The Measurement of Pessimism: The Hopelessness Scale." *Journal of Consulting and Clinical Psychology* 42(6): 861–865.

Betz, Nancy E., and Louise F. Fitzgerald. 1987. *The Career Psychology of Women.* Cambridge, MA: Academic Press.

Cooney, Kate. 2006. "Mothers First, Not Work First: Listening to Welfare Clients in Job Training." *Qualitative Social Work* 5(2): 217–235.

Diemer, Matthew A., and David L. Blustein. 2007. "Vocational Hope and Vocational Identity: Urban Adolescents' Career Development." *Journal of Career Assessment* 15(1): 98–118.

Duckworth, Angela Lee, Heidi Grant, Benjamin Loew, Gabriele Oettingen, and Peter M. Gollwitzer. 2011. "Self-Regulation Strategies Improve Self-Discipline in Adolescents: Benefits of Mental Contrasting and Implementation Intentions." *Educational Psychology* 31: 17–26.

Farmer, Helen S. 1985. "Model of Career and Achievement Motivation for Women and Men." *Journal of Counseling Psychology* 32(3): 363–390.

Gowdy, Elizabeth A., and Sue Pearlmutter. 1993. "Economic Self-Sufficiency: It's Not Just Money." *Affilia* 8(4): 368–387.

Hackett, Gail, and Nancy Betz. 1981. "A Self-Efficacy Approach to the Career Development of Women." *Journal of Vocational Behavior* 18(3): 326–339.

Harvey, Vorricia, Philip Young P. Hong, and Kweli Kwaza. 2010. "Shared Reflections on Transformative Practice: From Challenges to Client Empowerment in Workforce Development." *Reflections: Narratives of Professional Helping* 16(2): 70–78.

Heckman, James J. 2012–13. "Hard Evidence on Soft Skills." *Focus* 29(2): 3–8.

Herth, Kaye Ann. 1991. "Development and Refinement of an Instrument to Measure Hope." *Scholarly Inquiry for Nursing Practice* 5(1): 39–51.

Holland, Brian. 2015. "A Workforce Development Systems Model for Unemployed Job Seekers." *Journal of Adult and Continuing Education* 21(2): 55–76.

———. 2016. "Both Sides Now: Toward the Dual Customer Approach under the Workforce Innovation and Opportunity Act in the United States." *Local Economy* 31(3): 424–441.

Hong, Philip Young P. 2013. "Toward a Client-Centered Benchmark for Self-Sufficiency: Evaluating the 'Process' of Becoming Job Ready." *Journal of Community Practice* 21: 356–378.

———. 2016. "Transforming Impossible into Possible (TIP®): A Bottom-Up

Practice in Workforce Development for Low-Income Jobseekers." *Environment and Social Psychology* 1(2): 93–104.

———. 2019. "Transforming Opportunities into Productivity (TOP): A System-Change Model for Employer/Employee Engagement." Paper presented at the Network for Social Work Management Conference, held in Chicago, May 29–June 1.

Hong, Philip Young P., and Sangmi Choi. 2013. "The Employment Hope Scale: Measuring an Empowerment Pathway to Employment Success." *International Journal of Psychology Research* 8(3): 173–189.

———. 2017. "Measuring Transformative Workforce Activation: Validation of the Comprehensive Employment Hope Scale." In *Transforming Society: Strategies for Social Development in Singapore and around the World*, Ngoh Tiong Tan, ed. New York: Routledge, pp. 81–96.

Hong, Philip Young P., Sangmi Choi, and Whitney Key. 2018. "Psychological Self-Sufficiency: A Bottom-Up Theory of Change in Workforce Development." *Social Work Research* 41(1): 22–32.

Hong, Philip Young P., Sangmi Choi, and Joshua R. Polanin. 2014. "A Multi-Sample Confirmatory Factor Analysis of the Short Employment Hope Scale (EHS-14)." *Journal of Social Service Research* 40: 339–352.

Hong, Philip Young P., Rana Hong, Dara Lewis, and Dianne Williams. Forthcoming. "Pathway of Employment from Uncovering Barriers to Discovering Hope: Non-Traditional, Student-Centered, Relationship-Based Approach." *Families in Society*.

Hong, Philip Young P., Caleb Kim, Rana Hong, Jang Ho Park, and Dara Lewis. Forthcoming. "Examining Psychological Self-Sufficiency among African-American Low-Income Jobseekers in a Health Profession Career Pathway Program." *Social Work in Health Care*.

Hong, Philip Young P., Joshua R. Polanin, Whitney Key, and Sangmi Choi. 2014. "Development of the Perceived Employment Barrier Scale (PEBS): Measuring Psychological Self-Sufficiency." *Journal of Community Psychology* 42: 689–706.

Hong, Philip Young P., Joshua R. Polanin, and Terri D. Pigott. 2012. "Validation of the Employment Hope Scale: Measuring Psychological Self-Sufficiency among Low-Income Jobseekers." *Research on Social Work Practice* 22(3): 323–332.

Hong, Philip Young P., Vamadu A. Sheriff, and Sandra R. Naeger. 2009. "A Bottom-Up Definition of Self-Sufficiency: Voices from Low-Income Jobseekers." *Qualitative Social Work* 8(3): 357–376.

Hong, Philip Young P., In Han Song, Sangmi Choi, and Jang Ho Park. 2016. "A Cross-National Validation of the Employment Hope Scale in the U.S. and South Korea." *Social Work Research* 40(1): 41–51.

Hong, Philip Young P., In Han Song, Sangmi Choi, and Jang Ho Park. 2018. "Comparison of Perceived Employment Barriers among Low-Income Job-seekers in the United States and South Korea." *International Social Work* 61(1): 23–39.

Hong, Rana, and Philip Young P. Hong. Forthcoming. "Neurobiological Core Content in the Research-Supported Transforming Impossible into Possible (TIP®) Program Model." *Journal of Evidence-Based Social Work*.

Hong, Rana, Terry Northcut, Marcia Spira, and Philip Young P. Hong. 2019. "Facilitating Transformation in Workforce Training: Utilizing Clinical Theory to Understand Psychological Self-Sufficiency." *Smith College Studies in Social Work* 89(1): 66–82.

Iversen, Robert Rehner, and Annie Laurie Armstrong. 2006. *Jobs Aren't Enough: Toward a New Economic Mobility for Low-Income Families*. Philadelphia: Temple University Press.

Jacobs, Ronald L., and Joshua D. Hawley. 2009. "The Emergence of 'Workforce Development': Definition, Conceptual Boundaries and Implications." In *International Handbook of Education for the Changing World of Work: Bridging Academic and Vocational Learning*, Rupert Maclean and David Wilson, eds. Springer Science & Business Media, pp. 2537–2552.

Juntunen, Cindy L., and Kara Brita Wettersten. 2006. "Work Hope: Development and Initial Validation of a Measure." *Journal of Counseling Psychology* 53(1): 94–106.

Lent, Robert W., Steven D. Brown, and Gail Hackett. 1994. "Toward a Unifying Social Cognitive Theory of Career and Academic Interest, Choice, and Performance." *Journal of Vocational Behavior* 45(1): 79–122.

Lent, Robert W., Steven D. Brown, and Gail Hackett. "Social Cognitive Career Theory." In *Career Choice and Development*, 4th ed., Duane Brown, ed. San Francisco: Jossey-Bass, pp. 255–311.

Lincoln, Yvonna, and Egon G. Guba. 1985. *Naturalistic Inquiry*. Thousand Oaks, CA: Sage.

Luthans, Fred. 2002a. "The Need for and Meaning of Positive Organizational Behavior." *Journal of Organizational Behavior* 23(6): 695–706.

———. 2002b. "Positive Organizational Behavior: Developing and Managing Psychological Strengths." *Academy of Management Executive* 16(1): 57–72.

Luthans, Fred, Bruce J. Avolio, James B. Avey, and Steven M. Norman. 2007. "Positive Psychological Capital: Measurement and Relationship with Performance and Satisfaction." *Personnel Psychology* 60(3): 541–572.

Luthans, Fred, Carolyn M. Youssef, and Bruce J. Avolio. 2007. *Psychological Capital: Developing the Human Competitive Edge*. New York: Oxford University Press.

March, James G. 1994. *Primer on Decision Making: How Decisions Happen.* New York: Simon and Schuster.

March, James G., and Johan P. Olsen. 2011. "The Logic of Appropriateness." *Oxford Handbook of Political Science*, Robert E. Goodin, ed. Oxford: Oxford University Press, pp. 479–497.

McWhirter, Ellen Hawley, Gail Hackett, and Deborah L. Bandalos. 1998. "A Causal Model of the Educational Plans and Career Expectations of Mexican American High School Girls." *Journal of Counseling Psychology* 45(2): 166–181.

Oettingen, Gabrielle. 2000. "Expectancy Effects on Behavior Depend on Self-Regulatory Thought." *Social Cognition* 18(2): 101–129.

Oettingen, Gabrielle, Hyeon-ju Pak, and Karoline Schnetter. 2001. "Self-Regulation of Goal-Setting: Turning Free Fantasies about the Future into Binding Goals." *Journal of Personality and Social Psychology* 80(5): 736–753.

Oyserman, Daphna, Deborah Bybee, Kathy Terry, and Tamera Hart-Hohnson. 2004. "Possible Selves as Roadmaps." *Journal of Research in Personality* 38: 130–149.

Schreier, Margrit. 2012. *Qualitative Content Analysis in Practice.* London: Sage.

Seligman, Martin E. P. 2002. "Positive Psychology, Positive Prevention, and Positive Therapy." In *Handbook of Positive Psychology*, C. R. Snyder and Shane J. Lopez, eds. New York: Oxford University Press, pp. 3–12.

Snyder, C. R., Cheri Harris, John R. Anderson, Sharon A. Holleran, Lori M. Irving, Sandra T. Sigmon, Lauren Yoshinobu, June Gibb, Charyle Langelle, and Pat Harney. 1991. "The Will and the Ways: Development and Validation of an Individual-Differences Measure of Hope." *Journal of Personality and Social Psychology* 60(4): 570–585.

Thaler, Richard H., and Cass R. Sunstein. 2008. *Nudge: Improving Decisions about Health, Wealth, and Happiness.* New Haven, CT: Yale University Press.

Yakushko, Oksana, and Olga Sokolova. 2010. "Work Hope and Influences of the Career Development among Ukrainian College Students." *Journal of Career Development* 36(4): 310–323.

11

Concluding Observations and Policy Recommendations

Christopher T. King
University of Texas at Austin

Philip Young P. Hong
Loyola University Chicago

Contributors to this volume have offered findings, lessons, and, in many cases, recommendations flowing from their particular research efforts. But it is also instructive to look across the various contributions to suggest cross-cutting findings, lessons, and recommendations. We do this fully recognizing that most, though not all, of the research reported here is descriptive in nature or outcomes based rather than impact based.[1] More definitive guidance will follow when impact results become available over the next few years.

That said, the findings from these chapters are consistent with the results from more rigorous evaluations that have been published recently (e.g., Elliot and Roder 2017; Roder and Elliot 2019; Hendra et al. 2016; Schaberg 2017). This should be encouraging news for national policymakers and state and local program administrators as they seek to fully implement sector-based, career pathway approaches in their respective areas under WIOA and related programs, including TANF and SNAP workforce efforts.

It should be said that in many ways health care may constitute a best-case scenario for the type of sector-based, career pathway strategies promulgated and supported by Health Profession Opportunity Grants (HPOG). For starters, health care is a highly structured industry that has been and will be experiencing growth for years to come, given an aging population with increasing health care needs. The perception and reality of skill shortages in many health care occupations, ranging from nursing to various allied health fields, engender greater support in terms of policies and programs. In addition, health care is a sector where large acute care hospital employers dominate the industry, making coordination less intractable than it would be in a sector with more diffuse employment concentrations. Health care occupations also tend to be well structured, with highly articulated career progressions from bottom to top. They also have national and state licensing and credentialing in their respective areas, making it easier for employers and educational institutions—as well as individuals—to plot out and nurture progressions along career pathways. While other sectors present some of these features to varying degrees, few, if any, have all of them the way health care does.

CONCLUDING THOUGHTS AND LESSONS LEARNED

First, and not surprisingly, HPOG 1.0 programs featured many of the key program elements articulated in Chapter 3 and described in more detail in Chapters 4 and 5. For example, Werner et al. in Chapter 4 report that nearly 9 out of 10 participants enrolled in health care occupational training, and most of them were provided with an array of support services, including case management and tuition assistance, designed to make productive participation possible.

However, many of the elements highlighted by King and Prince in Chapter 2 on effective sector-based, career pathway programs were not fully incorporated into these programs. It is noteworthy that one of the key elements in particular did not seem to play the central role of engaging employers as the real "drivers" of the workforce strategy. Nor did these programs appear to be particularly creative in terms of blending and/or braiding potential funding streams (e.g., WIOA, TANF, SNAP E&T) to make their workforce approaches come together more systemically, probably because they were generally well funded by the U.S. Department of Health and Human Services (HHS) and the Administration for Children and Families via HPOG 1.0 itself and may not have felt the need to access these other sources to provide for supports like child care, transportation, and counseling with state and local dollars. There is still considerable room for improvement if such strategies are to become an integral part of the broader workforce development landscape and lead to sustainable systems change well into the future. We offer more on this topic below.

Second, it is striking that most of those served in HPOG 1.0 programs were women of color and that many of them were also mothers of young children. This was the case nationally and in the various tribal projects, as well as in the HPOG UP projects discussed. Health care generally tends to be a female-dominated field, and HPOG strongly encouraged programs to recruit from TANF and other efforts serving low-income populations, so the fact that women made up such a large share of HPOG 1.0 enrollees is not all that surprising; that so many of them also appear to have been mothers of young children may be a bit more so. This suggests that the experience of the highly intentional two-generation human capital strategy embodied by Tulsa's Career*Advance*® HPOG program may be highly informative of good practice in the health care sector and more broadly. CAP Tulsa has been successful with engaging the mothers of children enrolled in early childhood education as they pursue postsecondary training in health care fields, securing credentials and procuring jobs in health care by providing financial and social supports, coaching, and child care. As Sommer et al. report, these efforts have also led to higher attendance and lower chronic absenteeism among their children.

Third, HPOG 1.0 enrollees were successful in terms of near-term program outputs and outcomes on the whole, including those that are education and employment related. Most (78 percent) reported completing a health care course; a large share of them (65 percent of Tribal enrollees) obtained at least one health care credential as part of their participation in HPOG. Moreover, as the Tulsa results demonstrate, the rate of credential attainment was far higher than either the typical postsecondary student or comparison groups of similar individuals seeking to pursue health care education and training. Completion and certification rates tended to be higher in the shorter, less demanding occupations, such as certified nursing assistant. And, about three-quarters of participants (73 percent) obtained jobs, over half (53 percent) in the health care sector. Rates of employment and earnings levels increased over the three-year postprogram period. This is a respectable performance record that hopefully will be borne out over the longer run through ongoing impact analyses as well.

Fourth, HPOG 1.0 succeeded in recruiting and serving low-income persons, though admittedly not those with the lowest basic education and skill levels. As several chapters suggest, better program structures and a wide range of supports are required if sector-based, career pathway programs are going to succeed in serving those in the lower reaches of the labor market. This is more important than ever, given that the labor market nationally and in many local areas is at or near what many economists and policymakers consider full employment: in mid-2019, the national unemployment rate is at a 50-year low of 3.6 percent, while in communities like Austin, Texas, it is well under 3 percent, even as the Trump administration's large tax cuts and growing deficits add more fuel to economic and employment growth. Bringing more lower-skilled individuals into the marketplace as productive workers is necessary to support such growth. Models like Washington's Integrated Basic Education and Skills Training and its next-generation efforts in states such as Maryland and Texas and communities such as Tulsa offering credit for prior learning and related accelerated learning models are proven approaches to doing just that.

Fifth, HPOG 1.0 participants accessed a wide array of supports during their participation, many of which have been provided inconsistently at best by most workforce development programs in recent decades. The overwhelming majority of HPOG 1.0 enrollees received case management, social services, and related supports. Nearly 100 percent benefited from child care and counseling. And, beyond implementing cultural adaptations and offering more welcoming environments, programs tended to make use of extended family structures and family engagement to support effective participation. Some researchers (e.g., Sommer et al., Heuer et al.) report that participation had positive effects at home on the perception of the value of postsecondary education, which was increasingly seen as a priority for the entire family, not just the HPOG participant. This echoes feedback consistently received from participants in Tulsa's program in participant interviews and focus groups (see Sommer et al.).

Sixth, while most enrollees obtained at least one health care credential as part of their participation in HPOG 1.0, only a small share—21 percent nationally and slightly more than 10 percent in the Tribal programs—were able to pursue further credentials within the five-year study period, thus availing themselves of HPOG's intended career pathway goal. This experience highlights the difficulty with implementing career advancement strategies on the ground with further education and training leading to upward job mobility and responsibilities. This difficulty is likely a function of both individual barriers impeding their progress (e.g., cost, time) as well as policy, institutional, and demand-side (employer) issues. If U.S. workforce programs are going to fulfill the career pathway aspirations, they will need much greater support on the demand side (employer) and the supply side (individual participant/postsecondary education) of the market. Enhanced supports (e.g., child care, transportation assistance), tailored class scheduling, and increased access to and support for on-the-job and further upgrading training are needed.[2] This is demonstrably true for the health care sector, as shown here. It is also likely to be the case in other major sectors of the labor market as well.

Seventh, experience with Tribal as well as other HPOG 1.0 programs further highlights the importance of incorporating cultural dimensions directly into the fabric of these programs, including curriculum and the nature and the types of employer relationships. Meit and Miesfeld strongly make this point. Boguslaw et al. and Heuer et al. reinforce it in their chapters. A broader take-away here may be the importance of thoughtfully tailoring sectoral and career pathway strategies to the unique circumstances of the local market and its supporting institutions, as well as to the needs of the populations targeted for service. Not only does one size not fit all, but effectively adapting strategies to local situations and needs simply makes good sense if they stand a chance of producing positive results over time.

Eighth, important issues related to engaging and working with employers and supporting labor market institutions remain to be addressed. Many of these are long-standing issues in workforce development and are evident in the sector-based approaches in health care as well.[3] Engaging employers in substantive ways in workforce programs has never been easy or straightforward. Over the decades, various approaches to engage them more effectively have been tried, including structuring state and local governance to ensure they had the dominant role—for example, private industry councils under the Comprehensive Employment and Training Act and Job Training Partnership Act in the 1970s and 1980s and workforce investment boards under WIA in the 1990s and 2000s—and now mandating sector-based strategies statewide and encouraging the use of career pathway approaches under WIOA in 2014 (see Barnow and Spaulding [2015]). Yet, barriers to effective engagement remain. Even in relatively tight labor markets, employers tend to "buy rather than build" their workforces, preferring to poach from their competitors instead of training their existing workers (Cappelli 2012; Ton 2014). True employer engagement in identifying and documenting skill needs and helping local colleges and providers shape and tailor training curricula to meet their needs takes a serious commitment of time and effort that employers subject to intense competition and short-term financing often feel they can ill afford (Conway and Giloth 2014). And, as Boguslaw et al. point out in Chapter 6, in highly structured internal labor markets such as those in health care, many employers institutionalize discriminatory practices that can mitigate against hiring even highly qualified workers of color. Much work remains to be done on this persistent problem.

Ninth, the form of psychological capital referred to as psychological self-sufficiency (PSS) may be at the heart of moving the motivational needle forward for HPOG students. As presented by Hong et al., PSS, though not so readily apparent, is a dynamic process of navigating the perceived employment barriers and employment hope as one sets the drive toward reaching the employment and retention goal. Empirically, HPOG UP research by Hong et al. provided the longitudinal data to take a deeper look at the complexity of measuring the intrapersonal "process" element of self-sufficiency. Theoretically, PSS is posited to be the vessel that sails through the storms of barriers and delivers a sustained and resilient hope to arrive at the shores of economic self-sufficiency (Hong, Choi, and Key 2018). The intrapersonal skills in PSS are interpersonally cultivated and nurtured in the relational way. In the same vein, Heuer et al. emphasized the American Indian traditional values and virtues of care, respect, cooperation, patience, generosity, humor, harmony, and humility. These attributes are manifested in the form of strong supportive relationships with HPOG program specialists, peer groups, and instructors as a social support network (see Chapter 8). Sommer et al. focus on the parent-child relationship as the motivator to success that translates into intergenerational success outcomes. PSS can be demonstrated on the job in the form of soft skills and could provide the opportunity for employers, as Boguslaw et al. put it in Chapter 6, to create an organizational culture and environment for such strong leadership qualities to grow and build toward greater patient-centered outcomes for health care organizations.

Finally, the collaborative researcher/practitioner partnerships represented by the chapters in this volume—including both the more traditional National Implementation and Tribal Evaluations that HHS has contracted for, as well as the more focused University Partnerships— have contributed considerably to understanding the HPOG program since it began in 2011. HHS operates similar researcher/practitioner partnerships within other key programs, such as Head Start and Early Head Start, as have other federal agencies, including the U.S. Department of Education with its regional network of educational research laboratories.[4] HHS has long been a leader in fostering and conducting rigorous research and evaluation work and has a staff with cross-sector expertise and deep experience in their fields to both guide and carry out the work. Engaging high-quality, independent researchers in their efforts is essential. This foreshadows the final section of this chapter that addresses future research needs.

POLICY AND PRACTICE RECOMMENDATIONS

With these conclusions and lessons as background, we offer several recommendations for policymakers and program operators to consider. These span all levels of government and a range of workforce development partners, as well as touch on both the supply and demand sides of the labor market.

First, it is essential that the nation—governments and employers— invest more in sector-based and career pathway strategies as part of a positive workforce agenda. Relative to its highly developed counterparts in the Organisation for Economic Co-operation and Development, the United States is and has been underinvesting in workforce development and active labor market policies generally for years (King and Heinrich 2011; Wandner 2015). Although the figures vary somewhat from year to year, on average the United States devotes less than 0.5 percent of gross domestic product to support labor market policies compared to over 4 percent in Denmark. Furthermore, much of what the United States supports tends to be passive (e.g., unemployment benefits) rather than active (e.g., job readiness and skills training). Sector-based and career pathway strategies could be a key part of expanding our workforce investments in the future, possibly connected to an infrastructure agenda (e.g., National Skills Coalition 2018). WIOA offers a supportive framework, but the administration must propose and Congress must then approve federal budgets that support greater investments in such policies than has been the case.

Additionally, governors and state legislatures should not be given a pass on this score. Even within diminished funding for WIOA, governors can opt to devote more of their discretionary funding to support sectoral and career pathway strategies, including those in health care. Some (e.g., Pennsylvania, Washington) have even invested scarce state tax dollars to support sector strategies over time. Others could and should follow suit.

In the United States, as in Japan and some other developed economies, the primary role for workforce development resides squarely with employers, who account for upward of 90 percent of U.S. investment in workforce development overall (King and Heinrich 2011). If sector and career pathway strategies are to be fully implemented in labor markets and offer real, accessible opportunities for job seekers to pursue career advancement beyond their initial preparation, employers must do much more than they now do in health care as well as other sectors of the labor market. Several labor market analysts (e.g., Peter Cappelli) have found that employers currently may be backing away from this role despite widely reported skill shortages. This needs to change. Employers must invest more—not less—and also must engage more fully with local boards, community colleges, and other partners to play a leading role in driving sector and career pathway strategies in their local labor markets. As King and Prince note in Chapter 2, there are excellent examples around the country of leading-edge strategies spearheaded by employers working with local workforce boards. These can serve as a foundation on which to build.

Second, local workforce boards, which serve as the frontline for workforce programming in the United States, also should do more to implement thoughtful and measured sector and career pathway strategies. While some boards are doing an excellent job and appear to be well ahead of the curve, many are still largely reactive to labor market conditions in their local areas. As the contributors to this volume and related evaluations have shown, in order to implement effective sector and career pathway strategies, workforce boards need to do the following:

- Engage employers in key growth sectors as true "drivers" of local workforce strategies.

- Offer the broad range of supports that low-income, low-skilled job seekers, including parents of young children, need to access and take full advantage of, including tuition assistance, flexible child care, transportation assistance, career navigation/coaching, and peer supports.

- Take steps to ensure that the strategies are well adapted to the particular cultural contexts of the resident target populations, as well as the needs of the local labor market.

- Where local boards are legislatively and structurally limited in their span of control and their scope—such as Oklahoma and many other states, where local boards control only one or two WIOA funding streams—be proactive about developing collaborative relationships with other partners and blending and braiding funding to fully support such strategies.

- Work closely with community and technical college systems in their communities to design and implement well-structured career pathways for resident job seekers.

Third, Congress, as well as federal and state education agencies and area colleges, should foster efforts that complement and support effective and efficient sector-based career pathway strategies. As any number of researchers and practitioners have noted, time is the enemy. Most postsecondary students today would have been characterized as nontraditional just a few short years ago. Many of them now are student parents juggling education and family responsibilities. The overwhelming majority is also working while pursuing their credentials, which means they must balance education, work, and family needs, often attending school on a part-time basis so they can work and attend to other demands on their time. Actions that would help them study and reach their goals in a more timely manner include

- opening up Pell Grants and loans and other federal assistance programs to postsecondary students who are enrolled in non-credit and part-time education and training programs, and

- expanding the use of such accelerated learning strategies as competency-based education and credit-for-prior-learning, allowing students to gain college credits by testing out of certain coursework and thus shortening the time to degree or credential.[5]

Fourth, policymakers at all levels should provide the resources needed to offer the broad range of supports that parents in particular appear to require in order to pursue education and training in sector-based career pathways while helping their children simultaneously access quality child care and child development services. Support for so-called two-generation human capital approaches such as Tulsa's pioneering Career*Advance*® Program described by Sommer et al. in Chapter 9 is increasing, and related efforts are now emerging across the country supported by a varied mix of federal, state, local, and philanthropic sources. Noteworthy examples include comprehensive statewide efforts in Colorado, Connecticut, and Utah, as well as pilot projects funded by the Annie E. Casey Foundation in Atlanta, Tulsa, and rural Garrett County (Maryland), and the W.K. Kellogg Foundation in El Paso, Maricopa County (Arizona), and Montgomery County (Maryland) via the National Association of Workforce Boards and Innovate+Educate. The Aspen Institute's Ascend Program is a hub for documenting these two-generation initiatives and their expansion.

As noted above, if these parents are to succeed, they require a broad range of supports, including tuition assistance, flexible high-quality child care and early childhood development programs, transportation assistance, career navigation/coaching, and peer supports. These services are too often simply presumed to be available and accessible to parents but in fact are rarely there when—and in the amount and the form—they are needed.[6]

Fifth, career pathways and workforce development strategies should utilize psychological and community-based cultural resources as central to soft skills development rather than peripheral to hard skills attainment. While soft skills are found to be the number one desirable skill set that most employers mention in interviews for building a sustainable and growing human resource, there is no one widely used method of engaging the workers-to-be before or after being employed. Often, these skills are either expected to be there during the screening process or they are attempted to be taught under the assumption that attitudinal and behavioral modification needs to hit the target goal of presenting the job candidates with the cleanest outer look, manifested in the form of interviewing, communication, and life skills. PSS theory of change and metrics (Hong, Choi, and Key 2018) needs to be integrated into WIOA one-stop career centers and other contracted job readiness training programs and more widely incorporated into the formative and summative evaluation processes to help strengthen the career pathways and workforce development programs. As introduced in an OPRE report by Anderson et al. (2018) at Mathematica Policy Research, the Transforming Impossible into Possible (TIP®) program was noted as one of the top five research-informed social-emotional, self-sufficiency programs in the country. Conducting implementation research on the innovative program[7] as described in Chapter 10 by Hong et al. is a promising tool for integrating PSS as a bridging concept to match the labor supply and demand. It could be instrumental not only in terms of preparing and maximizing the potential of the newly entering workers (supply-side concern) but also empowering the incumbent workers for increased retention and productivity (demand-side concern) by connecting the purpose, motivation, aspirations, and goals in their vocational pursuit. TIP® can help lay the foundation for PSS to be the organizing principle for how the system truly can be job seeker–centered in an age when every service delivery is couched as a patient-, customer-, person-, and human-centered approach while bringing about the most innovative and desirable outcomes.

There are certainly other recommendations that follow from the research in this volume. These are just some that we believe are most important for policymakers and practitioners.

CONTINUING SUPPORT FOR RESEARCH

As noted in the foregoing chapters, none of the findings and lessons presented here would have been possible without strong and thoughtful support from and collaborative efforts with HHS/Administration for

Children and Families/Office of Planning, Research, and Evaluation and other federal agencies (e.g., the Department of Labor and the Department of Education) and a handful of philanthropic institutions, including the Annie E. Casey Foundation, the W.K. Kellogg Foundation, the JPMorgan Chase Foundation, and the Lloyd A. Fry Foundation. Bruck et al. in Chapter 3 have described the Office of Planning, Research, and Evaluation's efforts to date and their plans for the near future, which include producing and disseminating evaluation findings on sector-based, career pathway strategies as well as the evaluability of two-generation approaches nationally. In this period of uncertainty in terms of both federal and state policy and labor market transitions, it is important that the federal commitment to research and evaluation be reinforced and sustained. Evidence-based policymaking and investment in effective workforce and related services cannot and will not take place without the research to provide that evidence. Such efforts are not inexpensive, but they are vital. It is up to government, with the help of philanthropy, to support such research. Private markets generally may not do so because the provision of a substantial share of workforce and education services falls in the realm of public goods, where private markets are expected to underinvest and underperform.

Below is a list of issues that merit further research in the years to come—research that would foster more effective approaches along the lines of HPOG. It is by no means an exhaustive list. Also, note that these are presented largely in the order in which they arise programmatically, proceeding from enrollment/engagement to bolstering post-program outcomes.

- Identify and document, to the extent feasible, effective approaches for recruiting and enrolling at-risk populations into HPOG and similar sector-based, career pathway strategies. These are likely to vary by population, sector, and career pathway, which makes this a daunting topic to tackle.

- Conduct more rigorous research than has been done to date on productive approaches for engaging employers in sector-based, career pathway strategies. Employers control the jobs that job seekers are pursuing, so it is axiomatic that such strategies cannot succeed without their active engagement. Promising approaches for engagement have been identified over time, but serious research on their components or their effects has never been conducted.

- Determine the best mix of supports to help low-income, parent, and other at-risk populations enroll, persist, and complete post-secondary credentials valued in today's labor markets. While researchers have been able to gauge the importance of providing a broad range of supports offered together—affordable, quality child care; case management/career counseling; tuition and transportation assistance—they have not been able to measure the independent contribution ("value added") of any particular service. This, too, may be impossible, given the large sample sizes and evaluation design complexities required to produce such answers, but it would be worth at least conducting more feasibility analysis of such an effort.

- Expand research on effective accelerated learning and credentialing approaches and their effectiveness. Such approaches have shown great promise, but more rigorous research and testing are required in differing settings and with varying populations to ensure that the early findings from such efforts as City University of New York's Accelerated Study in Associate Programs hold up and can be applied elsewhere.

- Enhance ongoing research into two-generation human capital strategies for lifting both student-parents and their children simultaneously out of poverty. While Tulsa's Career*Advance*® Program, which has been funded by HPOG 1.0 and 2.0 and is described by Sommer et al., is one of the best examples of such an effort, others certainly exist—such as the Jeremiah Program in the Twin Cities and Austin and the Educational Alliance in New York City—and are beginning to expand around the country. Despite relatively high initial costs, the potential for such efforts to harness "mutual motivation" of parents and students in supporting program participation and successful exits from intergenerational poverty is quite high.[8]

- Conduct deeper and broader research into psychological self-sufficiency as an interlocking theory of change for pre- and post-employment empowerment practice utilizing a broader range of sectors, settings, and populations to determine the extent to which it has broader applicability in workforce and education programming. TIP® implementation studies can be scaled to widely test the degree to which such an intervention could help invigorate psychological self-sufficiency, thereby increasing self-regulation and executive functioning, to yield significant impacts on labor market outcomes and economic self-sufficiency.

- Increase analysis to gauge the value of key credentials—certificates, diplomas, and degrees—in today's changing labor market and the benefits and costs of attaining them. Georgetown's Center on Education and the Workforce (https://cew.georgetown.edu/) is one of several groups that has engaged in studies on this important issue. More rigorous research remains to be conducted.

- Implement effective career advancement strategies in the workplace after initial training has been completed—it is critical to fulfilling the vision of HPOG as well as the goals for workforce progress in other sectors of the labor market if the nation is going to address the issue of widening wage inequality. Too little is known about the prevalence and the effectiveness of these strategies and what makes them work. Given that the overwhelming share of training in the United States (more than 90 percent) is the purview of employers[9]—whether in the workplace or via voucher-supported education programs at postsecondary institutions—and given that such a small share of HPOG participants were able to avail themselves of further education and training, this topic calls for much more information and analysis.

Diving deeper into these topics would enhance the broad-based research agenda HHS is already pursuing, especially its work on two-generation strategies and Pathways for Advancing Careers and Education, as well as HPOG 2.0. As noted, its agenda is complemented by research fostered by its partner agencies at the federal level (i.e., the Department of Labor and the Department of Education), as well as initiatives supported by the Annie E. Casey Foundation, the W.K. Kellogg, and others.

Notes

1. Exceptions are Chapter 2, which summarizes the impacts from sector-based, career pathway program evaluations, and Chapter 9, which shares initial, quasi-experimental impact results from Tulsa's CareerAdvance® program.

2. In too many instances, employers in health care and other sectors become motivated to undertake upgrading training by the immediate pressures of employee turnover and concerns over shortages of skilled workers, only to drop them when market conditions loosen and shortages abate. A decade ago, in response to nursing retention issues, national foundations, including Robert Wood Johnson and Hitachi, launched an initiative to train lower-skilled frontline workers (e.g., food preparation, janitors) who had already exhibited a strong commitment to employment in their organizations for higher-level work as nursing assistants, LPNs, and other positions. When the effects of the Great Recession led to reductions in turnover among nurses, participating hospitals seemed to lose interest. Their time horizon appears to be very short when it comes to interest in human capital investments for their workforce.

3. For example, the 1977 Amendments to CETA launched the Private Sectors Initiatives Pilot, which was followed by the 1978 CETA Amendments that mandated the creation of Private Industry Councils to oversee local job training programs across the country. JTPA in 1982 took this even further. These were policy developments in response to perceived shortcomings in employer engagement. The 2014 WIOA mandate for governors to implement sector strategies statewide is the latest development in this arena.

4. The National Parks Service has supported a regional network of research learning centers since 2001, "places where science and learning come together" (https://www.nps.gov/rlc/index.htm). The USDOL's Employment and Training Administration supported a dissertation research program and regional Manpower Institutional Grantees, typically research and technical assistance and training centers at public universities, working with state and local policymakers and program administrators until the program was eliminated in 1982. One of the editors (King) was fortunate to have worked in Manpower Institutional Grantees at the University of Utah and the University of Texas at Austin in the 1970s and 1980s and collaborated with a number of others during that time (e.g., the University of Maryland, George Washington University, the University of Houston).

5. The City University of New York's Accelerated Study in Associate Programs is an excellent example of these types of efforts (http://www.cuny.edu/academics/programs/notable/asap.html). The Accelerated Study in Associate Programs, which was the focus of a rigorous evaluation conducted by MDRC (Gupta 2017), is being expanded to communities in other states as well. For more information on these and other strategies, see Ganzglass, Bird, and Prince (2011).

6. Many recent reports are available on this topic, detailing the scope of the problem and, more importantly, offering a series of tools, guides, and program prescriptions for addressing it. The Institute for Women's Poverty Research's National

Student-Parent Success Initiative (https://iwpr.org/issue/special-websites/student
-parent-success-initiative/) has assembled a comprehensive body of research on
this topic. Also see Duke-Benfield (2015), Goldrick-Rab (2016), Green (2013),
and Kelly and Goldrick-Rab (2014).

7. TIP was developed by the Loyola research team at the Center for Research on
Self-Sufficiency using data obtained from HPOG UP 1.0 as an evidence-informed
model at the request of HPOG program partners and community-based organizations (Hong 2016). Because PSS was conceptualized based on the grassroots
community definition of self-sufficiency (Hong 2013; Hong, Sheriff, and Naeger
2009), it was echoed by the community partners that there is a need to deliberately use the embedded metrics—perceived employment barriers and employment
hope—and implement programs to improve the scores on the metrics. TIP® was
a response to the community call to provide a cultural resource that supports PSS
development as the core driver to achieving ESS. More information can be found
at http://www.tipprogram.org.

8. For more on two-generation programs, visit the Ascend Program at the Aspen
Institute website: https://www.aspeninstitute.org/programs/ascend/. Also, see
King, Chase-Lansdale, and Small (2015); King et al. (2016); and Sommer et al.
(2018).

9. King and Heinrich (2011) discuss this issue and present statistics for the United
States and other Organisation for Economic Co-operation and Development
countries.

References

Anderson, Mary Anne, Elizabeth Brown, Elizabeth W. Cavadel, Michelle
Derr, and Jacqueline F. Kauff. 2018. *Using Psychology-Informed Strate-
gies to Promote Self-Sufficiency: A Review of Innovative Programs*. OPRE
Report No. 2018-41. Washington, DC: Office of Planning, Research and
Evaluation, Administration for Children and Families, U.S. Department of
Health and Human Services; Mathematica Policy Research.

Barnow, Burt S., and Shayne Spaulding. 2015. "Employer Involvement in
Workforce Programs: What Do We Know?" In *Transforming U.S. Work-
force Development Policies for the 21st Century*, Carl Van Horn, Tammy
Edwards, and Todd Greene, eds. Kalamazoo, MI: W.E. Upjohn Institute for
Employment Research, pp. 221–263.

Cappelli, Peter. 2012. *Why Good People Can't Get Jobs: The Skills Gap and
What Companies Can Do About It*. Philadelphia: Wharton Digital Press.

Conway, Maureen, and Robert P. Giloth, eds. 2014. *Connecting People to
Work: Workforce Intermediaries and Sector Strategies*. New York: American Assembly Press.

Duke-Benfield, Amy Ellen. 2015. *Bolstering Non-Traditional Student Suc-*

cess: A Comprehensive Student Aid System Using Financial Aid, Public Benefits, and Refundable Tax Credits. Washington, DC: Center for Law and Social Policy. http://www.clasp.org/resources-andpublications/ publication-1/Bolstering-NonTraditional-Student-Success.pdf (accessed November 16, 2018).

Elliott, Mark, and Anne Roder. 2017. *Escalating Gains: Project QUEST'S Sectoral Strategy Pays Off.* New York: Economic Mobility Corporation. https://economicmobilitycorp.org/wp-content/uploads/2018/01/Escalating -Gains_WEB.pdf (accessed November 16, 2018).

Ganzglass, Evelyn, Keith Bird, and Heath Prince. 2011. *Giving Credit Where Credit Is Due: Creating a Competency-Based Qualifications Framework for Postsecondary Education and Training.* Washington, DC: Center for Law and Social Policy, Center for Postsecondary and Economic Success.

Goldrick-Rab, Sara. 2016. *Paying the Price: College Costs, Financial Aid, and the Betrayal of the American Dream.* Chicago: University of Chicago Press.

Green, Autumn. 2013. "Babies, Books, and Bootstraps: Low-Income Mothers, Material Hardship, Role Strain and the Quest for Higher Education." Doctoral diss. Boston College. http://www.proquest.com/products-services/ pqdtglobal.html (accessed November 16, 2018).

Gupta, Himani. 2017. *The Power of Fully Supporting Community College Students: The Effects of the City University of New York's Accelerated Study in Associate Programs after Six Years.* New York: MDRC. https://www .mdrc.org/publication/power-fully-supporting-community-college-students (accessed November 16, 2018).

Hendra, Richard, David H. Greenberg, Gayle Hamilton, Ari Oppenheim, Alexandra Pennington, Kelsey Schaberg, and Betsy L. Tessler. 2016. *Encouraging Evidence on a Sector-Focused Advancement Strategy: Two-Year Impacts from the WorkAdvance Demonstration.* New York: MDRC.

Hong, Philip Young P. 2013. "Toward a Client-Centered Benchmark for Self-Sufficiency: Evaluating the 'Process' of Becoming Job Ready." *Journal of Community Practice* 21(4): 356–378.

———. 2016. "Transforming Impossible into Possible (TIP): A Bottom-Up Practice in Workforce Development for Low-Income Jobseekers." *Environment and Social Psychology* 1(2): 93–104.

Hong, Philip Young P., Sangmi Choi, and Whitney Key. 2018. "Psychological Self-Sufficiency: A Bottom-Up Theory of Change in Workforce Development." *Social Work Research* 41(1): 22–32.

Hong, Philip Young P., Vamadu A. Sheriff, and Sandra R. Naeger. 2009. "A Bottom-Up Definition of Self-Sufficiency: Voices from Low-Income Jobseekers." *Qualitative Social Work* 8(3): 357–376.

Kelly, Andrew P., and Sara Goldrick-Rab, eds. 2014. *Reinventing Financial*

Aid: Charting a New Course to College Affordability. Cambridge, MA: Harvard Education Press.

King, Christopher T., P. Lindsay Chase-Lansdale, and Mario Small, eds. 2015. *Two Generations. One Future: An Anthology from the Ascend Fellowship.* Washington, DC: Ascend Program of the Aspen Institute.

King, Christopher T., and Carolyn Heinrich. 2011. *How Effective Are Workforce Development Programs? Implications for U.S. Workforce Policies.* Austin, TX: Ray Marshall Center for the Study of Human Resources, Lyndon B. Johnson School of Public Affairs, University of Texas. Prepared for the Fall 2011 APPAM Policy Research Conference, Washington, DC, November 5.

King, Christopher T., Cynthia J. Juniper, Rheagan Coffey, and Tara C. Smith. 2016. *Promoting Two-Generation Strategies: A Getting-Started Guide for State and Local Policy Makers (Revised and Updated).* Austin, TX: Ray Marshall Center for the Study of Human Resources, Lyndon B. Johnson School of Public Affairs, University of Texas at Austin.

National Skills Coalition. 2018. *Skills for Good Jobs Agenda 2018: Steps Congress and the Administration Can Take to Stand behind America's Greatest Asset: Its People.* Washington, DC: National Skills Coalition. https://www.nationalskillscoalition.org/resources/publications/file/Skills-for-Good-Jobs-Agenda-2018.pdf (accessed November 16, 2019).

Roder, Anne, and Mark Elliott. 2019. *Nine-Year Gains: Project QUEST's Continuing Impact.* New York: Economic Mobility Corporation.

Schaberg, Kelsey. 2017. *Can Sector Strategies Promote Longer-Term Effects? Three-Year Results from the WorkAdvance Demonstration.* New York: MDRC, September.

Ton, Zeynep. 2014. *The Good Jobs Strategy: How the Smartest Companies Invest in Employees to Lower Costs and Boost Profits.* New York: New Harvest/Houghton Mifflin Harcourt.

Wandner, Stephen A. 2015. "The Future of the Public Workforce System in a Time of Dwindling Resources." In *Transforming U.S. Workforce Development Policies for the 21st Century.* Carl Van Horn, Tammy Edwards, and Todd Greene, eds. Kalamazoo, MI: The W.E. Upjohn Institute for Employment Research, pp. 129–166.

Authors

Janet Boguslaw is a senior scientist at the Heller School for Social Policy and Management, Brandeis University.

Hilary C. Bruck is a senior social science research analyst at the Administration for Children and Families, U.S. Department of Health and Human Services.

Patricia Lindsay Chase-Lansdale is the Frances Willard Professor in Human Development and Social Policy, and vice provost for academics at Northwestern University

Karin M. Eyrich-Garg is the director of the Masters in Social Work program and an associate professor at Temple University.

Catharine Fromknecht is a principal research analyst at NORC at the University of Chicago.

Carol Hafford is a principal research scientist at NORC at the University of Chicago.

Loretta Jean Heuer is a professor in the School of Nursing at North Dakota State University.

Brian Holland is the training and technical assistance manager at BLH Technologies and an adjunct lecturer in the School of Public Affairs, American University.

Philip Young P. Hong is associate dean for research and a professor in the School of Social Work, Loyola University Chicago; he is also the founding director of the Center for Research on Self-Sufficiency

Rana Hong is a senior research associate at the Center for Research on Self-Sufficiency in the School of Social Work at Loyola University Chicago.

Cheryl A. Hyde is an associate professor at Temple University.

Molly Irwin is the vice president for research and science at the Pew Charitable Trusts.

Christopher T. King is a senior research scientist at the Ray Marshall Center for the Study of Human Resources at the University of Texas at Austin's LBJ School of Public Affairs.

Marilyn G. Klug is an associate professor at the University of North Dakota.

Robin Koralek is a senior associate at Abt Associates.

Mary Leff is the research/evaluation project coordinator in the Department of Nursing at North Dakota State University

Cynthia Lindquist is president of Cankdeska Cikana Community College.

Pamela Loprest is a senior fellow at the Urban Institute.

Michael Meit is codirector of the NORC Walsh Center for Rural Health Analysis.

Noelle Miesfeld is a principal research analyst at NORC at the University of Chicago.

Timothy E. O'Brien is a professor in the Department of Mathematics and Statistics and Institute for Environmental Sustainability, Loyola University Chicago

Jang Ho Park is a PhD student in the School of Social Work, Loyola University Chicago Data Analyst, Center for Research on Self-Sufficiency

Emily Phillips is a principal research analyst at NORC at the University of Chicago.

Terri Pigott is a professor in the School of Public Health and College of Education and Human Development, Georgia State University

Amelia Popham is a senior social science research analyst at the Administration for Children and Families, U.S. Department of Health & Human Services.

Heath J. Prince is a research scientist and the director of the Ray Marshall Center for the Study of Human Resources at the University of Texas at Austin's LBJ School of Public Affairs.

Terri Sabol is an assistant professor in human development and social policy and faculty fellow at the Institute for Policy Research, Northwestern University.

Jessica Santos is a lecturer and scientist at the Heller School for Social Policy and Management at Brandeis University.

Teresa Eckrich Sommer is a research associate professor at the Institute for Policy Research, Northwestern University.

Kim Stupica-Dobbs is HPOG Program Manager at the Administration for Children and Families, U.S. Department of Health & Human Services.

Trinidad Tellez is the director of the Office of Health Equity at the New Hampshire Department of Health and Human Services.

Alan Werner is a principal associate at Abt Associates Inc.

Index

Note: The italic letters *f, n,* or *t* following a page number indicate a figure, note, or table, respectively, on that page. Double letters mean more than one such consecutive item on a single page.

IASP. *See* Institute on Assets and Social Policy
Icahn School of Medicine, 235–236, 237–238, 250, 251*n*2
Illinois, career pathway programs and partners in, 17, 84*t*, 93*t*, 291–292, 305, 306
IMPLAN®, economic development data derived from, 32, 48
Independence, economic, 17–19, 38–39, 76
Industry engagement, improve sector-based and career pathway strategies with, 39–40
Industry-recognized certificates
apprenticeships with, 71, 143, 308
barriers to, 36–37
health care employers and, 127, 128*t*
sector partnerships with foundation support for, 21, 23, 29, 44*n*4
as sector strategy for workforce development, 2–5, 20*n*1, 23, 281, 283, 287
state investment in sectoral strategies, 30–32, 45–62
Innovate+Educate, two-generation human capital approach of, 360
Institute for Women's Poverty Research, need for support services and, 20*n*2, 360, 365–366*n*6
Institute on Assets and Social Policy (IASP), Brandeis University
HPOP and, 196–197
as OMHRA partner, 187, 191–192, 194–195, 224*n*2
(*see also* Health Care Employer Research Initiative)
Institutional review boards, research in tribal communities and, 149, 151
Instituto del Progreso Latino, Chicago, as HPOG 1.0 program partner, 84*t*
Integrated Basic Education and Skills Training, 354
Issksiniip Project. *See under* Blackfeet Community College (BCC), evaluation of

Japan, employers and workforce development in, 358
Jeremiah Project, two-generation human capital approach of, 363
Job growth, health care expectations of, vii, 1–2
Job placement, 145*n*33, 246
career navigators for, 11, 273
career pathways with, 24, 73
effect of PSS and ESS on, for HPOG students, 17, 303–304
Job quality, 224
dead-end jobs and, 257, 284
hospital system and, in New Hampshire, 198–199
Job readiness, 358
PSS integration into, services, 19, 361, 366*n*7
Job retention services, as HPOG support, 121, 123, 123*t*
Job search assistance
HPOG programs and, 121, 123, 123*t*
innovative sector strategies *vs.* traditional supply-side methods for, 3–4, 4*f*, 22–23
Job seekers, 16, 26, 359
barriers to education and employment by, 240, 313, 342–343
employability of, and PSS, 342–344
low-income populations as, 13–14, 257–274, 305
networking and, 259, 263–266, 266*t*, 267*f*
Job Service North Dakota, as TMCC partner, 160
Job Training Partnership Act (JTPA, 1982)
lackluster results of, 281, 365*n*3
served job seekers exclusively, 26, 355
Jobs for the Future, Boston, National Fund for Workforce Solutions and, 25
JOBS Initiative, funded by Annie E. Casey Foundation, 25
JPMorgan Chase Foundation, support from, 21, 29, 362

About the Institute

The W.E. Upjohn Institute for Employment Research is a nonprofit research organization devoted to finding and promoting solutions to employment-related problems at the national, state, and local levels. It is an activity of the W.E. Upjohn Unemployment Trustee Corporation, which was established in 1932 to administer a fund set aside by Dr. W.E. Upjohn, founder of The Upjohn Company, to seek ways to counteract the loss of employment income during economic downturns.

The Institute is funded largely by income from the W.E. Upjohn Unemployment Trust, supplemented by outside grants, contracts, and sales of publications. Activities of the Institute comprise the following elements: 1) a research program conducted by a resident staff of professional social scientists; 2) the Early Career Research Award program, which provides funding for emerging scholars to complete policy-relevant research on labor-market issues; 3) a publications program and online research repository, which provide a vehicles for disseminating the research of staff and outside scholars; 4) a regional team that conducts analyses for local economic and workforce development; and 5) the Employment Management Services Division, which administers publicly funded employment and training services as Michigan Works! Southwest in the Institute's local four-county area.

The broad objectives of the Institute's activities are to 1) promote scholarship and evidence-based practices on issues of employment and unemployment policy, and 2) make knowledge and scholarship relevant and useful to policymakers in their pursuit of solutions related to employment and unemployment.

Current areas of concentration for these programs include the causes, consequences, and measures to alleviate unemployment; social insurance and income maintenance programs; compensation and benefits; workforce skills; nonstandard work arrangements; and place-based policy initiatives for strengthening regional economic development and local labor markets.

CPSIA information can be obtained
at www.ICGtesting.com
Printed in the USA
FSHW020658031219